Gravitation and Relativity

PHYSICAL INVESTIGATIONS OF THE UNIVERSE

A. G. W. Cameron, Editor

Interstellar Matter in Galaxies   *L. Woltjer, Editor*

Interstellar Communication   *A. G. W. Cameron, Editor*

Gravitation and Relativity   *H.-Y. Chiu and W. F. Hoffmann, Editors*

GRAVITATION AND RELATIVITY

Edited by

HONG-YEE CHIU

NASA Goddard Institute for Space Studies
New York, New York

and

WILLIAM F. HOFFMANN

Sloane Physics Laboratory
Yale University

W. A. Benjamin, Inc.   New York   Amsterdam   *1964*

GRAVITATION AND RELATIVITY

*The final chapter of manuscript was received on
August 27, 1963; this volume was published
January 15, 1964*

*The publisher is pleased to acknowledge the assistance
of Cecilia Duray-Bito, who produced the illus-
trations, and William Prokos, who designed the
jacket*

W. A. BENJAMIN, INC.
New York, New York

Foreword

While astronomy and geology have traditionally been sciences involving observation and classification of phenomena in the universe, the other physical sciences have been largely restricted to laboratory investigations of the laws of nature and their manifestations in simple forms of matter. In recent years, however, immense progress has been made in understanding how the laws of nature operate in the universe itself—in the cosmic laboratory—where man cannot perform simple experiments but must attempt to analyze nature as he finds it. Progress has been particularly vigorous in such fields as astrophysics, geophysics, geochemistry, and meteoritics. In particular, the space research program has stimulated large numbers of people from various physical disciplines to participate in the physical exploration of the solar system.

This series of books will be concerned with any line of scientific inquiry which attempts to achieve a better understanding of the physical mechanisms that operate in the universe. Pure investigations of the laws of nature, and laboratory investigations of the properties of matter, will not be included. If a laboratory scientist turns his experimental and theoretical talents to the investigation of his physical environment, the results of his investigations are of interest for this series.

The primary aim of the series will be to further communication between scientists investigating nature, and the mode of publication will be varied to minimize the diversion of a scientist's energy from his active participation in teaching and research. The series will include monographs on various specialized topics, proceedings of conferences and symposia, collections of scientific reprints with critical commentary, and publication of lecture-note volumes.

A. G. W. CAMERON
Series Editor

New York, New York
February 1963

v

Preface

This book is a presentation of fundamental concepts, theoretical structure, and experimental foundations of gravitation theory in the light of present-day experimental and theoretical research. It provides an opportunity for physicists, geophysicists, astronomers, and mathematicians not in the field to become acquainted with several aspects of current research in gravitation. In addition, it provides professional relativists with a unique collection of subject matter, some of which has not been previously available in published form.

Topics range from formal questions concerning the structure of general relativity to possible observable implications of gravitational theory for geophysics, atomic physics, and astrophysics.

The material included, with the exception of Chapter 15, is derived from a series of lectures presented at a seminar on gravitation and relativity at the NASA Goddard Institute for Space Studies, New York City, in 1961–1962. This seminar was organized by Professor Dicke as an introduction to the subject, emphasizing the observational implications of the theory and the potential contributions that modern experimental techniques may make.

The approach in those lectures was conceptual rather than axiomatic. For this reason, a complete mathematical development of the subject was not presented. Rather, a review of the fundamental notions, notation, and equations of general relativity was provided as an introduction to subsequent mathematical elaboration of the conceptual arguments.

The text of Chapters 1 through 14 was prepared from notes and tape recordings with further revision by the lecturers. Chapter 15 was first presented at the Conference on Relativistic Theories of Gravitation, Warsaw, Poland, 1962, and subsequently adapted for lectures at the Summer Institute for Theoretical Physics, University of Colorado, Boulder, Colorado, 1962. The present form of this chapter is derived both from a lecture delivered by Professor Wheeler at the Institute for Space Studies and from the lecture notes of the Summer Institute for Theoretical Physics in Boulder.

A general discussion of current experimental and theoretical work in gravitation physics and a survey of the book's contents is presented in the Introduction. Subsequent chapters follow the order in which the lectures were given. Chapters 1 through 4 introduce the basic content of gravitation theory; the remaining chapters discuss various theoretical and experimental questions according to the interests of the lecturers. This method of choice of topics leads to many omissions. It is hoped that the reader will be rewarded by the freshness and novelty of approach rather than by a comprehensive coverage of the subject.

The editors would like to thank Dr. Robert Jastrow for the hospitality of the NASA Goddard Institute for Space Studies where these lectures were presented, and for his personal encouragement of their publication. We express our appreciation to the National Academy of Sciences and the National Research Council for the fellowships that we held during part of the preparation of this material. We wish to thank the Summer Institute for Theoretical Physics at the University of Colorado for permission to use some of the material appearing in Chapter 15. We should also like to acknowledge our pleasant collaboration with the several lecturers and with the publisher during the preparation of this volume.

H.-Y.C.
W.F.H.

New York, New York
New Haven, Connecticut
August 1963

The Authors

James L. Anderson, Stevens Institute of Technology, Hoboken, N.J.

Robert H. Dicke, Palmer Physical Laboratory, Princeton University, Princeton, N.J.

Vernon W. Hughes, Sloane Physics Laboratory, Yale University, New Haven, Conn.

Robert F. Marzke, Palmer Physical Laboratory, Princeton University, Princeton, N.J. (Presently at Columbia University, New York.)

Joseph Weber, Department of Physics and Astronomy, University of Maryland, College Park, Maryland

John A. Wheeler, Palmer Physical Laboratory, Princeton University, Princeton, N.J.

Contents

Introduction

Special relativity has been successful in interpreting electromagnetic phenomena and in determining the dynamics of particles not moving in strong gravitational fields. Gravitational phenomena are well described by Newtonian mechanics to the extent that terms involving ϕ/c^2 or v^2/c^2 can be neglected. ϕ is the gravitational potential, v is the velocity of the particle with respect to the source of the gravitational field, and c is the velocity of light. General relativity describes the motion of bodies in strong gravitational fields, and interactions among gravitational fields.

The most important and unique characteristic of general relativity is its identification of gravitational fields with the geometrical structure of the space-time continuum, using concepts developed in Riemannian geometry. These concepts are described in Chapter 2. Although the structure of Riemannian geometry is fairly well established, the contents of general relativity are only partly understood.

Part of the reason is due to the nonlinearity of the Einstein field equations, which makes mathematical treatment difficult. An even greater problem is the difficulty of carrying out experiments to verify the predictions of general relativity, and to distinguish this theory from other theories of gravity.

This volume emphasizes the overriding principles which determine the content and form of the theories of gravity and those experiments and observations which guide the form and verify the predictions of these theories. This introduction provides a general discussion of the subject and a brief survey of the contents of the subsequent chapters.

Theoretical Foundations of General Relativity as a Theory of Gravitation

The Principle of Equivalence

After an extensive study of the invariance properties of Maxwell's equations under Lorentz transformations, and of the nature of the null result of the Michelson-Morley experiment, Einstein postulated two basic principles upon which his geometrical analysis of space and time is founded.[1] These two principles are now known as the principle of equivalence and the principle of covariance. The two principles as Einstein stated them are as follows:

The Principle of Equivalence: "*In a homogeneous gravitational field (acceleration of gravity γ) let there be a stationary system of coordinates K, oriented so that the lines of force of the gravitational field run in the negative direction of the axis of z. In a space free of gravitational fields let there be a second system of coordinates K', moving with uniform acceleration (γ) in the positive direction of the axis of z* . . . [The equations of motion in the two systems K and K' are the same.] *But we arrive at a very satisfactory interpretation of this law of experience, if we assume that the systems K and K' are physically exactly equivalent, that is, if we assume that we may just as well regard the system K as being in a space free from gravitational fields, if we regard K as uniformly accelerated* . . .*"*

The Principle of Covariance: "*The general laws of nature are to be expressed by equations which hold good for all systems of coordinates, that is, are co-variant with respect to any substitutions* [of coordinates] *whatever (generally covariant).*"

Before we proceed to discuss further how the field equations are derived, we must examine these two principles in greater detail.

In Chapter 1 Dicke subdivides the principle of equivalence into two principles, one called the strong principle, and the other called the weak principle. The weak principle has its origin in the following observation. If the gradient of the gravitational field times the square of the dimension of a physical laboratory or the square of the space-time distance over which experiments can be performed, is much less than c^2, then any gravitational effects on the laboratory can be transformed away by letting this physical laboratory fall freely. This characteristic of gravity manifests itself in Riemannian geometry through the possibility of always obtaining a coordinate system which is locally Cartesian.

On the other hand, according to the strong principle of equivalence, in a freely falling, nonrotating laboratory, one observes the same set of physical laws identical in both form and numerical content, independent of the space-time locality and the velocity of the laboratory. Here also it is necessary to neglect the effects of gradients of the gravitational field. In the above sense, the strong principle of equivalence *excludes* the possibility of variation of physical laws in both space and time.

The weak principle of equivalence is supported to a high precision by the Eötvös experiment as performed originally by Eötvös[2] and more recently by Dicke.[3] These experiments verify the following: The ratio of the inertial to the gravitational mass of nearby objects composed of various materials is essentially the same to an accuracy of a few parts in 10^9 (Eötvös) and one part in 10^{11} (Dicke).

Two conclusions may be drawn on the basis of Eötvös's experiment:

1. All material bodies describe unique trajectories in space and time when affected by gravitational fields only, provided the restrictions on the strength of the gradient of the gravitational field described earlier remain true.* This is the weak principle of equivalence. It provides a basis for establishing the structure of space-time.

2. The strong principle of equivalence can be inferred to a limited accuracy. That is, one can infer within some limits that the laws of physics (e.g. the ratios of the strengths of fundamental forces) are the same throughout space-time. This is done by the following argument.

If the ratios of various interaction strengths should vary from place to place, then so would the ratios of their contributions to the inertial mass of different objects vary with position. Such position dependent mass energy would lead to an anomalous force which would be different for materials exhibiting different ratios of mass-energy content due to these various interactions. The experimental absence of such anomalous forces implies the constancy of the interaction ratios to a precision depending on their fractional contribution to the total mass of the various materials. In particular, the contribution of strong interactions, electromagnetic interactions, weak interactions, and gravitation to the energy of a body is roughly $1 : 10^{-2} : 10^{-12} : 10^{-40}$ for an atom (the contribution from the strong interaction is normalized to unity.) For a macroscopic body of mass about 1 gram and density unity the total gravitational energy is about 10^{-8} erg and the above ratios become $1 : 10^{-2} : 10^{-12} : 10^{-29}$.

The Eötvös experiment demonstrates that the inertial and gravitational masses of material bodies have the same ratio to an accuracy of 1 part in 10^{11}. Hence to great accuracies the constancy of the electromagnetic and the strong interactions must follow the strong principles of equivalence. Nothing can be said about weak interactions and the gravitational interaction. Hence, the Eötvös experiment rules out the possibility that the coupling constants of strong interactions and electromagnetic interactions vary appreciably with time and position. It does not rule out the variability of the weak coupling constant and the gravitational coupling constant. This possibility may be closely connected with Mach's principle (Chapters 8 and 15).

One way to test the validity of the equivalence principle in gravitation is to observe the trajectories of objects whose self-gravitational energy is large. Only for astronomical bodies is this possible. For example, for the

---

* This restriction is necessary since the trajectory of a spinning test particle is different from the trajectory of ordinary particles in the presence of a nonuniform gravitational field.[4]

sun the above interaction strength ratios are $1 : 10^{-2} : 10^{-12} : 10^{-6}$. For Jupiter the ratios are $1 : 10^{-2} : 10^{-12} : 10^{-8}$. A study of the trajectory of Jupiter might lead to more precise limits for the applicability of the strong principle of equivalence to gravitational self-energy.

The Principle of Covariance

This principle states: "*The general laws of nature are to be expressed by equations which hold good for all systems of coordinates, that is, are covariant with respect to any substitutions whatever (generally covariant).*"[1]

There are two interpretations of this principle:

1. We may interpret this principle as the statement that a coordinate system is just a particular choice of imaginary lines in space and time whose intersections characterize events. Hence, the choice of coordinate systems has nothing to do with the contents of the theory. This is a restricted sense of covariance. And in a sense is an empty statement; for any physical theory may be made to be covariant without increasing its physical content. For example, Maxwell's equations may be written in a form which appears to be generally covariant [Chapter 11, Eq. (34)], without enlarging its physical content as long as the metric is restricted to that of a flat space. Then the metric can always be restored to the familiar diagonal Lorentz form by an ordinary coordinate transformation. In this restricted sense, all laws of physics may be written in a covariant form without introducing any new physics and the principle of covariance thus interpreted is an empty statement.

2. What Einstein had in mind when he stated the principle of covariance is entirely different (Chapter 9). What he meant is that the laws of nature are geometrical statements about geometrical objects and that such laws must be applicable to spaces of arbitrary geometry. In a completely geometrized theory, the geometry is determined from the theory and is not given a priori (as an *absolute* element). For example, in the Einstein field equations, the geometry is determined from the field equations, whereas in special relativity the geometry is a priori restricted to that which is Lorentz-invariant.

All known descriptions of physical laws utilize geometrical objects and concepts. It may be that the concept of geometry is so deeply imprinted in our minds that we cannot think of other ways to describe physical theories. The distinction we wish to emphasize here is that the geometry used in a theory may be either given a priori (like that for a flat space, used in most physical theories) or determined by the theory. If the geometry is given a priori, it is an absolute element of the theory and all laws of physics which are written in geometrical form only relate different geometrical objects and do not determine the geometry. To this date, only in the theory of relativity is the geometry determined by the theory.

Furthermore, no microscopic theory has been profitably written in a form applicable to spaces of arbitrary geometry. The microscopic laws of physics usually apply to a spatial dimension of around 10^{-8} cm (atoms) or to 10^{-13} cm (nuclei and fundamental particles). Unless the spatial variations of curvature are so large that the curvature changes substantially over such small distances, one can always transform to a coordinate system in which the metric is locally flat and free from gravitational effects. Hence it may not be necessary to require that the physical laws describing the microscopic phenomena be applicable to spaces of arbitrary geometry.*

Moreover, the requirement of covariance introduces additional complications (Chapter 9). The solutions of the Einstein field equations must admit a general coordinate transformation in order to be generally covariant. This is reflected by the fact that the ten equations satisfy four identities (Chapter 4). These are the conservation laws of energy and momentum expressed in the form

$$T^{\mu\nu}{}_{;\nu} = 0 \tag{1}$$

Thus, out of the ten Einstein field equations for ten unknown metric components $g_{\mu\nu}$ only six equations are independent. In this way an arbitrary coordinate transformation is automatically permitted by the theory.

However, no definite solutions can be found from such a set of equations, unless an additional four equations are imposed. These four equations are known as *coordinate conditions*. Once a solution is obtained one must be able to transform the solution freely to other coordinate systems compatible with the geometry. Hence, the role of coordinate conditions is to aid obtaining a solution. Once a solution is obtained they may be discarded. However, without having them imposed first and then discarded, no solution may be found.

Fock[6] argued that a certain set of noncovariant coordinate conditions exists. According to him there exists a set of preferred coordinate systems in general relativity, which are not contained in Einstein's theory but must be obtained from other arguments. This question is discussed in Chapter 9.

Identification of Gravitational Fields with the Geometrical Structure of Space-Time

To the accuracy of the Eötvös experiment, all material bodies follow unique trajectories in space-time, if gravitational forces alone act. Would not this imply that the gravitational field is a property of the space? That is, can one replace gravitational fields by a geometrical structure of space-time? This can and has been done for gravitation theory.

* However, this conclusion may not follow if the topology of the space-time is non-Euclidean.[5]

One way to achieve geometrization of gravitation theory is to define the geometry in such a way that particle trajectories coincide with unique curves contained in the geometry. Einstein suggested that the extremal paths of the geometry should be identified with particle trajectories. Then the gravitational field is replaced by the curvature of space and the equations of motion are equations for geodesics. However, this is not the only way by which the theory of gravitation may be geometrized. It is possible to define a geometry in such a way that particles do not move along geodesics of the metric. Geodesics and other curves are discussed in detail in Chapter 1.

Classical Measurements of Space-Time Distances

In the geometrized theory of gravitation, the gravitational field is replaced by the curvature of space, which is characterized by a set of metric coefficients $g_{\mu\nu}$ (metric tensor). They are defined in such a way that the line element ds (the distance between two neighboring space-time points) is given by

$$(ds)^2 = g_{\mu\nu}\, dx^\mu\, dx^\nu \tag{2}$$

where $\{x^\mu\}$ are the coordinates used and a summation over repeated indices is understood. In order to use this notion of distance operationally one must have a scheme for measuring distances. This is necessary not only for infinitesimal distances as described by Eq. (2) but also for large distances.

Classically, Einstein discussed space and time measurements in terms of rods and clocks. In a frame in which the rods and the clocks are at rest relative to each other, the two measuring instruments perform orthogonal measurements, that is, a clock measures the distance along the time axis, and a rod measures the distance along the spatial axis. If the strong equivalence principle is to hold exactly and precisely, then all coupling constants will indeed be constant. Then rods and clocks can be relied on to be unchanged from place to place and the comparison of measurements (such as the velocity of light) from place to place will have a clear meaning.

However, according to one version of gravitational theory (Dicke, Chapter 8), the gravitational coupling constant $Gm_p^2/\hbar c$ is not really a constant, but may vary with time. It is even conceivable that other fundamental constants are not constant. The ratio of distance measurements performed by using a material rod (composed of atoms) to those performed by counting the number of wavelengths of a red spectral line of Kr[86] is proportional to $e^2/\hbar c$ (Chapter 3). Hence, if the strong principle of equivalence is in doubt (Chapters 1 and 8) all measurements performed by using clocks and rods of various constitution are subject to question. Statements like "the velocity of light has a constant numerical value measured locally in all frames of reference" may not be meaningful.

On the other hand, it is not necessary to use clocks and rods at all to measure space-time intervals. It is possible to combine the measurement of space and time intervals into a single operation. This operation, Marzke and Wheeler show in Chapter 3, can be defined entirely in terms of light beams and particle trajectories independent of the constitution of matter. The constancy of the velocity of light measured in any local system then becomes—as Weyl[7] long ago suggested—a postulated principle by which measurements are interpreted.

Marzke and Wheeler also spelled out one way by which the intercomparison of space-time distance intervals may be carried out over a long distance even in the presence of gravitational fields. The heart of the procedure is a particle moving on a geodesic and a nearby particle moving on a parallel world line which in general is not a geodesic. Light is scattered back and forth between the particles. The number of scatterings yields a well-defined measurement of the space-time interval.

The Einstein Field Equations

The Einstein field equations provide a means for constructing the geometry when the stress tensor (the source of the gravitational field) and suitable boundary conditions are given. From the field equations we can also derive equations of motion of test particles which must reduce to the Newtonian equations of motion in the case of weak fields and low velocities. The Eötvös experiment indicates that the source of gravitational interaction is the total mass energy. Any matter distribution will have in addition to the rest energy of matter, also the stress energy. (Rigid bodies have no invariant meaning since a strain wave cannot be transmitted instantaneously.) Hence the source term for the gravitational equations is usually taken to be the stress-energy tensor $T_{\mu\nu}$, which includes the matter distribution as one of its components. However, one may also use the contracted stress tensor $T = T^{\mu}_{\mu}$ as a source of a scalar field, as is described in Chapter 8.

In Chapter 4 Wheeler discusses the derivation of the field equations. It is demanded that the theory be generally covariant, that it involve only the metric tensor and various geometrical objects obtained from its components and derivatives of these, and that the equations be the lowest order possible. With these requirements and the additional assumption that the stress-energy tensor $T_{\mu\nu}$ be the source of gravitational effects, the Einstein field equations follow uniquely.

Experimental Foundations of General Relativity and Other Theories of Gravity

General relativity theory, and other theories of gravity, are based on one or more of the following principles:

1. The equivalence principle
2. The local Lorentz character of space and time
3. The principle of covariance (discussed above)
4. The constancy of electric charge independent of its velocity
5. The concept that the ratio of two space-time intervals has a well-defined value independent of the route of intercomparison (Riemannian geometry!).

What is the experimental support for these principles?

The Equivalence Principle and the Principle of the Locally Lorentz Character of Space-Time

Associated with the idea of the local Lorentz character of space-time is the idea of the isotropy of space-time. Mach's principle requires that the inertial properties of matter be determined by the distribution of matter in the universe. A naïve interpretation of Mach's principle is that the inertial property of matter depends on the *local* distribution of matter, and therefore, it is expected to depend on the direction of motion. However, every attempt to detect such anisotropy has failed (Chapter 7).

Beltran-Lopez, Robinson, and Hughes[8] performed experiments to determine if the inertia of matter depends on the spatial direction (Chapter 6). The local source of mass anisotropy is the sun and the galaxy. These experiments have been done both with paramagnetic resonance absorption measurements of the Zeeman splitting in chlorine and oxygen and by nuclear magnetic resonance in lithium. In the case of Zeeman splitting, an atomic electron with nonzero orbital angular momentum moves in different directions with respect to an external magnetic field in different magnetic substates. Hence, if the mass depends on the direction of motion, the energy difference between different magnetic substates will depend on the orientation in space. A similar situation occurs with the different nuclear magnetic states in the lithium experiment. Because of the much higher binding energies in the nucleus compared with those of the atomic electrons, the lithium experiment is the more precise one. The results of this experiment place an upper limit of 1 part in 10^{22} to the anisotropy of mass.

The Constancy of Electric Charge Independent of Its Velocity

The constancy of electric charge independent of its velocity is implied by the invariance of Maxwell's equations under a Lorentz transformation. This constancy is the basis of electrodynamics as well as of special relativity from which general relativity evolved. It has been established to a high degree of precision as a by-product of several experiments carried out to measure the electron-proton charge ratio. Some of these experiments are described by Hughes in Chapter 13. In one of these, performed by Zorn,

Chamberlain, and Hughes[9], the deflection of a neutral molecular beam passing through an electric field perpendicular to the direction of motion was measured and found essentially to be zero. From the sensitivity of the apparatus for a beam of cesium atoms the equality of electron and proton charge is established to 1 part in 10^{19}.

In other experiments using a gas efflux method King[10] established the charge equality to about 1 part in 10^{20} in hydrogen and helium and Hillas and Cranshaw[11] determined the equality to about 1 part in 10^{21} with argon and nitrogen. These experiments not only demonstrate that the electric charges for electrons and protons are equal and opposite but also as a byproduct, demonstrate that the electric charge is a constant independent of its velocity to an extremely high degree of precision.

The principle behind this interpretation is the following. In a hydrogen atom the proton and the electron move around their common center of mass. Because of the lighter mass, the velocity of the electron is higher than that of the nucleus by three orders of magnitude. In a many-electron system the velocity ratio is even greater. In the case of argon ($z = 18$), the velocities of the k-shell electrons are about 4×10^9 cm/sec and the charge equality limit is 1 part in 10^{21}. If we use $(v/c)^2$ as a parameter for the dependence of electric charge with respect to its velocity, we find the coefficient of the dependence is less than 10^{-9}. This may be regarded as the accuracy to which the electric charge is independent of the velocity.

The Justification for Using Riemannian Geometry to Describe the Space-Time Structure of the World

One of the most important postulates concerning the structure of space-time is that the ratio of two intervals should be independent of the route of intercomparison. The evidence on this point is discussed by Wheeler in Chapter 3.

Experimental and Observational Tests of Gravitation Theory

For a theory of such seemingly pervasive importance underlying the structure of space-time and, as is sometimes suggested, perhaps the structure of elementary particles as well, general relativity has led to remarkably little successful experimental research. The few predictions the theory does make about observable phenomena require an almost impossible precision for any decisive measurement. Such precision has been realized for only three experiments in the past: Analysis of the orbit of the planet Mercury for a small relativistic precession of the perihelion of the orbit, gravitational bending of starlight passing by the sun, and the red shift of spectral lines emitted and observed at two different gravitational potentials. Significant precision is currently being sought for two more tests: Precession of a gyroscope in the field of the rotating earth, and gravitational radiation. In view of this paucity of tests it is no surprise that gravitation has met with limited interest in the past as an object of experimental research.

In the last few years there has been an increase in activity and interest in the field. This has come about variously by the availability of new and precise experimental techniques (e.g., earth satellites, precise electronics systems); by a broadening base of theoretical work in gravitational theory, and by an increasing feeling among some physicists of the ultimate role gravity may play in other fields of physics, such as the structure of elementary particles. The new experimental work is proceeding along several lines, some of which have already been discussed. All of these approaches are listed here for the sake of completeness.

1. A refinement of the measurements of the "three famous checks" of general relativity: the precession of the perihelion of Mercury, the bending of starlight by the sun, and the gravitational red shift.

2. Attempts to measure previously undetected general relativistic effects, in particular the Lense-Thirring precession of a gyroscope in the gravitational field of the earth, and the gravitational radiation from oscillating laboratory or astronomical masses.

3. Fundamental precision measurements which are prerequisite to any theory of gravity: the experiments concerning the equivalence of gravitational and inertial mass, mass isotropy, and charge equality.

4. Attempts to detect effects not predicted by general relativity but suggested by alternative theories: gravitational "ether drift"; time varying gravitational "constant"; the interaction of scalar matter waves with the solar system.

5. Incorporation of general relativity into the astrophysical analysis of very dense stars with the hope that the comparison of prediction with observation will lead to new conclusions.

6. Search for cosmological effects such as the over-all curvature and closure of space.

Refinements of Measurements of the Three Famous Checks

These standard three experiments are not emphasized in the subsequent chapters of this book, so we shall go into some detail here.

The field equations of general relativity are nonlinear. The principle of superposition cannot be applied to gravitational fields without caution. To discuss general relativistic effects, one examines the motion of very small bodies (test bodies) or light rays whose perturbing effect on the gravitational field is negligible. In particular, the three experimental tests to be discussed here involve the behavior of such test bodies in the Schwarzschild geometry to the order of $(v/c)^2$ or (ϕ/c^2).

The Schwarzschild geometry is an *exact* solution of Einstein's field equations with the following properties.

1. It is time-independent (static).
2. It is spherically symmetric around some point.
3. Its predictions reduce at moderate distances to those of Newtonian gravitational theory.
4. The geometry becomes asymptotically flat for large distances.

The Schwarzschild solution for the line element *ds* in the so-called isotropic coordinate system, r', θ, φ, t, is

$$ds^2 = \left(1 + \frac{m^*}{2r'}\right)^4 (dr'^2 + r'^2 \, d\theta^2 + r'^2 \sin^2\theta \, d\varphi^2) - \frac{(1 - m^*/2r')^2}{(1 + m^*/2r')^2} c^2 \, dt^2 \tag{3}$$

where m^* is the geometrized mass related to ordinary mass m by the relation

$$m^* = \frac{Gm}{c^2} \tag{4}$$

In the weak field limit for which $m^*/2r' \ll 1$ we can replace r' by an expression involving the spherical coordinate r and express the coefficients for the terms in this line element in the form of a power-series expansion in (m^*/r):

$$ds^2 = -\left(1 - \frac{2\alpha m^*}{r} + \frac{2\beta(m^*)^2}{r^2}\right)c^2 \, dt^2 + \left(1 + \frac{2\gamma m^*}{r}\cdots\right)(dr^2) + r^2 \, d\Omega^2 \tag{5}$$

The relation of isotropic coordinates r', θ, φ, t to the spherical coordinates, r, θ, φ, t (used by Schwarzschild himself) is given in Eqs. (6).

$$r = r'\left(1 + \frac{m^*}{2r'}\right)^2$$

$$r' = \tfrac{1}{2}[(r^2 - 2m^*r)^{\frac{1}{2}} + r - m^*] \tag{6}$$

$$\theta = \theta \qquad \varphi = \varphi \qquad t = t$$

Both coordinate systems reduce to the ordinary three-dimensional spherical coordinate system in the weak field limit.

For the Schwarzschild solution the coefficients α, β, γ in Eq. (5) are unity. Other theories of gravity may lead to a similar power series expansion for the line element with coefficients not equal to 1. This method of analyzing the experimental implications of the Schwarzschild geometry follow the approach of Schiff[12] and Robertson.[13]

In general relativity the value of α is determined to be unity by the requirement (3) above that Einstein's theory yield an inverse square

Newtonian gravitational field at great distances. This term also accounts for the gravitational red shift. The difference in clock rates, hence in atomic spectral frequencies at different distances from a mass point, is given by

$$\frac{\Delta \nu}{\nu} = \Delta \frac{Gm}{rc^2} \tag{7}$$

The angle of deflection of light at the limb of the sun is given by

$$\theta = 2(\alpha + \gamma) \frac{Gm_\odot}{R_\odot c^2}$$

$$= 0''.875 \, (\alpha + \gamma) \tag{8}$$

In Einstein's theory $\alpha = \gamma = 1$, so that

$$\theta = 1''.75 \tag{9}$$

The value of α is given by the Newtonian inverse square law of gravitation and may also be inferred by the principle of equivalence and the results of observations of the gravitational red shift. Arguments have also been presented by Schiff[14] to derive the bending of light (which involves γ) using the principle of equivalence in a flat space geometry. However, this derivation requires additional assumptions about the relationships of accelerating coordinate systems separated in space which are not implied by the Eötvös experiment. It has been shown in at least one case[15] that it is possible to formulate a theory which satisfies the principle of equivalence and predicts a value for the bending of light which differs from general relativity. This case, the theory of Dicke and Brans, implies a value for the light bending given by

$$\theta = \left(\frac{3 + 2\omega}{4 + 2\omega} \right) \frac{4Gm}{R_\odot c^2} \tag{10}$$

where ω is a coupling constant for a scalar field. Its value is determined to be greater than six from the observation of the relativistic precession of the perihelion of Mercury.

The prediction of general relativity for the precession of the perihelion of a planet can also be given in terms of the coefficients α, β, and γ. In this case the predicted precession is $[2\alpha(\alpha + \gamma) - \beta]$ multiplied by a geometrical factor for the particular orbit.

Of these three tests of general relativity, only the observation of the precession of the perihelion of Mercury predates the theory of general relativity. Discrepancies in Mercury's orbit had confounded astronomers since the middle of the nineteenth century. In 1859 LeVerrier noted an unexplained excess in the advance of the perihelion of Mercury over the theoretical value of approximately 39 seconds of arc per century.[16] Twenty-five years later Newcomb determined this discrepancy to be 43 seconds of arc per century.[17] The most extensive modern analysis is that of Clemence,[18] which yields a value of 42.9 ± 0.2 seconds of arc per century. This is to be compared with the general relativistic prediction of 43.03 sec.

This comparison furnishes the best support for general relativity, both because of the impressive agreement between experiment and theory and because the theoretical prediction of the precession, unlike the other two tests, depends both on the effect of gravitation on time and length measurements to terms quadratic in the mass and on the general relativistic modification of the equations of motion of a mass particle. Hence it is all the more important to confirm these results and to be sure that the calculated geometrical and dynamical corrections which total approximately 5600 seconds of arc per century are not subject to systematic error.

Unfortunately, the test for Mercury is unique. That is, it depends on a single planetary analysis of motion for relativistic precession. Because of the large number of corrections required which may be subject to systematic error, it is unreasonable to weight this measurement as heavily as the random error would suggest without independent corroboration from accurate observation of the precession of other planets. Unfortunately, the relativistic precession of other planets is less by a factor of 10 than that of Mercury. Of these the earth and Venus have been observed with accuracies of only 50 per cent. The situation for earth satellites is even worse, with the nonspherical shape of the earth producing perturbations on the orbit far in excess of the relativistic precession.

One of the possible perturbing effects on Mercury's orbit is that due to the nonsphericity (oblateness) of the sun. This effect on the precession is given for a nearly circular orbit by

$$(\text{Precession angle per revolution}) = \frac{6\pi}{5}\,\epsilon\left(\frac{R_\odot}{R}\right)^2 \qquad \epsilon = \frac{\Delta R_\odot}{R_\odot} \qquad (11)$$

where $\Delta R_\odot$ is the difference between the polar and equatorial radii of the sun. The oblateness of the sun (given by ϵ) has not been reliably measured but is estimated on the basis of a simple model of the rotating sun to produce a negligible precession of Mercury.

Dicke and his associates, Hill and Goldenberg, are undertaking a measurement of the oblateness of the sun to determine an accurate measure of this correction. The experiment is discussed briefly in Chapter 1.

The second "classical" test of general relativity in historical order is the observation of the bending of starlight as it passes through the gravitational field of the sun. The theoretical prediction for the bending of starlight both by Newtonian corpuscular theory and by general relativity is discussed in Chapter 11. Observations have been carried out at a number of solar eclipses since 1917. These experiments, subject to many uncalculable systematic errors, average about 20 per cent above the general relativity theoretical value for the average extrapolated limb shift, that is, the shift in apparent star position for a line of sight between star and observer barely grazing the edge of the sun. Unfortunately, these results are not decisive because of the difficulty in interpreting the observational data and eliminating systematic errors.[19] Furthermore, these observations give only the limb shift and do not establish the radial dependence of the bending.

An experiment is being undertaken at Yale to measure the deflection of starlight by the sun during the day without an eclipse. This approach has the advantage of permitting continuous monitoring of star separations while the sun passes through the star field, and of allowing very much increased observing time for isolating systematic errors. In addition, by using photoelectric rather than photographic detection one can eliminate the problems of photographic plate deformation in the determination of the scale function for converting the observed star displacements to angles in the celestial sphere. On the other hand, the presence of a bright background sky and bright sun present a difficulty of high background and low signal-to-noise ratio not present in the eclipse observations.

The third classical check on relativity, both in point of time and in importance, for distinguishing the prediction of general relativity from other gravitational theories is the gravitational red shift. The theory of this effect is discussed in Chapter 11. The theoretical prediction given by general relativity, and by other arguments involving only the principle of equivalence and the Doppler shift, is

$$\frac{\Delta \nu}{\nu} = \Delta \left(\frac{Gm}{rc^2} \right) \tag{12}$$

The gravitational red shift was first measured astronomically for light from the companion of Sirius,[20] a white dwarf whose mass is determined from its motion relative to Sirius and whose radius is determined from the theory of Chandrasekhar for white dwarfs. The results from these observations are very uncertain, both because of the problem of isolating the light of Sirius B from that of Sirius A and because of subsequently recognized spectral line shifts resulting from pressure in the stellar atmosphere and from the Doppler shift associated with convection. Somewhat better results were obtained more recently by Popper[21] on the dwarf 40 Eridani B. These attempts to measure this effect on stars and the sun have resulted in an acknowledgment of the complexity of the problem of disentangling the gravitational red shift from a variety of Doppler and pressure shifts which occur in the stellar photosphere. Only recently have these difficulties been avoided or partly overcome.

In a more recent terrestrial experiment Pound and Rebka[22] measured the frequency shift to be 1.05 ± 0.10 times the theoretical value. They used the Mössbauer effect for resonant absorption of gamma rays by iron-57 for a source at a vertical separation of 74 feet from the absorber. Later Brault[23] has measured the red shift in absorption lines in the sun's photosphere for the sodium Dl line, which is free of many of the disturbing effects, since the absorption for strong lines is high in the solar atmosphere. He obtained 1.05 ± 0.05 of the theoretical value.

Measurements of New Relativistic Effects

The second area of current experimental work in gravitation involves the detection of other effects predicted by general relativity but not yet observed. One of these is the effect on the orientation of the spin axis of a gyroscope in the field of the rotating earth. The theory of this effect has recently been discussed by Schiff.[12] We shall summarize his discussion here.

According to Newtonian theory, such a gyroscope, in the absence of bearing friction and structural asymmetries, should point indefinitely in its initial direction relative to "space" as determined by the "fixed" stars. General and special relativity predict a precession of the spin axis which arises from three causes:

1. As the gyroscope is carried around by the rotation of the earth, its orientation should behave according to the law of parallel transport of a vector in general relativity. The notion of parallel transport of a vector is discussed in Chapter 2 in connection with the ideas of covariant differentiation and affinity. Such a vector, transported in a circle around a mass center, will not return to its initial orientation. This effect is spoken of as the "geodetic precession."

2. In the vicinity of a rotating mass the inertial frame is "dragged around" slightly at a small fraction of the angular velocity of the mass. Thus a gyroscope, even at rest near the earth with its axis not coaxial with the earth, will experience a changing orientation relative to the fixed stars. This precession is referred to as the Lense-Thirring precession.

3. A spinning object on the earth in motion (owing to the earth's rotation) experiencing non-gravitational forces (the bearing supports) will precess according to special relativity.

For a gyroscope on the earth at the equator with spin axis normal to the earth's axis, all three effects have approximately the same value, 0.4 seconds of arc per year. For a gyroscope in a satellite, the first two effects are somewhat smaller, depending on the orbit parameters, and the third is absent.

These effects on gyroscope precession are extremely small and hence normally completely obscured by instrumental defects. However, it would be interesting to observe them. Two approaches are currently being followed to develop adequately stable gyroscopes for this experiment. One involving a superconducting spinning sphere, magnetically supported, has been investigated by Fairbank and Little at Stanford.[24] Another approach, utilizing an electrostatically supported spinning sphere, is being developed at the University of Illinois Coordinated Science Laboratory.[25]

Gravitational radiation is a particularly interesting area of research both on the theoretical and the experimental sides. It is not known whether gravitational radiation from galactic sources is of sufficient strength to be detectable. In Chapter 5, Weber reviews briefly the theoretical grounds for believing gravitational radiation exists and describes a bold and skillful attempt by himself and his collaborators to observe such radiation.

Gravitational Effects Predicted or Suggested by Alternative Theories and Hypotheses

In view of the small number of now testable predictions given by general relativity, one can try to find effects which are not predicted by general relativity but which are supported by reasonably plausible arguments or by alternative theories. Dicke has initiated several experiments along these lines, both by his work in indicating the scope of alternative theories equally compatible with the experimental evidence and by the variety of experiments which he has suggested (Chapters 7, 8, and 12).

Several of these experiments have centered around the effort to observe effects of a preferred reference frame for gravitational field effects which might be expected in accordance with Mach's principle. In one sense it is clear that there is a preferred frame of reference given by Newton's first law, that is, the inertial frame with respect to which bodies not subject to forces continue in uniform motion (or rest) and with respect to which a gyroscope maintains a constant orientation. Observationally, this reference frame with regard to rotation turns out to be coincident with the frame determined by the distant fixed stars up to an arbitrary uniform relative motion. Furthermore, one can imagine singling out an unambiguous fixed preferred reference frame by choosing one which is static relative to the average motion of the receding galaxies in the expanding universe, that is, the frame for which distant matter exhibits no net rotation and the recession velocities of galaxies are isotropic, independent of the direction of observation.

The tantalizing question is then, does uniform motion relative to this "cosmological" coordinate system produce any effect on gravitation, on strong interactions, or on weak interactions? The search for such effects on strong interactions and electromagnetic propagation is represented by the attempts to observe ether drift effects by Michelson and Morley[26] and Kennedy and Thorndike[27] and their successors, and by the modern experiments of Townes, Cedarholm, Bland, and Havens,[28] of Turner and Hill,[29] and of Jaseja, Javan, and Townes.[30] The experiment of Jaseja, Javan, and Townes verifies the Lorentz-Fitzgerald contraction due to the earth's orbital velocity to 1 part in 1000.

Does motion relative to the coordinate system of the fixed stars affect the strength of the gravitational interaction? Hoffmann[31] has attempted to detect such an effect. He monitored the period of a precision pendulum gravimeter as the earth moves in its orbit about the sun. The elliptical motion of the earth is superimposed on the motion of the sun in the galaxy, and ultimately on the motion of the galaxy relative to the cosmological coordinate system. Consequently the square of the velocity of the earth relative to this system is modulated with a period of a year. This experiment, with an accuracy of 2 parts in 10^8, implies that if gravitational attraction is affected by this motion with a term quadratic in (v/c), then the coefficient of this term is less than 1.

This search for subtle gravitational effects by direct measurements of g presents a struggle for precision and stability. Although a pendulum is capable of very precise measurement, it is subject to drift and aging. Another approach, with potentially much greater long-term stability, is that of dropping an interferometer plate for making "absolute" measurements of g. This approach has been developed by Faller.[32] Other possible observable effects due to a varying gravitational constant and to scalar gravitational waves are discussed in Chapters 8 and 12.

General Relativity in Astrophysics

The departures in the metric from that of flat space due to a mass distribution are of the order of the dimensionless number defined below:

$$\xi \equiv \frac{Gm}{rc^2} \sim \frac{Gr^2\rho}{c^2} \tag{13}$$

where ρ is the density, r is the radius of the object, and m is its mass.

For ordinary laboratory-sized objects this dimensionless number ξ is approximately 10^{-25}. At the "surface" of a proton it is 10^{-39} and at the surface of the sun 10^{-6}. It is most likely that in advanced stages of stellar evolution, the core of a massive ($M = 30$ solar masses, solar mass $= 2 \times 10^{33}$ g) star becomes a degenerate neutron gas, with a very high density.[33] This dimensionless number ξ then becomes nearly 1. In such cases, the distortion of the metric may have a large effect on stellar structure theory. This question is discussed in Chapter 10 in connection with the collapse of a "superdense" dwarf star. Gravitation theory may also play an important role in the evolution of stars if the gravitational constant varies in time, as suggested by Dicke in Chapter 8.

Cosmological Effects of Gravitational Theory

What are the boundaries of the universe? Is it open and infinite or finite in extent? Is it curved into closure? Einstein's equations permit all three possibilities. In Chapter 15 Wheeler reviews Einstein's arguments in favor of a closed universe. He also shows that the demand for closure supplies a boundary condition for the field equations of general relativity which can be interpreted as a mathematical formulation of Mach's principle.

Observationally, the question of closure is unsettled. The present state of the observational evidence for various theoretical models has been discussed in detail by Sandage.[34] He summarizes the observational data for four cosmological phenomena.

A Minimum Size for Distant Galaxies

Galaxies of a standard linear dimension in a closed universe will never show an angular diameter less than a certain minimum value. This effect is illustrated for a two-dimensional closed space (a spherical surface) in Figure I-1.

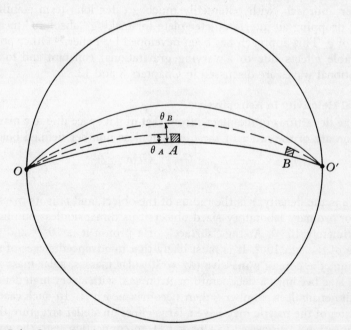

Figure I-1 On a closed two-dimensional spherical surface an object at position *A* subtends a minimum angle for an observer at O. The same-sized object at *B* subtends a larger angle as shown. The lines drawn on the surface are the geodesics (lines of shortest distance) for a sphere. O′ is the antipodal point.

The relationship between the angular diameter and magnitude of distant galaxies for a Friedman model of the universe for several different values of the deceleration parameter q is given in Figure I-2. q is a parameter used by Robertson[35] and Hoyle and Sandage[36] in describing an isotropic and homogeneous universe. For such a universe the line element can be given by

$$ds^2 = c^2 dt^2 - R^2(t) du^2 \qquad (14)$$

where du represents an auxiliary three-space of constant Riemannian curvature. $R(t)$ is a measure of distance and is determined by substituting Eq. (14) into Einstein's equations [Eq. (54), Chapter 4].
The deceleration parameter q is given by

$$q = \frac{\ddot{R}}{RH^2} \qquad (15)$$

where H is the Hubble expansion parameter:

$$H \equiv \frac{\dot{R}}{R} \qquad (16)$$

For a steady-state universe the angular diameter approaches a constant value asymptotically. For a closed universe ($q > \frac{1}{2}$) the angular diameter of distant galaxies exhibits a minimum size. This minimum size occurs at a distance greater than the distance for which the 200-inch telescope can be of use. Perhaps in the future one will be able to determine if a minimum exists (and hence be able to determine whether the universe is closed or not).

Variation in Density of Galaxies with Distance

Assuming that galaxies are distributed uniformly in the universe on the average, in a curved universe the distribution would appear to be nonuniform. Unfortunately, the data now available for the galaxy-count magnitude relation are not adequate to discriminate between various cosmological models.

Non-linearity in Redshift Observation

The observation that spectral lines from distant galaxies appear to be shifted in proportion to their distance from us has led to the model of the expanding universe with velocity of recession of galaxies proportional to their separation.

$$v = \frac{R}{T} \qquad (17)$$

where T is the reciprocal of the Hubble constant. T is currently determined to be 1.3×10^{10} years.[37]

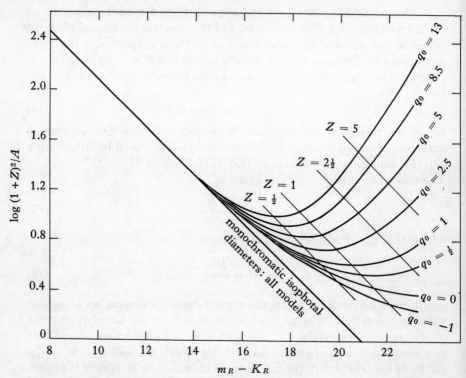

Figure I-2 *Metric* diameters of either individual galaxies or of clusters of galaxies computed on the magnitude system of the brightest cluster galaxy. No normalization of the ordinate to agree with observational data has been made. The steady-state model ($q_0 = -1$) and seven exploding models are shown. Lines of constant red shift are given. The straight line gives the *isophotal* diameters for all models by the equation $\theta_i = \text{const.}/A$. The metric diameters are defined by the actual boundary of the galaxy (as a standard rod) whereas the isophotal diameter refers to the sizes of the isophotal contours. The significance of this distinction is discussed by Sandage. (*From A. R. Sandage.*[34])

How the velocity of recession depends upon the distance varies from one cosmological model to another. For example, for a closed (Friedman-type) universe ($q > \frac{1}{2}$) the calculated recessional velocity increases more rapidly than linearly with distance.

The 200-inch Palomar telescope was built in part to answer this question. The ability of this telescope to distinguish distant objects from the sky background is limited to the 23rd magnitude. For a normal galaxy this limitation corresponds to a distance of 4.5×10^9 light-years. Unfortunately

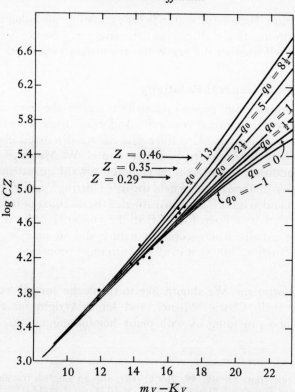

Figure I-3 The theoretical red-shift magnitude relation for various values of the deceleration parameter q_0. For a steady-state universe $q_0 = -1$, and for an open Euclidean universe $q_0 = \frac{1}{2}$. For all models with $q_0 > \frac{1}{2}$, the universe is closed. z is the red shift, $\Delta\lambda/\lambda_0$, and C is a calibration constant on the absolute magnitude scale. Data for 18 clusters of galaxies are plotted as given by Humason, Mayall, and Sandage.[37] Arrows are placed at the observed red-shift values for those distant clusters whose magnitudes are not yet available, The magnitude gives a measure of the distance; for a Euclidian space the relation is given by $R \propto$ (magnitude)[5]. (*From A. R. Sandage.*[34])

this range has not been adequate to resolve this question. Figure I-3 summarizes the predictions with respect to the universe for several values of the acceleration parameter.

Time Scales

The comparison of time scales drawn from cosmological models, stellar evolution, and the dating of rocks and meteorites has proved to be one of the most successful methods for evaluating cosmological models. These measurements are discussed extensively in Chapter 8 as a means ultimately to tell whether the gravitational constant varies with time.

Quantization of General Relativity

The quantization of general relativity is one of the most active areas of present-day gravitational research. Anderson discusses some aspects of this work in Chapter 14. (Other aspects are discussed elsewhere by B. DeWitt[38] and R. Arnowitt, S. Deser, and C. W. Misner,[39] and also in Ref. 5.) In addition, active work is going on toward quantizing relativity by perturbation methods used in field theory (Thirring[40] and Feynman[41]).

Salecker and Wigner[42] have investigated the meaning of measurements in general relativity. They found that the concepts utilized in general relativity are usually macroscopic in nature and so may be limited by quantum fluctuations inherent in all measurement processes.

Acknowledgement. We should like to thank the several lecturers and Drs. Dieter Brill, Charles Misner, and James Wright for reading the manuscript and providing us with many helpful suggestions.

References

1. A. Einstein, *Ann. Physik*, **49,** 769 (1916); also an English translation in *The Principle of Relativity*, Dover, New York, 1923, pp. 109–164.
2. R. v. Eötvös, D. Pekár, and E. Fekete, *Ann. Physik*, **68,** 11 (1922).
3. R. H. Dicke, *Sci. Am.*, **205,** 84 (1961). R. H. Dicke, P. G. Roll, and R. Krotkov, The Equivalence of Inertial and Passive Gravitational Mass (to be published).
4. A. Papapetrou and E. Corinaldesi, *Proc. Roy. Soc. (London)*, **A209,** 259 (1951).
5. J. A. Wheeler, *Geometrodynamics*, Academic, New York, 1962, p. 225.
6. V. A. Fock, *The Theory of Space-time and Gravitation*, translated by N. Kemmer, Pergamon, New York, 1959.
7. H. Weyl, *Space, Time, Matter*, translated by H. L. Brose, Dover, New York, 1950.
8. V. Beltran-Lopez, H. G. Robinson, and V. W. Hughes, *Phys. Rev. Letters*, **4,** 342 (1960); *Bull. Am. Phys. Soc.*, **6,** 424 (1961).
9. J. C. Zorn, G. E. Chamberlain, and V. W. Hughes, *Phys. Rev.*, **129,** 2566 (1963).
10. J. G. King, *Phys. Rev. Letters*, **5,** 562 (1960).
11. A. M. Hillas and T. E. Cranshaw, *Nature*, **184,** 974 (1959).
12. L. I. Schiff, *Proc. Natl. Acad. Sci.*, **46,** 871 (1960).
13. H. P. Robertson, NASA Conference on Experimental Tests of Theories of Relativity, Stanford University, July 1961, Conference Notes, p. 1.
14. L. I. Schiff, *Am. J. Phys.*, **28,** 340 (1960).
15. C. Brans and R. H. Dicke, *Phys. Rev.*, **124,** 925 (1961).
16. U. J. LeVerrier, *Annales de l'Observatoire de Paris*, **5,** 1 (1859).
17. S. Newcomb, *Astronomical Papers of the American Ephemeris*, **1,** 472 (1882).

18. G. M. Clemence, *Rev. Mod. Phys.*, **19**, 361 (1947). The value of the observed relativistic precession of the perihelion of Mercury given in the text was kindly furnished by Dr. Clemence in a private communication. This value has been corrected for the most recent determination of planetary masses.

19. B. Bertotti, D. Brill, and R. Krotkov, Experiments in Gravitation, in *Gravitation: An Introduction to Current Research*, L. Witten (ed.), Wiley, New York, 1962, pp. 30–40.

20. W. S. Adams, *Proc. Natl. Acad. Sci.*, **11**, 382 (1925).

21. D. M. Popper, *Astrophys. J.*, **120**, 316 (1954).

22. R. V. Pound and G. A. Rebka, Jr., *Phys. Rev. Letters*, **4**, 337 (1960).

23. J. Brault, *Bull. Am. Phys. Soc.*, **8**, 28 (1963).

24. This experiment is discussed by L. I. Schiff, *Phys. Rev. Letters*, **4**, 215 (1960); *Proc. Natl. Acad. Sci.*, **46**, 871 (1960).

25. A. Nordsieck, in *Progress in Astronautics and Rocketry*, R. E. Robertson and J. S. Farrior (eds.), vol. 8, Academic, New York, 1962, p. 435.

26. A. A. Michelson and E. W. Morley, *Am. J. Sci.*, **34**, 333 (1887).

27. R. J. Kennedy and E. M. Thorndike, *Phys. Rev.*, **42**, 400 (1932).

28. J. P. Cedarholm, G. F. Bland, B. L. Havens, and C. H. Townes, *Phys. Rev. Letters*, **1**, 342 (1958).

29. K. C. Turner and H. A. Hill, *Bull. Am. Phys. Soc.*, **8**, 28 (1963).

30. T. S. Jaseja, A. Javan, and C. H. Townes, *Phys. Rev. Letters*, **10**, 165 (1963).

31. W. F. Hoffmann, *Bull. Am. Phys. Soc.*, **8**, 29 (1963).

32. J. E. Faller, *Bull. Am. Phys. Soc.*, **2**, 29 (1963).

33. H.-Y. Chiu, Supernovae, Neutrinos, and Neutron Stars, preprinted NASA Institute for Space Studies, New York, 1963 (to be published in *Ann. Phys.*).

34. A. R. Sandage, *Astrophys. J.*, **133**, 355 (1961).

35. H. P. Robertson, *Publ. Astron. Soc., Pacific* **67**, 82 (1955).

36. F. Hoyle and A. Sandage, *Publ. Astron. Soc. Pacific*, **68**, 301 (1956).

37. M. L. Humason, N. U. Nayall, and A. R. Sandage, *Astron. J.*, **61**, 97 (1956).

38. B. DeWitt, The Quantization of Geometry, in *Gravitation, an Introduction to Current Research*, L. Witten (ed.), Wiley, New York, 1962, pp. 266–381.

39. R. Arnowitt, S. Deser, and C. W. Misner, The Dynamics of General Relativity, in *Gravitation, an Introduction to Current Research*, L. Witten (ed.), Wiley, New York, 1962, pp. 227–265.

40. W. E. Thirring, *Ann. Phys.*, **3**, 91 (1958).

41. R. P. Feynman, Quantization of General Relativity, lecture series (Recent Developments of Contemporary Physics) given at Yeshiva University, September 24, 1962 (unpublished).

42. H. Salecker and E. P. Wigner, *Phys. Rev.*, **109**, 571 (1958).

Gravitation and Relativity

I
Remarks on the observational basis of general relativity

R. H. Dicke

The Observational as Opposed to Formal Approach to General Relativity

In this chapter, I shall talk about the observational basis for gravitational theories, general relativity in particular. To start out in this way is a bit different from the usual procedure. Specialists working in this field are now primarily concerned with formal questions. They take it as axiomatic that general relativity is correct in all its details and that one must compute with this theory. However, if one actually examines the observational basis for general relativity, one finds that the assumption that general relativity is valid rests, primarily, on the beauty and elegance of the theory rather than on the direct observations. There is nontrivial, observational support for general relativity, and we shall see what it is. However, we shall see also that the observational support is not sufficient to eliminate other possible theories of gravitation.

With this introduction, I shall go on to a discussion of the places in which observations come into play, the bearing that they have on the structure of general relativity, and the type of observational facts most important to theories of gravitation.

Limitations and Future Possibilities of Planetary Orbit Observations

Any serious theory of gravity must reduce to Newtonian gravitation in the limit of sufficiently weak fields, or sufficiently small velocities for the moving parts that are interacting gravitationally. The observational

1

evidence in terms of planetary motion is quite good, and Newtonian gravitational theory is good, at least within certain limits. The question is: What are these limits?

The first thing we note is that the periods of the planets are known with considerable precision. The planets, at least the inner ones, have revolved a good many times during the interval of time they have been observed, and this enables quite good periods to be determined. A question naturally arises: With what kind of clock are these periods measured?

If one talks about measuring periods in terms of the earth's rotation, one is using a rather bad clock—one that is affected by tidal interactions and that undergoes random fluctuations. The most precise statement that one can make concerning planetary periods is that their ratios are known with considerable accuracy. The accuracy with which the ratios of the periods are known is of the order of 1 part in 10^8. (If one were to trace back to ancient times, perhaps the accuracy could be improved somewhat, but the interpretation of ancient records is rather tricky.) On the other hand, the ratios of the radii of the planetary orbits to each other are not known with anything like this precision. These relative-distance measurements depend on our ability to measure angles; and the accuracy here is more like a few parts in 10^6 rather than 1 part in 10^8. This means that Kepler's third law cannot be checked with an accuracy greater than a few parts in 10^6 by using planetary orbits.

The new space-science techniques are already giving hints of more accurate observations to be obtained in the future. Radar ranges on the moon and Venus have given more precise measurements of distance. Also, a light pulse derived from an optical maser reflected from a corner reflector placed on the moon appears to be capable, in principle, of a distance measurement with an accuracy of 1 part in 10^9. As discussed below, accurate radar transponder techniques as applied to Mariner-type space probes may someday give even more precise distance measurements.

Relativistic effects usually appear to the order of $(v/c)^2$. For the earth, this is around 10^{-8}. Thus, if the measurements of the radii of planetary orbits were made with an accuracy of 1 part in 10^8, we could check Kepler's third law to a limit that would be significant with respect to relativistic effects. This is where the space program can make important contributions. Accurate radar transponder experiments on planets could be used to determine these orbital dimensions with considerably more precision than they are now determined. We are not concerned with absolute distance measurements but rather with the ratio of planetary radii.

An example of a space experiment that might improve these distance measurements is an artifical planet surrounded by some gas shield to eliminate gas drag and light pressure difficulties that would interfere with the gravitational orbit. A radar technique could then be used to determine

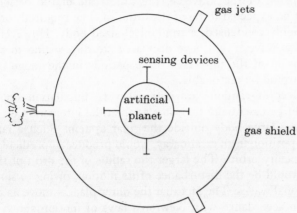

Figure 1-1   Artificial planet with a gas shield.

the distance to this device with great precision. This would give us precise orbital data for both the earth and the planetoid. The gas-shield technique has been independently suggested by a number of people, probably first by M. Schwarzschild. His suggestion is to surround a small artificial planet with a hollow spherical shell equipped with small gas jets as in Figure 1-1. When the artificial planet gets near the wall, the gas jets are turned on by a servomechanism to compensate the drag and to keep the shell from touching the inner sphere. In this way the artificial planet moves on a proper planetary orbit, not being influenced by radiation pressure and gas drag. This is a nice device, which could be used to tell us something rather interesting about gravitation theory by making possible a test of the form of the force law to the accuracy required for relativistic effects to appear.

An alternative and simpler technique would be to set two or three vehicles, externally identical but of different density, on substantially the same initial orbit. The effect of gas drag (and light pressure) on their orbits could be inferred then from their different motions. With this technique there is a substantial advantage in using heavy orbiters and uranium would be an excellent material for the densest.

Another interesting possible effect on planetary orbits involves one of the more nebulous concepts appearing in general relativity, the gravitational wave. Only recently has much of the theoretical confusion surrounding this concept been lifted. With the assumption that such waves are physically meaningful, it would be interesting to enquire about their possible effects on the solar system. If gravitational waves were produced, in a manner not yet understood, in some primeval explosion at the beginning of the expansion of the universe, the time scale of the period of such waves might be expected to be of the order of time required for sound to traverse a highly condensed, astronomical-sized body. However, the frequency of this wave would have decreased steadily, owing to the subsequent expansion of the universe. Wave periods in the range of days to many years would be reasonable.

The effect of random gravitational-wave fluctuation on the solar system would be essentially the same as the tidal interaction on planetary orbits of some large body outside the solar system. Such a large body, changing its position in an erratic way, would produce unpredicted disturbances of planetary orbits. The larger the radius of the orbit of the planet, the greater would be the disturbance of its motion, owing to slowly varying gravitational waves. The fact that the outer planets move as accurately as they do in accordance with Newton's laws of motion shows that disturbances resulting from long-period gravity waves, if they exist, are small.

Although this probably has nothing to do with gravitational waves, it is distressing to note that, although the calculations of celestial mechanics are quite good and the agreement of the observations is excellent, the agreement is not as good as it should be. It has been remarked by one of the experts that no planet is observed to move on its calculated orbit to the accuracy of the observations. The causes for the discrepancies are unknown. Small inconsistencies continue to appear.

To give an example of the type of inconsistency that shows up, the masses given in Table 1–1 have been assigned to Saturn in the last hundred years or so. These are typical reciprocal masses of Saturn in units of the sun's reciprocal mass.

As you can see, this is not a happy situation. The adopted masses have frequently changed by substantially more than the assigned errors.

Table 1-1
Reciprocal Masses of Saturn

M^{-1}	Source
3501.6 ± 0.8	Bessel (1833), from Saturn's moon Titan
3494.8 ± 0.3	Jeffrey (1954) and Struve (1924–37), (Titan)
3502.2 ± 0.53	Hill (1895), Saturn's perturbations of Jupiter
3497.64 ± 0.27	Hertz (1953), Saturn's perturbations of Jupiter
3499.7 ± 0.4	Clemence (1960), Saturn's perturbations of Jupiter

Table 1–2

Solar Parallax

Source	Parallax
Rabe (1950), from the dynamics of Eros orbit	8."79835 ± 0.00039
McGuire et al. (Space Tech Lab) (1960), from the dynamics of the orbit of Pioneer V	8."79738 ± 0.0008
Pettengill (1961), radar range of Venus	8."794491 ± 0.000024

The latest series of discrepancies involves the absolute value of the astronomical unit (the mean distance from the earth to the sun). The value one gets from the radar range of Venus does not agree very well with the value obtained from gravitational theory. Again no one knows the cause.

The most recent and precise measurements of the value of the astronomical unit imply the solar parallax given in Table 1–2. The large disagreement needs no comment.

Now, I come to the famous relativistic effect of the advancement of the perihelion of the orbit of Mercury. This is the only general relativistic effect on planetary orbits that seems to be significant in terms of measurements of present accuracy. Here the results are quite good. With an elliptical orbit, one expects a relativistic contribution to the rotation of the line of apsides, an effect over and above that which would be computed from the perturbations of other planets, using standard Newtonian mechanics. This effect is large only in the case of Mercury, where it amounts to an anomalous rotation of 43.03 seconds of arc per century. The observations suggest 42.9 ± 0.2. I would say that this is very good agreement. However, there are serious doubts about the significance of this error.

It must be remembered that the perihelion precession rate of Mercury is actually ∼5600″ of arc per century, 130 times the relativistic effect. Of this, 5026″ is geometrical, being caused by the motion of the coordinate system, and the remaining 575″ is dynamical, owing primarily to planetary perturbations. The small relativistic residual is only as accurate as these various subtracted quantities permit. The biggest contributed planetary perturbation is 278″ from Venus. Any uncertainty in the mass of this planet would be mirrored in a proportional uncertainty in this perturbation.

The recent determination of the mass of Venus, a value derived from the orbit of a space probe, increases our confidence in the accuracy of this computed contribution to perihelion rotation. There remains, however, one gnawing uncertainty about this test of general relativity, the most important of the three classical tests. A very small flattening of the sun would distort its gravitational field and hence affect planetary motion. The inner planets move in orbits almost in the solar equatorial plane, and the only important orbital effect from such a flattening is the rotation of the line of apsides (perihelion rotation). An oblateness of 10^{-4} (difference between equatorial radius and polar radius of 0.09″) would increase the perihelion rotation rate of Mercury by 7″ per century, 18 per cent of the relativistic effect. The velocity and magnetic fields at the photosphere are sufficiently small that the equipressure surfaces in the lower solar atmosphere are approximately the same as the gravitational equipotential surfaces. Hence the gravitational field due to the sun (external to it) can be reliably determined from the sun's oblateness.

Owing to turbulence in the earth's atmosphere, the limb of the sun is smeared out by 5″ and an oblateness as small as 0.05″ could be detected only with great difficulty. Present measurements are not believed to be sufficiently accurate to exclude this possibility. New improved measurements are presently being attempted at Princeton.

The Eötvös Experiment: Equivalence of Inertial and Gravitational Mass

I turn now to a different kind of experimental evidence that has a bearing on gravitational theories. You may be surprised that I do not consider immediately the remainder of the famous three checks of general relativity (I mentioned previously the perihelion advancement, but only because it ties into orbit theory). The gravitational deflection of light and the gravitational red shift are, in my opinion, secondary to several other lines of evidence that are much more important from the standpoint of the construction of theories.

The most important experiment, I believe, is the Eötvös experiment, which shows that different bodies fall with very nearly the same acceleration.[1] This experiment was performed by Eötvös in 1906 or 1908. In simplified terms, he observed the balance between gravitational and inertial forces in the following way: When an object is suspended, it is acted upon by (1) a centrifugal force resulting from the earth's rotation, (2) the earth's gravitational force directed inward, and (3) the tension in the supporting string. The equilibrium position is determined by a balance of these three forces as shown in Figure 1–2.

Eötvös used several materials, ranging from snakewood (Schlangenholtz) to copper sulfate. In principle, one would observe whether the vertical lines, as defined by the line of suspension for different objects, are the same. Within the accuracies of his experiment (5 parts in 10^9), Eötvös

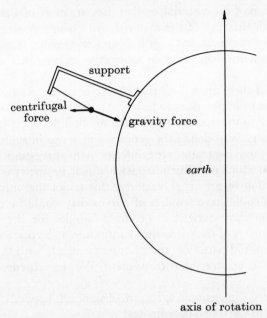

support

centrifugal
force

gravity force

earth

axis of rotation

Figure 1-2 A greatly oversimplified version of the Eötvös experiment for comparing the ratio of inertial to gravitational mass of various objects.

concluded that the centrifugal-force term and the gravitational term balanced each other, independent of the kind of material he put there.

Naturally, the experiment was not done in quite such a naïve way. Eötvös used a torsion balance with weights of different material suspended from the ends of the torsion rod.

At Princeton, Peter Roll, Robert Krotkov, and I repeated this experiment and reduced the error to less than 1 part in 10^{11}.[1] This is the accuracy to which the gravitational acceleration is presently known to be independent of the composition of the materials compared.

An Implication of the Eötvös Experiment: Gravitation Described by Geodesics of the Geometry of Space

The null result of the Eötvös experiment provides a basis for a gravitational theory. What kind of theory can one construct, knowing only this: that bodies fall gravitationally with the same acceleration, independent of the type of material falling?

The first thing one could conclude is that, to the accuracy of the experiments, the trajectories in space-time are unique curves independent of the composition of the material, so that they are more of a characteristic of the space than they are of the material. And, since these gravitational curves are unique curves in space, it becomes reasonable to ask what kind of unique curves does one find in geometry, curves that characterize space?

We note that there are curves that characterize the geometrical structure of space: for example, the geodesics (extremal paths between pairs of points). One way to incorporate the results of the Eötvös experiment into gravitational theory is to define the geometry of space in such a way that the trajectories of moving matter are geodesics in the space-time continuum. This is the way in which non-Euclidian Riemannian geometry is introduced into the description of gravity. Of course, this is not the only choice we could make. We could have families of curves that would be unique, but still could not be characterized as geodesic families for the space. Our choice of the geometry of the space-time continuum, to be that for which the trajectories of material particles (and photons) coincide with the geodesics of the geometry, is arbitrary but convenient. We shall discuss other possibilities later.

In a flat, three-dimensional space, the distance ds between two neighboring points is (in Cartesian coordinates)

$$ds^2 = dx_1^2 + dx_2^2 + dx_3^2 \tag{1}$$

Analogously, the distance between two neighboring space-time points in the presence of gravity (curved Riemannian space) is

$$ds^2 = g_{ij}\, dx^i\, dx^j \tag{2}$$

where g_{ij} is the *metric tensor* and is a function characterized by (1) the gravitational field and (2) the particular coordinate system we use. [The sum over the repeated indices i and j is assumed. As for (2), the g_{ij} transform under coordinate transformations according to certain laws (those of tensors), which are discussed by J. Anderson in Chapter 2.] Here we have left open the possible choice of a coordinate system that one could introduce.

With the introduction of the concept of infinitesimal distance between two neighboring points, one could characterize the geodesics as the line of shortest paths. That is, the geodesics are given by the variation of s:

$$\delta s = \delta \int ds = 0 \tag{3}$$

The meaning of geodesics is more extensively discussed in Chapter 2.

From the way the quantity ds was introduced in relation to the Eötvös experiment, we assume that the space-time path of free gravitational fall of a small object is given by Eq. (3). This is an idealization because other forces may be present. Also, the so-called *tidal interactions* of gravitational origin must be negligible. The smaller the spatial extent of the falling body, the less important are the tidal effects. [One form of a possible deviation from the trajectory given by Eq. (3) is discussed in Appendix A.]

We now return to the problem of the equation of motion. We first define the four-velocity. The four-velocity u^i is defined to be

$$u^i \equiv \frac{dx^i}{ds} \tag{4}$$

From Eq. (4) and the relation

$$ds^2 = g_{ij}\, dx^i\, dx^j \tag{5}$$

we obtain

$$g_{ij}u^i u^j = 1 \tag{6}$$

The variational principle that

$$\delta \int ds = \delta \int \sqrt{g_{ij}u^i u^j}\, ds = 0 \tag{7}$$

gives (from Euler's equation) the equation of minimum path length as

$$\frac{d}{ds}g_{ij}u^j - \tfrac{1}{2}g_{jk,i}u^j u^k = 0 \tag{8}$$

where $g_{ik,j} \equiv \partial g_{ik}/\partial x_j$ is the notation for ordinary differentiation. The first term is essentially an ordinary acceleration (in a flat space $u^j \to$ velocity, $g_{ij} = \delta_{ij'}$, and $ds \to c\, dt$) and may be interpreted as the inertial force ma. The second term may be thought of as a gravitational force. In other words, the particle moves in such a way that there is always a balance between the inertial and the gravitational force.

An interesting feature of this interpretation of the terms in Eq. (8) arises if Eq. (8) is modified to include a term for nongravitational forces (for example, electromagnetic forces). Since the magnitude of the terms in Eq. (8) depend on the coordinate system who choose, we can choose a coordinate system for which either the gravitational force or inertial force is zero at a point. In the former case, the external force balances the gravitational force and the body appears to be stationary; in the latter case, the external force balances the inertial force and the body appears to be accelerated in the absence of gravitational field. Therefore, the criterion, whether we are dealing with an inertial force or a gravitational force, is not a unique criterion: It depends on the coordinate system we choose.

The fact that the inertial force is like a gravitational force is an important aspect of Mach's principle, to which we shall return in Chapter 7.

It has been emphasized, in particular by Sciama, that, according to Mach's principle, one can regard the inertial forces acting on an observer

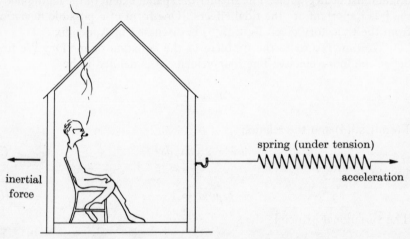

Figure 1-3   Inertial forces in an accelerated laboratory.

in a laboratory as due to the acceleration of matter at great distance which, interacting with the object inside, produces these inertial forces.

Consider a physicist inside a laboratory (Figure 1-3). We imagine this laboratory to be acted upon by a spring, which accelerates it. The phenomena we observe inside are influenced by inertial forces. From the point of view of Mach's principle, these inertial forces are gravitational in origin and are but a particular aspect of gravitation. We see a hint of this idea appear in the variational equation [Eq. (7)]: Both types of forces arise from the same term in the variational equation.

Thus, we have seen (if we neglect all such forces as the electromagnetic force, and the tidal force, as we have mentioned previously), that from the Eötvös experiment has come, in a rather natural way, the idea that particles move along geodesic paths. This identification of particle trajectories with geodesic paths constitutes the definition of the geometry.

For the moment, I shall raise the interesting question of whether these space-time paths that particles travel would be geodesic paths at all—if we could look at them with sufficient accuracy. Are there other ways of getting unique paths? Yes! One possibility is to use a two-tensor field such that the equations of motion would be of the following form:

$$\frac{d}{ds}\left(\frac{m_1 g_{ij}u^j}{\sqrt{g_{ij}u^iu^j}}\right) + \frac{d}{ds}\left(\frac{m_2 h_{ij}u^j}{\sqrt{h_{ij}u^iu^j}}\right) - \frac{1}{2}\frac{m_1 g_{jk,i}u^ju^k}{\sqrt{g_{ik}u^iu^k}} - \frac{1}{2}\frac{m_2 h_{jk,i}u^ju^k}{\sqrt{h_{jk}u^ju^k}} = 0 \tag{9}$$

This follows from the variational principle:

$$\delta \int (m_1\sqrt{g_{ij}u^iu^j} + m_2\sqrt{h_{ij}u^iu^j})\, ds = 0 \qquad (10)$$

It turns out (not surprisingly) that, if the equation of motion is in this form, one cannot, in general, define a geometry such that the paths, as defined by these equations, are geodesics. These equations are usually not in the form of geodesic paths, although they are nonetheless unique equations. Another possibility is the introduction of vector fields. It is found, however, that a vector interaction does not lead to a unique space-time path. (See Appendix B.) We shall assume for the present that the paths of particles are geodesics.

Definition of Units of Measurement; Are Physical "Constants" Constant?

Now we have the important question: How are measurements made? To answer this, we must first define the units of measure. There is a great deal of arbitrariness in this. First, if I have a meter stick and put another next to it, I can say that the two meter sticks have the same length in the sense of congruence. I cannot make such a direct congruence comparison for a meter stick here on the earth and one on Sirius. When I say that a meter stick on Sirius has the same length as one on the earth, I am talking nonsense or else I am making a definition of some kind.

There is a question as to what one may or may not define. If our approach to the geometry (definining geometry by the use of geodesics and the paths of test particles) is correct, we have already built into the geometry definitions of length and time such that the maximum velocity of a particle ($ds = 0$) is a constant. With the assumption that light travels as a maximum-velocity particle, the light paths in this geometry can be characterized by the fact that the path integral $\int ds$ is zero for a light ray. As stated above, this is the upper limit of velocity any particle can have. Therefore, we postulate the constancy of the velocity of light. It must be emphasized that, from this slightly queer point of view, the velocity of light is constant by definition, and its equality at two different points in space is built into this kind of a geometry, as long as I decide that I shall measure length and time by the same measure $\int ds$, and that $ds = 0$ for a light ray.

If actual meter sticks and clocks should fail to give the same velocity of light, independent of the position of the measurement, we would, with this scheme of things, say that the rod and/or clock was affected by some field—a field that changed the rod and/or clock. Fortunately, as nearly as we can tell, we are not faced by this problem for, to the accuracy of the observations, real rods and clocks do appear always to measure the same velocity for light.

There is still the question of the constancy of other physical constants, such as Planck's constant $\hbar$. We simplfy our work by assuming this quantity to be constant also.

We can continue to define other physical "constants" as constant (by definition) until they can be combined to form dimensionless combinations. After this happens, we must stop, for it becomes a question of experiment, not definition, as to whether such a dimensionless constant varies from point to point. We may *define* a *complete set* of quantities as constant when it is the largest number that can be defined in such a way as to generate no dimensionless numbers. Note, for example, that the constancy of electronic charge cannot be defined, having previously defined $\hbar$ and c constant.

Variation of Inertial Mass; The "Weak" versus the "Strong" Principle of Equivalence

There also is a problem of what we mean by the inertial masses of particles. Before I proceed, let me describe another experiment: This is an experiment that sets drastic limits to the kind of electromagnetic theories that one can construct. The experiments of King[2] and of Hughes (Chapter 13) showed that the charge of an electron and proton are equal to within 2 parts in 10^{20}. These are extremely precise experiments and enable one to conclude that the electromagnetic interaction is a vector interaction to a very great precision, because the atom does contain rapidly moving electrons, and, if there is any velocity dependence in the charge of the particle, it would certainly show up in these experiments.

Thus, we can conclude, with very great precision, that we understand the electromagnetic interactions. If we understand them, they can constitute a pillar upon which—again with considerable meaning and significance —we can base what we mean by inertial mass. We define the inertial mass in relation to the acceleration given to a particle that has one standard of charge and is a standard distance from a like charge. It should be remembered that length has already been defined through the geometry.

Now, one of the questions that we might consider is the problem of whether the mass ratio of two different particles (for example the mass ratio of a proton to an electron, or a hydrogen atom to a proton) is the same when we move them from one place to another. These mass ratios may be defined, as stated above, in terms of the electrically produced acceleration. Does the Eötvös experiment say anything about the constancy of mass ratios from one place to another? There is some indirect evidence that is rather compelling.

Let us imagine, for the moment, that we have defined our geometry in such a way that a particular particle, say the neutron, moves gravitationally on a geodesic path, and that the neutron obeys the geodesic equation of motion:

$$\frac{d}{ds}g_{ij}u^j - \tfrac{1}{2}g_{jk,i}u^j u^k = 0 \tag{11}$$

Now let us imagine that some other particle (e.g., hydrogen atom) is characterized by the fact that the ratio of its mass to that of the neutron is different in different places. Under this condition, it would be expected, and is found, that a new force term appears in the equation of motion; Eq. (11) must be modified to become

$$\frac{d}{ds}(mg_{ij}u^j) - \tfrac{1}{2}mg_{jk,i}u^j u^k - m_{,i} = 0 \tag{12}$$

where m is the (variable) mass of the hydrogen atom. The extra term $m_{,i}$ results from the fact that, if the mass of hydrogen changes relative to that of the neutron, some extra work has to be done to change its internal energy when it is moved. This extra work is mirrored by the extra force $m_{,i}$. But this extra force leads to an anomalous gravitational acceleration of the hydrogen atom relative to the neutron.

Therefore, the assumption that the hydrogen atom, and the neutron, have different mass ratios at different places would lead to the conclusion that, if we observe them fall with great accuracy, they should fall with different accelerations. But this is in contradiction to the results of the Eötvös experiment. Therefore, if these assumptions are valid, the mass of the hydrogen atom does not change relative to the neutron mass, at least not by much, or else we would get into difficulty with the Eötvös experiment.

This consideration leads directly to that principle which Einstein called the *principle of equivalence*. I would like to break up the principle of equivalence into two principles: a weak principle of equivalence and a strong principle.

By the weak principle, I mean that, up to the great accuracy of the Eötvös experiment, all bodies move along the same kind of geodesic paths (under the conditions for which the experiment was performed). The strong principle says something more than this. It says that, in a free-falling laboratory, if one does experiments locally, one observes the same laws of physics—including all the numerical content—that one observes anyplace else, including any gravity-free place. This is the principle that is the basis of general relativity. In order for this to be true, the mass ratio of the neutron to the hydrogen atom must be the same everywhere, or else we would see different laws of physics from one place to another; that is, the numerical content expressed in this mass ratio would be different.

Can we, therefore, conclude that the Eötvös experiment supports the *strong principle of equivalence*? The answer to this is a *qualified yes*. The experiment suggests that the ratios of the masses of elementary particles are constant. Also, in so far as the *strong interactions* are concerned, the Eötvös experiment suggests that the coupling constants (such as the electro-magnetic coupling constant $e^2/\hbar c = 1/137$) are constant to a good approxi-mation. However, the weak interactions, and the gravitational interaction, contribute so little to the self-energy of a small body that the Eötvös experiment is unable to contribute any information as to the constancy of their coupling constants.

We conclude, therefore, that the Eötvös experiment lends support to the *strong principle of equivalence*, but that it has nothing to say about the constancy of gravitation and the weak interaction. (See Appendix A for a discussion of a gravitational trajectory under conditions for which the gravitational self-energy is not negligible.)

How compelling is this argument? Is it possible that the anomalous force $m_{,i}$ in Eq. (12) could be compensated for by some other long-range field, scalar, vector, or tensor? This question was investigated by one of my students, J. Peebles. It was found that the scalar interaction is already implied by the mass variation, the mass of the particle being a function of the scalar. It is easily seen that a vector interaction is unsuitable because gauge invariance of the field leads to an interaction strength independent of binding energy (see Appendix B). The third possibility, a second tensor field, was shown to be suitable and could be so constructed as to avoid difficulties with the Eötvös experiment. However, the very stringent limits on space isotropy imposed by the experiments of Hughes, Robinson and Beltrow-Lopez,[3] also Drever,[4] were shown to require the elimination of the second tensor field. (See Chapter 6.)

This experiment demonstrated that, with tremendous precision, there is no preferred direction in space, locally. This implies that there is at least one coordinate system where all tensors of cosmic origin are spatially diagonal. As this conclusion is independent of the earth's velocity, two or more such tensors must be substantially identical, except for a possible multiplicative scalar. This appears to limit long-range fields to a single-tensor field. It is concluded, therefore, that the Eötvös experiment does support the strong principle, with the exception of the weak interactions, and gravitation.

Conclusion: The Familiar Experimental Checks; Inadequate Support for a Theory

As for those famous experimental checks of relativity—the gravita-tional deflection of light and the gravitational red-shift—the accuracy is relatively poor. There are many theories that have been constructed which agree with these experiments to the accuracy of the observations. I do not think the fact that a particular theory agrees with these observations to their present poor accuracy is very strong support for it. In particular the gravitational red shift follows from a simple energy conservation principle. What we must do, it seems to me, is to construct theories that are compatible with the precision null experiments—that of Eötvös, the space-isotropy experiment of Hughes et al. and Drever, and the charge-constancy experiments of King and of Hughes. Of course, it goes without saying that the resulting theories must also be compatible with the "three checks" *to within their accuracy*.

We have seen how Riemannian geometry gets into such gravitation theories. Also we have discovered the extent to which the "strong principle of equivalence" is supported by the Eötvös experiment and must be satisfied by such theories. However, the assumption that the weak-interaction "constant" and the gravitational-coupling "constant" are constant need not be made. This assumption is based, not upon observations, but upon certain philosophical considerations of dubious validity. In Chapters 7 and 8, I shall explore the consequences of a possible nonconstancy of the gravitational coupling "constants."

Appendix A

Effects on Planetary Motion of Gravitational Self-Energy

Jupiter is almost large enough that its gravitational self-energy could come into its dynamics in a measurable way. This suggests a possible important experiment for the future. The fractional part of the total energy of Jupiter represented by the gravitational self-energy E_{self} is

$$\frac{E_{self}}{Mc^2} = \frac{GM_J^2}{RM_Jc^2} \approx 10^{-8}$$

It might be asked whether this part of Jupiter's total energy contributes to its weight in the normal fashion. If not, an anomaly in its acceleration of this order of magnitude would be expected.

This particular number is too small now, with the present accuracy of the radius measurement of Jupiter's orbit, to say anything about its gravitational acceleration, to this accuracy. I think it is too small by two orders of magnitude. But, if we can use Mariner-type vehicles with radar transponders or radar echoes to measure the radius of Jupiter's orbit, we could investigate the question of whether there is anything anomalous about Jupiter's acceleration by reason of the fact that we already have a precise measure of its period. The self-energy for the sun is 100 times bigger, but, unfortunately (or fortunately for us), the sun is not part of a double-star system, and its inertial mass cannot be measured separate from its gravitational mass.

Appendix B

Limitation on the Possible Strength of a Lee–Yang Vector Field from the Eötvös Experiment

A long-range (zero-mass) vector field has some interesting features. Some years ago Lee and Yang suggested,[5] in connection with baryon conservation, that there might be some vector field in space that would play a role in connection with baryon conservation, a role analogous to electromagnetism in relation to charge conservation.

If such a field existed, it could interact with the nucleons and lead to long-range interactions just like electromagnetic interactions. This kind of interaction is a nongeodesic type. However, the Eötvös experiment sets very drastic limits to how strong this interaction can be. In fact, it must be extremely weak indeed, if it exists at all. The reason is this: A vector field is such that the force is independent of the motion of the charged particle. Inside an atom, with an electron going around the nucleus, the charge of the electron is independent of how fast it is moving. Analogously, the strength of the vector interaction is independent of the way that the nucleons are bound.

But, the inertial mass does depend on the binding. Therefore, one can consider the problem of how hydrogen would fall in relation to how iron would fall. In the case of iron, the nucleus consists of many nucleons strongly bound and rapidly moving. Thus the inertial mass per nucleon is smaller for iron than for hydrogen. If the vector force (which depends only on how many nucleons there are) exists, the accleration of this tightly bound system would be different from the acceleration of a system without the binding energy, not because the force is different, but because the inertial mass is different.

This kind of an argument can be used to set very drastic limits to the strength of this Lee and Yang force, if it exists. It has been shown[6] that it must be weaker than gravitation by a factor of 10^7.

References

1. For details of this experiment, see R. H. Dicke, *Sci. Am.*, **205,** No. 6, 84 (1961).
2. J. G. King, *Phys. Rev. Letters*, **5,** 562 (1960).
3. V. W. Hughes, H. G. Robinson, and V. Beltrow-Lopez, *Phys. Rev. Letters*, **4,** 342 (1960).
4. R. W. P. Drever, *Phil. Mag.*, **6,** 683 (1961).
5. T. D. Lee and C. N. Yang, *Phys. Rev.*, **98,** 1501 (1955).
6. R. H. Dicke, *Phys. Rev.*, **126,** 1580 (1962).

2

Riemannian geometry

J. L. Anderson

Geometry as an Experimental Science

Euclidean geometry was considered by Immanuel Kant to be one of the *a priori* categories of thought. For him, there was no other way of thinking about geometry. By the time Kant wrote his *Critique of Pure Reason*, the historic origins of geometry had long since been forgotten. For Euclidean geometry had its inception as an experimental science with the work of the ancient Egyptians and Babylonians. It began with the attempt to portion out land after the Nile overflowed its banks. Later, it was codified by Euclid and was developed into a subject of pure thought. By the time of Kant, Euclidean geometry was considered the only geometry one could conceive of. However, mathematicians were soon to construct other geometries. Although their origins were not experimental, they did demonstrate that Euclidean geometry was not the only conceivable one.

Not long after Kant's writings, about 1829, Bolyai and Lobatchewsky attacked one of the main postulates of Euclidean geometry, the parallel postulate. This postulate was that through a point only one line can be drawn parallel to another given line. By modifying that postulate they developed the so-called non-Euclidean geometries.

It was not until 1915, however, that geometry was recognized again as an experimental science by Einstein in his general theory of relativity. The way in which this came about was discussed by Professor Dicke in Chapter 1.

I shall review this briefly. The principle of equivalence states that it is impossible to distinguish locally, by a purely gravitational observation, between a uniform gravitational field and a uniformly accelerated frame

17

of reference in the absence of the field. Thus it is possible to describe gravitational effects either in terms of a flat space with a gravitational field present, or in terms of a curved four-dimensional space without a gravitational field. The second alternative is the origin for the geometric interpretation of gravitation and brings geometry back to an experimental science for which the problem is to determine the geometry of the physical world. It was the attempt of Einstein in 1915 to revive this question that led to the development of general relativity.

Unfortunately, general relativity is somewhat of a mathematical subject built upon the concepts and structures of tensor calculus and Riemannian geometry. This chapter is devoted to a discussion of the four-dimensional Riemannian geometry as a prerequisite to understanding general relativity. I shall approach the subject in a synthetic fashion starting with the simplest kind of geometry, namely, no geometry at all.

The Element of Geometry: A Differentiable Manifold; Geometric Structure

The simplest geometry is that of a bare topological space. Such a space is a collection of points with a topology. The topology specifies the notion of points being near each other. It enables us to define the neighborhood of a point in the manifold, that is, all the points that are near this point. When it is possible to make a one-to-one correspondence between these points and the points of an Euclidean space in such a way that, whenever two such correspondences overlap the relationship between them is continuous and differentiable, we call the topological space a differentiable manifold. Eventually we shall make an association between the points of the manifold and the points of actual space-time.

The usual topology of space-time is assumed to be the same as that of an ordinary Euclidean plane. For example, with this kind of topology any closed curve can be shrunk to a point in a continuous manner. There are other topologies in which this is not the case. For instance, on the surface of a doughnut where the topology is not Euclidean, there are two different classes of curves that cannot be shrunk to a point.

Perhaps even the assumption that the topology of space-time is euclidean is open to question, to be decided by physical observation. Recently, Wheeler and Misner have constructed models for electric charge by actually introducing non-Euclidean manifolds, containing so-called worm holes.

Much of the following discussion will be independent of the type of topology possessed by our manifold. When this is not the case, we shall assume Euclidean topology unless we state otherwise.

Because a bare manifold is not of much interest in physics, we must enrich it by assigning to it some geometric structure. Then we can attempt to make a correspondence between this geometric structure and the physical quantities we wish to describe. We shall find that there are geometric objects called vectors and tensors which can be associated with actual physical structures. As an example, we usually associate an antisymmetric tensor with an electromagnetic field. We must always keep in the back of our mind, however, that these geometric quantities are merely superimposed on an otherwise bare manifold that has only a topology associated with it.

Coordinates: A Practical Convenience

Now, let me say a word about coordinates in geometry. The geometry that we are familiar with is the so-called intrinsic geometry. The properties of such a geometry are independent of the particular coordinate system we choose. One of the central features of general relativity is the independence of geometry on the particular way of coordinatization. For example, the intrinsic geometry of a plane is not affected by the way we draw coordinate lines on it. It does not matter if they are drawn curved (e.g., polar coordinates) or straight (Cartesian coordinates).

Thus, one can build up an intrinsic geometry on a manifold and construct the intrinsic quantities, that is, the tensors and vectors, without ever making reference to coordinates. However, for practical purposes, this has not proved to be convenient, So, instead we introduce coordinates and use the tools of analytic geometry to associate numbers with points in the manifold.

As we use the notion of a coordinate system, we must always keep in mind the fact that this coordinate system is merely an aid in helping us to do calculations. Our results should be independent of the particular coordinate system chosen. We do not prefer one coordinate system over any other. This is sometimes referred to as *the principle of general covariance*. But, the physical meaning of this principle is a far-more-involved question than what we have stated simply above.

To introduce coordinates onto our space-time manifold, we shall associate the points of the manifold with those of a Euclidean space; that is, with every point P of the manifold, we shall associate a set of four numbers $\{x^\mu\}$, where $\mu = 1, 2, 3$, or 4. We can do this in many ways. We can make another association with a set of different numbers $\{x'^\mu\}$. Since associations $\{x^\mu\}$ and $\{x'^\mu\}$ describe the same point, there must be functional relations between $\{x^\mu\}$ and $\{x'^\mu\}$. We write

$$P \leftrightarrow \{x^\nu\} \tag{1}$$

$$P' \leftrightarrow \{x'^\mu\} \tag{2}$$

Hence

$$x'^{\mu} = x'^{\mu}(\{x^{\nu}\}) \tag{3}$$

Since the manifold is assumed to be differentiable, the functions x'^{μ} must be continuous and differentiable functions of the x^{ν}. It is also assumed that the inverse to Eq. (3) exists. However, unless the manifold possesses Euclidean topology, it will not be possible to cover the manifold by a single coordinate system that satisfies these conditions. For example, if we try to coordinatize the surface of a sphere, we run into difficulties at the poles or branch cuts. Thus, we can coordinatize this manifold only by pieces, with one coordinate system covering one patch and another covering another patch. However, wherever the patches overlap, the two coordinate systems used to coordinatize them must satisfy the relations (3) for all points in the intersection of the two patches.

Contravarient and Covariant Tensors

We shall now proceed to define vectors and tensors according to the way in which they transform under coordinate transformations of the form of Eq. (3). We begin by defining contravariant quantities. The simplest contravariant quantity is a scalar. A scalar has the property that its numerical value at a point does not change under a coordinate transformation. Not all numbers defined at a point are scalars. Only those to which this particular invariant transformation law applies are scalars. An example of a number associated with a point that does not transform like a scalar is the kinetic energy of a particle at a point. Under a transformation involving time-dependent translations the kinetic energy changes. So it is not a scalar, although it is a number.

We represent this mathematically by the following. Let $\phi(x)$ be a scalar. When a coordinate transformation $\{x\} \to \{x'\}$ is made, $\phi(x) \to \phi'(x')$. But, although the functional dependence of ϕ on x is different from ϕ' on x', it is true that

$$\phi(x) = \phi'(x') \tag{4}$$

if $\{x\}$ and $\{x'\}$ both refer to the same point.

Next we define the contravariant vector. A contravariant vector is a set of four numbers (we shall always be working in a four-dimensional space) which have certain transformation properties at a point P. The transformation law for a contravariant vector A^{μ} is

$$A'^{\mu} = A^{\nu} \frac{\partial x'^{\mu}}{\partial x^{\nu}} \tag{5}$$

This is a linear transformation since the A''s and A's are related linearly. (We use the convention of summing over repeated indices.) Here again,

$\{x\}$ and $\{x'\}$ refer to the same point P. Thus: In order to transform a contravariant vector, we first transform its components, as in Eq. (5), then we insert the transformed coordinates. For example, if we want to obtain the Lienard–Wiechart potential from the field of a stationary particle, we perform a Lorentz transformation to a frame of reference in which the particle is moving, calculate the transformed components of the field from the Lorentz transformation, and substitute the transformed coordinates.

One example of a contravariant vector is a line joining two points that lie close to each other. In one coordinate system, it is dx^μ, and in the other coordinate system (primed system), it is

$$dx'^\mu = \frac{\partial x'^\mu}{\partial x^\nu} dx^\nu \tag{6}$$

Covariant quantities may be defined similarly by their transformation laws. A covariant scalar transforms like a contravariant scalar.

A covariant vector B_μ (we denote contravariant vectors by using superscript indices and covariant vectors by using subscript indices) transforms as

$$B'_\mu = \frac{\partial x^\nu}{\partial x'^\mu} B_\nu \tag{7}$$

The gradient of a scalar function is an example of a covariant vector:

$$\frac{\partial \phi}{\partial x'^\nu} = \frac{\partial x^\mu}{\partial x'^\nu} \frac{\partial \phi}{\partial x^\mu} \tag{8}$$

These quantities have been defined without referring to a metric. In this way, we have introduced geometric structure into this manifold. We may generalize these vector-transformation laws in order to define a whole class of quantities that satisfy linear homogenous transformation laws. These quantities are called tensors and may have an arbitrary number of covariant and contravariant indices.

The transformations of a tensor $T \cdots ^\mu_\nu \cdots$ is

$$T' \cdots ^\mu_\nu \cdots = \cdots \frac{\partial x'^\mu}{\partial x^\rho} \cdots \frac{\partial x^\sigma}{\partial x'^\nu} \cdots T \cdots ^\rho_\sigma \cdots \tag{9}$$

That is, for each contravariant (or covariant) index, the tensor transforms as a contravariant (or covariant) vector. The total number of indices (contravariant or covariant) is the rank of the tensor.

Tensor Algebra

We next define the algebra of tensors. Since we have defined tensors only by their transformation characteristics, the algebra is not specified.

We must define addition and multiplication laws for tensors that are consistent with their transformation properties. The addition law is defined as

$$A \cdots ^{\mu} \cdots + B \cdots ^{\mu} \cdots = (A + B) \cdots ^{\mu} \cdots \qquad (10)$$

Only tensors of the same rank and contravariant or covariant properties may be added, and then only at the same point.

A particular tensor can be defined at every point of space. This is called a tensor field. The addition of two tensor fields must be carried out point by point. It makes no sense to add them at different points since they transform differently at different points. Such a sum would have no meaningful transformation properties. Thus, if we want to maintain the tensor character, we must add tensors of the same kind and rank at the same point.

We define the multiplication of tensors such that components of the product tensor are given by the products of the components of the two tensors:

$$A \cdots ^{\mu} \cdots B \cdots ^{\nu} \cdots = (AB) \cdots ^{\mu} \cdots \cdots ^{\nu} \cdots \qquad (11)$$

where $A \cdots ^{\mu} \cdots$ and $B \cdots ^{\nu} \cdots$ need not be of the same kind or rank. The rank of the resulting tensor AB is the sum of the ranks of A and B. We can verify that $(AB) \cdots ^{\mu} \cdots ^{\nu} \cdots$ does transform like a tensor.

We now define further algebraic operations. A tensor may be contracted by summing over a pair of contravariant and covarient indices to obtain a new tensor:

$$A \cdots \cdots ^{\mu} \cdots \cdots _{\mu} \cdots \qquad (12)$$

The rank of the contracted tensor is two less that of the original tensor. For example, we may multiply two vectors A^{μ} and B_{ν} to obtain a tensor of the second rank $(AB)_{\nu}^{\mu}$. A contraction of $(AB)_{\nu}^{\mu}$ gives $A^{\mu}B_{\mu}$, which is the scalar product of the two vectors and is a tensor of the zeroth rank.

A useful property of tensors, which is preserved under transformations, is its symmetry property. This refers to the change of sign of a tensor under the interchange of a pair of like indices:

$$A \cdots ^{\mu} \cdots ^{\nu} \cdots = \pm A \cdots ^{\nu} \cdots ^{\mu} \cdots \qquad (13)$$

A is said to be symmetric or antisymmetric with respect to the pair of indices μ and ν according to whether the plus or minus sign applies. The symmetry property of a tensor is an invariant property under coordinate transformation.

A special tensor, the Kronecker delta, is defined as

$$\delta^{\mu}_{\nu} = \begin{array}{cc} 1 & \mu = \nu \\ 0 & \mu \neq \nu \end{array} \tag{14}$$

δ^{μ}_{ν} can be shown to transform like a tensor.

As a consequence of the homogeneity of the tensor-transformation law, if a tensor has all its components equal to zero in one coordinate system, they will vanish in all other coordinate systems as well.

Tensor Densities

There are other objects that transform according to a linear homogeneous transformation law. These objects are called tensor densities and are of some importance in general relativity. Following the usual practice, we use German capitals to denote a tensor density. A tensor density can carry contravariant as well as covariant indices. Under a coordinate transformation $\{x\} \rightarrow \{x'\}$, the components of $\mathfrak{F}$ transform as

$$\mathfrak{F}' \cdots ^{\mu} \cdots = \left| \frac{\partial x^{\alpha}}{\partial x'^{\beta}} \right|^{w} \cdots \frac{\partial x'^{\mu}}{\partial x^{\nu}} \cdots \mathfrak{F} \cdots ^{\nu} \cdots \tag{15}$$

$|\partial x^{\alpha}/\partial x'^{\beta}|$ is the Jacobian of the coordinate transformation, and w (an integer) is the weight of the tensor density $\mathfrak{F} \cdots ^{\nu} \cdots$.

A useful tensor density is the Levi-Civita tensor density $\epsilon^{\mu\nu\rho\sigma}$, defined as

$$\epsilon^{\mu\nu\rho\sigma} = \begin{cases} +1 \text{ when } \mu, \nu, \rho, \sigma \text{ is an even} \\ \quad\quad \text{permutation of } 1, 2, 3, 4 \\ -1 \text{ when } \mu, \nu, \rho, \sigma \text{ is an odd} \\ \quad\quad \text{permutation of } 1, 2, 3, 4 \\ 0 \text{ when any pair of } \mu, \nu, \rho, \sigma \\ \quad\quad \text{are identical} \end{cases} \tag{16}$$

It may be shown that $\epsilon^{\mu\nu\rho\sigma}$ is a tensor density of weight 1. It has the property that the determinant of any tensor of second rank $h_{\mu\nu}$ is given as

$$|h_{\mu\nu}| = \tfrac{1}{4}\epsilon^{\mu\alpha\rho\gamma}\epsilon^{\nu\beta\sigma\delta}h_{\mu\nu}h_{\alpha\beta}h_{\rho\sigma}h_{\gamma\delta} \tag{17}$$

ϵ serves to arrange the different terms of h in accordance with the definition of a determinant.

So far, we have considered only geometric objects whose transformation law is linear and homogeneous. There are other types of geometric objects in addition to these. For example, the affinity is a geometric object. Its transformation law is not homogeneous, although it is linear. This will be discussed later. There are other geometric objects that have even more complicated transformation laws, but, because they have at present no application in physics, we shall not discuss them further.

Differentiation of Tensors

Now we shall define the operation of differentiation of tensors. This operation is designated by a comma. For example, $\phi_{,\mu}$ means the partial differentiation of ϕ with respect to x. In general,

$$T \ldots {}_{\mu,\nu} \ldots \equiv \frac{\partial T \ldots {}_{\mu} \ldots}{\partial x^\nu} \tag{18}$$

However, $T \ldots {}_{\mu,\nu} \ldots$ is *not* a tensor. We can illustrate this by considering the transformation law for the derivative of a vector:

$$A_{\mu,\nu} = \frac{\partial A_\mu}{\partial x^\nu}$$

Under the coordinate transformation $\{x^\mu\} \to \{x'^\nu\}$ the $A_{\mu,\nu}$ becomes

$$A'_{\mu,\nu} = \frac{\partial x^\rho}{\partial x'^\mu} \frac{\partial x^\sigma}{\partial x'^\nu} A_{\rho,\sigma} + \frac{\partial^2 x^\rho}{\partial x'^\mu \partial x'^\nu} A_\rho \tag{19}$$

Clearly, this is not the tensor transformation law. However, there are certain differential operations that can be performed to construct tensors. The following quantities do satisfy the tensor transformation law:

$$A_{\nu,\mu} - A_{\mu,\nu} \tag{20}$$

$$\phi_{\mu\nu,\rho} + \phi_{\rho\mu,\nu} + \phi_{\nu\rho,\mu} \quad (\text{for} \quad \phi_{\mu\nu} = -\phi_{\nu\mu}) \tag{21}$$

and

$$\sum_{permutation} A_{\mu\nu\rho,\sigma} \tag{22}$$

if $A_{\mu\nu\rho}$ is antisymmetric with respect to interchange of any two of the three indices.

We can also construct tensor densities with differential operations. The following are tensor densities:

$$\mathfrak{A}^\mu{}_{,\mu} \quad (\text{rank zero}) \tag{23}$$

$$\mathfrak{A}^{\mu\nu}{}_{,\nu} \quad (\text{for} \quad \mathfrak{A}^{\mu\nu} = -\mathfrak{A}^{\nu\mu}) \tag{24}$$

$$\mathfrak{A}^{\mu\nu\rho}{}_{,\rho} \quad (\text{for } \mathfrak{A}^{\mu\nu\rho} \text{ totally antisymmetric}) \tag{25}$$

$$\mathfrak{A}^{\mu\nu\rho\sigma}{}_{,\sigma} \quad (\text{for } \mathfrak{A}^{\mu\nu\rho\sigma} \text{ totally antisymmetric}) \tag{26}$$

Now we may ask ourselves: How much physics can we construct from tensors, tensor densities, and their derivatives alone? We may, for example, construct the following equations from the second-rank tensors $T^{\mu\nu}$ and $\phi_{\mu\nu}$, which are taken to be antisymmetric:

$$T^{\mu\nu}{}_{,\nu} = j^\mu$$
$$\phi_{\mu\nu,\rho} + \phi_{\rho\mu\,\nu} + \phi_{\nu\rho,\mu} = 0 \tag{27}$$

They turn out to be the celebrated Maxwell equations, if we write

$$T^{\mu\nu} = \begin{pmatrix} 0 & H_z & -H_y & -D_x \\ -H_z & 0 & H_x & -D_y \\ H_y & -H_x & 0 & -D_z \\ D_x & D_y & D_z & 0 \end{pmatrix} \tag{28}$$

and

$$\phi_{\mu\nu} = \begin{pmatrix} 0 & B_z & -B_y & -E_x \\ -B_z & 0 & B_x & -E_y \\ B_y & -B_x & 0 & -E_z \\ E_x & E_y & E_z & 0 \end{pmatrix} \tag{29}$$

and let j^μ be the current density. But we cannot obtain any solutions for these uncoupled equations in the absence of any subsidiary equations for connecting B and E with H and D. Hence these equations alone can have no physical content. It appears that the first nontrivial theory that can be built upon a manifold will require, in addition to antisymmetric quantities as introduced above, a symmetric tensor of the second rank. Anything less will either give no theory at all or will give one with a uniquely determined trivial solution. Therefore, on the basis of what we have done, we can obtain the superficial form of Maxwell equations, but not their detailed content.

The need for some additional structure defined on the manifold leads us into the various kinds of geometries. The first kind of geometry we will consider is *affine geometry*.

Affine Geometry: The Notion of Covarient Differentiation

To construct an affine geometry we start with some particular coordinatization of our manifold and assign to each point a set of 64 numbers $\Gamma^\rho_{\mu\nu}$, which is called the affine connection or simply the affinity of our space. The choice of the Γ's determines the particular kind of affine geometry imposed on the space. But this alone is not sufficient to define the affinity. We must specify, as well, how to construct the Γ's in

some other coordinate system, given them in the original one. This transformation law should be such that a knowledge of the original Γ's alone,
together with the coordinate transformation, uniquely determine the Γ's
in this other system.

We shall define the transformation law for the Γ's through the introduction of the notion of the covariant derivative of a covariant vector
(denoted by a semicolon before the index of coordinate of differentiation).

$$A_{\mu;\nu} \equiv A_{\mu,\nu} - \Gamma^{\rho}_{\mu\nu}A_{\rho} \tag{30}$$

We require the Γ's to transform in such a way that $A_{\mu;\nu}$ itself transforms
like a covariant tensor of the second rank. Then the transformation law
for the Γ's must be

$$\Gamma'^{\rho}_{\mu\nu} = \frac{\partial x'^{\rho}}{\partial x^{\sigma}} \frac{\partial x^{\gamma}}{\partial x'^{\mu}} \frac{\partial x^{\delta}}{\partial x'^{\nu}} \Gamma^{\sigma}_{\gamma\delta} + \frac{\partial x'^{\rho}}{\partial x^{\sigma}} \frac{\partial^2 x^{\sigma}}{\partial x'^{\mu} \partial x'^{\nu}} \tag{31}$$

Because of the last term in Eq. (31), the Γ's do not transform like the components of a tensor. Nevertheless, their components in any one coordinate
system are uniquely determined by their components in any other system
by means of the transformation law (31). Hence, they depend only on the
geometry imposed on the space and thus have an intrinsic significance.

Given an affinity Γ specified in some coordinate frame, it is always
possible to find another coordinate system in which all components of the
affinity are zero at one point. At that point, the covariant derivative reduces
to the ordinary derivative

$$A_{\mu;\nu} = A_{\mu,\nu} \tag{32}$$

In the small region in the neighborhood of that point, the geometry is
Minkowskian (a flat space). Thus, any law that we set up with ordinary
derivatives (valid in flat space) may be translated into a law that is valid in
general relativity (where the space is no longer flat) by just replacing ordinary derivatives by covariant derivatives.

Covariant differentiation of a contravariant vector is obtained by the
following rule:

$$B^{\mu}_{;\nu} = B^{\mu}_{,\nu} + \Gamma^{\mu}_{\rho\nu}B^{\rho} \tag{33}$$

This satisfies the requirement that

$$(A_{\mu}B^{\mu})_{;\nu} = A_{\mu;\nu}B^{\mu} + A_{\mu}B^{\mu}_{;\nu} \tag{34}$$

For the remainder of this chapter we shall assume for convenience
that Γ is symmetric in the lower indices:

$$\Gamma^{\mu}_{\rho\nu} = \Gamma^{\mu}_{\nu\rho} \tag{35}$$

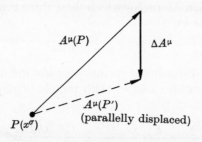

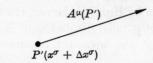

Figure 2-1   Parallel displacement of a vector.

Parallel Displacement; The Geometrical Meaning of Covariant Differentiation

In the following, we shall describe another way of introducing the affinity from a more physical approach. This involves the notion of parallel displacement of a vector and the definition of a derivative of a vector field.

The derivative of a function is usually defined by the limit

$$\lim_{\Delta x \to 0} \left\{ \frac{f(x^\nu + \Delta x^\nu) - f(x^\nu)}{\Delta x^\nu} \right\} = \frac{\partial f(x^\nu)}{\partial x^\nu} \tag{36}$$

where $f(x^\nu + \Delta x^\nu) - f(x^\nu)$ is the difference between the values of the function f defined at two neighboring points P' and P. But this definition cannot be applied directly to a vector field. We cannot meaningfully subtract two vectors at different points because, in general, vectors at different points transform differently. In order to overcome this difficulty we must define the operation of parallel displacement of a vector from a point $P'(x^\sigma + \Delta x^\sigma)$ to a neighboring point $P(x^\sigma)$ (Figure 2-1). The components of the vector $\overline{A^\mu(P')}$ obtained by parallelly displacing $A^\mu(P')$ from P' to P can be written

$$\overline{A^\mu(P')} = A^\mu(P') - \delta A^\mu \tag{37}$$

δA^μ is not a vector. Its form is determined by the requirements that $\overline{A^\mu(P')}$ transforms like a vector (at P), that $A^\mu(P')$ transforms like a vector (at P'), that $\delta A^\mu = 0$ when $A^\mu = 0$, and that $\delta A^\mu = 0$ when $\Delta x^\sigma = 0$.

The simplest functional form for which these three conditions are satisfied is the bilinear vector form:

$$\delta A^\mu = -\ \Gamma^\mu_{\rho\sigma} A^\rho \Delta x^\sigma \tag{38}$$

where $\Gamma^\mu_{\rho\sigma}$ is some three-index quantity which defines the meaning of parallel displacement of a vector. With the above requirements, and the relation that

$$\frac{\partial x'^\nu(P')}{\partial x^\mu} = \frac{\partial x'^\nu(P)}{\partial x^\mu} + \frac{\partial^2 x'^\nu(P)}{\partial x^\mu \partial x^\sigma} \Delta x^\sigma$$

Eqs. (37) and (38) define the transformation law for $\Gamma^\mu_{\rho\sigma}$. This turns out to be identical with that given by Eq. (31). Hence, the introduction of the affinity through the notion of parallel displacement is consistent with its introduction directly through the invariant requirement for covariant differentiation.

Now we continue to describe geometrically covariant differentiation of a vector field. To obtain the covariant derivative of a vector field at a point P, we first parallelly displace in a parallel direction the vector given by the field at a point P' to the point P by the law given in Eqs. (37) and (38). Then we subtract from that the vector which actually exists at point P to obtain

$$\Delta A^\mu = \overline{A^\mu(P')} - A^\mu(P) = A^\mu(P') - \delta A^\mu - A^\mu(P) \tag{39}$$

Since $\overline{A^\mu(P')}$ and $A^\mu(P)$ are both defined at the same point, their difference will be a vector. For small Δx^σ

$$A^\mu(P') = \frac{\partial A^\mu(P)}{\partial x^\sigma} \Delta x^\sigma + A^\mu(P) \tag{40}$$

Substituting this into Eq. (39), we obtain

$$\Delta A^\mu = A^\mu + \frac{\Delta A^\mu}{\Delta x^\sigma} \Delta x^\sigma + \Gamma^\mu_{\rho\sigma} A^\rho \Delta x^\sigma - A^\mu \tag{41}$$

The covariant derivative is the limit of the ratio of this difference divided by the separation of the points Δx^σ:

$$A^\mu_{;\sigma} = \lim \frac{\Delta A^\mu}{\Delta x^\sigma} = A^\mu_{,\sigma} + \Gamma^\mu_{\rho\sigma} A^\rho \tag{42}$$

Introduction of Geodesics without a Metric

Thus, an affine space includes the notion of a parallel displacement. With this notion alone, without the aid of a metric, we may construct

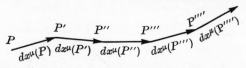

Figure 2-2 Obtaining a geodesic from successive infinitesimal parallel displacement of a vector.

geodesics in the following manner: Starting with some infinitesimal displacement vector at a point P, we may parallel displace this vector along its own direction to the point P'. This gives us a new infinitesimal vector at P' that we can then displace along its own direction to P''. Continuing this process, we obtain the broken-line curve of Figure 2-2. Thus, one can parallel-transport the vector dx^μ from any point to some other point. As the size of each displacement goes to zero, this broken line becomes a continuous curve. Thus curve starts from P with a well-defined direction and continues to another point at a finite distance. Such a curve is called a *geodesic*.

Now we use a parameter to designate points along the curve. Let s be chosen to transform as a scaler and to have an invariant value at P and P'. Then dx^μ/ds is a vector. The condition for a geodesic is that the components of the vector $dx^\mu(P)/ds$ displaced to a point P' are identical with those of the vector dx^μ/ds at P':

$$\frac{dx^\mu(P)}{ds} - \Gamma^\mu_{\rho\sigma}\frac{dx^\rho}{ds}\Delta x^\sigma = \frac{dx^\mu(P')}{ds} \tag{43}$$

We may divide this equation by the displacement from P to P', Δs, and take the limit as $\Delta s \to 0$:

$$\lim_{\Delta s \to 0}\left\{\frac{[dx^\mu(P')/ds] - [dx^\mu(P)/ds]}{\Delta s} + \Gamma^\mu_{\rho\sigma}\frac{dx^\rho}{ds}\frac{\Delta x^\sigma}{\Delta s}\right\} = 0 \tag{44}$$

or

$$\frac{d^2x^\mu}{ds^2} + \Gamma^\mu_{\rho\sigma}\frac{dx^\rho}{ds}\frac{dx^\sigma}{ds} = 0 \tag{45}$$

This is the equation for a geodesic in terms of the invariant parameter s for the curve. It is interesting that we have obtained this equation without recourse to the notion of a metric. With this construction of a geodesic, we can use the parameter s to compare the lengths of two intervals along the same curve but not along two different curves.

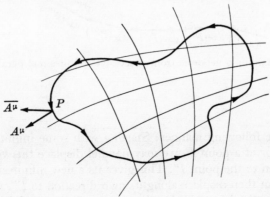

Figure 2-3 Parallel transport of a vector around a closed curve.

In a flat space the Γ's may be chosen to be zero everywhere and the geodesic equation [Eq. (45)] becomes

$$\frac{d^2x^\mu}{ds^2} = 0 \tag{46}$$

This is the equation for straight lines. This conclusion is independent of the choice of the particular coordinate system and prevails even if the Γ's are not zero. It is an intrinsic property. If there is any one coordinate system in which all Γ's are identically zero, the space is flat and the geodesics are straight lines.

There is a simple criterion to determine if it is possible to construct a coordinate system, with the Γ's zero. It is that any vector A^μ transported parallel around any closed curve must return to its initial value. In general, this will not be the case (Figure 2-3).

For A^μ to return to its initial value,

$$\oint \Gamma^\mu_{\rho\sigma} \frac{dA^\rho}{ds} \, ds = 0 \tag{47}$$

A more convenient criterion for flat space without involving integration uses the tensor $B^\iota_{\kappa\lambda\mu}$ (called the *key tensor*):

$$B^\iota_{\kappa\lambda\mu} = -\,\Gamma^\iota_{\kappa\lambda,\mu} + \Gamma^\iota_{\kappa\mu,\lambda} + \Gamma^\iota_{\alpha\lambda}\Gamma^\alpha_{\kappa\mu} - \Gamma^\iota_{\alpha\mu}\Gamma^\alpha_{\kappa\lambda} \tag{48}$$

One may show (1) $B^\iota_{\kappa\lambda\mu}$ is a tensor; (2) if $B^\iota_{\kappa\lambda\mu} = 0$ everywhere, there exists a coordinate system in which all the Γ's vanish everywhere, and the space is flat. This key tensor plays an important role in Riemannian geometry and consequently will play a key role in the theory of general relativity.

The Metric Tensor

The fundamental assumption of general relativity is that a free particle will move along a geodesic in four-dimensional space-time. The affinities are in some way connected to the geometric properties of the space and, consequently, to the gravitation and dynamic properties of the space. However, we cannot use the geodesics alone to describe the geometry. To go further, we must introduce a way of comparing distances along different geodesics. We do this by finding a mechanism for assigning an invarient distance between any pair of points in the space.

As previously mentioned, we can always find a coordinate system for which the Γ's vanish at some point. Then, a small region of space in the neighborhood of that point appears like a flat space, and we may introduce the metric of special relativity. This means we can define the space-time distance between two neighboring points. This is given as

$$ds^2 = \eta_{\mu\nu}\, dx^\mu\, dx^\nu \tag{49}$$

where

$$\eta_{\mu\nu} = \begin{pmatrix} -1 & 0 & 0 & 0 \\ 0 & -1 & 0 & 0 \\ 0 & 0 & -1 & 0 \\ 0 & 0 & 0 & 1 \end{pmatrix} \tag{50}$$

This is the Minkowski metric.

It is interesting to note that it is not always possible to introduce a metric into an affine geometry in a consistent manner. We can take, for example, a space-time that is invariant under the galilean group of transformations:

$$\begin{aligned} x' &= x - v_x t \\ y' &= y - v_y t \\ z' &= z - v_z t \\ t' &= t \end{aligned} \tag{51}$$

This space contains the notion of parallel displacement and affinity. In fact, one can talk about parallel transport over a finite distance. This means we can speak of two vectors as parallel at large distances and, consequently, this is a flat space. But, we cannot introduce a nonsingular metric into such a space.

The reason for this is that, when the time separation Δt is not zero, the space separation can be transformed to any value by Eq. (51), whereas the time separation is invariant. Hence, there is no way to assign a unique space-time separation. Only when the time separation of the points is zero can distances between points be uniquely defined. This is the case of a flat three-dimensional geometry for a single point of time. This trouble does not occur in a Minkowskian space, for time is not invariant, and there is a limiting velocity.

The metric given by $\eta_{\mu\nu}$ in Eq. (50) has a natural extension in a general Riemannian space-time continuum. We may simply define the infinitesimal distance ds between two neighboring points as

$$ds^2 = g_{\mu\nu}\, dx^\mu\, dx^\nu \qquad (52)$$

where $g_{\mu\nu}$ is taken to be some tensor field.

Having made this definition, we may inquire whether there is any relationship between the metric $g_{\mu\nu}$ and the affinity $\Gamma^\alpha_{\beta\gamma}$, which was obtained from parallel transport. It turns out that there is a connection if we require that a geodesic constructed by parallel transport is the shortest distance between two points. The equation for the curve of shortest distance between two points in a space, for which the distance is given by Eq. (52), is

$$\frac{d^2 x^\mu}{ds^2} + \left\{ {\mu \atop \rho\sigma} \right\} \frac{dx^\rho}{ds} \frac{dx^\sigma}{ds} = 0 \qquad (53)$$

where $\left\{ {\mu \atop \rho\sigma} \right\}$ is known as the Christoffel symbol and is defined as

$$\left\{ {\mu \atop \rho\sigma} \right\} = \tfrac{1}{2} g^{\mu\nu} (g_{\nu\rho,\sigma} + g_{\sigma\nu,\rho} - g_{\rho\sigma,\nu}) \qquad (54)$$

The $g^{\mu\nu}$ have yet to be defined in terms of $g_{\mu\nu}$. Comparing Eqs. (45) and (53), we see that the coincidence between the geodesic and the line of shortest distance may be established if we set

$$\Gamma^\mu_{\rho\sigma} \equiv \left\{ {\mu \atop \rho\sigma} \right\} \qquad (55)$$

Using this identity, we can express the key tensor $B^\iota_{\kappa\lambda\mu}$ defined in Eq. (48) in terms of the metrical quantities. This tensor is also known as the Riemann–Christoffel tensor. The metric $g_{\mu\nu}$ can be taken to be symmetric, since antisymmetric components cannot contribute to the value of ds^2. It has thus only 10 independent components. This is to be compared with the 40 components for a symmetrical affinity and 64 for a general affinity. The geometric structure of general relativity is contained in these 10 components of the $g_{\mu\nu}$.

We have defined separately contravariant and covariant vectors without giving any rule for obtaining the covariant components of a given vector from the contravariant components. We shall simply define the covariant components of any contravariant vector A^ν to be

$$A_\mu = g_{\mu\nu}A^\nu \tag{56}$$

Thus,

$$A^\nu g_{\mu\nu}A^\mu \equiv A_\mu A^\mu \tag{57}$$

Further, we may define $g^{\alpha\beta}$ to be the inverse of $g_{\mu\nu}$ by the condition

$$g^{\alpha\beta}g_{\beta\gamma} = \delta^\alpha_\gamma \tag{58}$$

where

$$\delta^\alpha_\gamma = \begin{cases} 1 & \text{for } \alpha = \gamma \\ 0 & \text{for } \alpha \neq \gamma \end{cases}$$

It then follows that

$$A^\nu = g^{\nu\mu}A_\mu \tag{59}$$

Equations (56) and (59) prescribe how to raise and lower tensor indices.

We now give an interpretation of covariant and contravariant components of a vector. For an oblique coordinate system, there are two ways to describe the components of a vector. In one case, one projects this vector onto a set of vectors perpendicular to the basis vectors that form the coordinate system. These projectors are the covariant components of the vector. In the other case, one resolves the vectors into components parallel to the basic vectors of the coordinate system. These are the contravariant components. This is why raising or lowering indices does not change the intrinsic properties of the vector. It only changes the representation of the vector.

Curvature in Riemannian Geometry

The tensor that is obtained from the B (key) tensor by lowering its only upper index is known as the Riemann–Christoffel tensor:

$$R_{\alpha\beta\gamma\delta} = g_{\mu\alpha}B^\mu{}_{\beta\gamma\delta} \tag{60}$$

This tensor has the following geometric interpretation: For any two vectors ξ^μ and η^μ given at a point in four-dimensional space, we may define a set of vectors w^μ as all possible linear combination of ξ^μ and η^μ:

$$w^\mu \equiv \xi^\mu u + \eta^\mu v \tag{61}$$

u and v are scalars that may take any value.

Now construct all geodesics tangent to w^μ from this single point of space. These geodesics will generate a two-dimensional surface in our four-dimensional space. The curvature of this two-dimensional surface may be defined as the curvature of a sphere that is made to fit the surface at the point to second order.

This curvature called K and thus defined by the use of the two vectors ξ^μ and η^μ is given by

$$-K = \frac{R_{\mu\nu\rho\sigma}\zeta^{\mu\nu}\zeta^{\rho\sigma}}{(g_{\alpha\gamma}g_{\rho\delta} - g_{\alpha\delta}g_{\beta\gamma})\,\zeta^{\alpha\gamma}\,\zeta^{\beta\delta}} \tag{62}$$

where $\zeta^{\alpha\beta}$ is

$$\zeta^{\alpha\beta} \equiv \xi^\alpha\eta^\beta - \xi^\beta\eta^\alpha \tag{63}$$

Thus, R, together with the g's, describes the curvature of the surface defined by ξ^μ and η^μ.

There is another vital tensor that plays an important role in the theory of relativity. This is the Ricci tensor $R_{\mu\nu}$, defined as

$$R_{\mu\nu} \equiv B^\iota_{\mu\nu\iota} \tag{64}$$

$R_{\mu\nu}$ is also known as the curvature tensor.

The curvature scalar R is defined as

$$R = g^{\mu\nu}R_{\mu\nu} \tag{65}$$

A simple geometric interpretation may be given to R. We first define the meaning of orthogonality: Two vectors A^μ, B^μ are said to be orthogonal to each other if

$$g_{\mu\nu}A^\mu B^\nu = 0 \tag{66}$$

This is an invariant property. In an n-dimensional space, n such mutually orthogonal vectors may be constructed. Out of each pair of such orthogonal vectors a surface may be constructed. In a four-dimensional space, six such surfaces exist through a given point. The average curvature of the six surfaces is R.

Next, we consider the average scalar curvature of a three-dimensional subspace orthogonal to any given vector ξ^μ. The curvature K of this subspace is given as

$$K = \frac{G_{\mu\nu}\xi^\mu\xi^\nu}{\xi^\mu\xi_\mu} \tag{67}$$

where $G_{\mu\nu}$ is defined by

$$G_{\mu\nu} = R_{\mu\nu} - \tfrac{1}{2}g_{\mu\nu}R \tag{68}$$

This quantity $G_{\mu\nu}$ plays the fundamental role in the structure of field equations in general relativity.

Symmetry Properties of Geometry

Having seen how we can impose various geometric objects upon a bare manifold to obtain the various types of geometries, we shall now look at the symmetry properties of these various geometries. We are all aware of the role symmetry has played in the formulation of physical theory and especially in the relativity theories of Einstein. Symmetries have their main importance in the restrictions that they impose on the possible theories one might construct to describe a given physical system. Thus, the requirement of special relativistic invariance has served to limit the possible number of particle fields.

What then are the symmetry properties of the bare manifold? The essential feature of the bare manifold is that it is impossible to distinguish any one point in the manifold from any other point. If we should ever happen to get lost on a bare manifold, we would have no way of telling where we were, since there are no distinguishing geometric signposts. The only properties that the bare manifold possesses are topological properties, such as its connectivity. These properties are unaffected by any deformation of the manifold, such as twisting or stretching, short of actually tearing it.

In order to formulate these ideas more precisely, we introduce the idea of a mapping or transformation of the points of the manifold onto themselves. Thus, with each point P of the manifold we associate a new point P', the only restriction being that we do not tear the manifold; i.e., points that are topologically near each other must be mapped onto points which are also topologically near each other. Of course, when we go from point P to point P' we must drag along the topology at P and replace the topology at P' with it. Since the local topology is always assumed to be Euclidean, it is clear that replacing the topology at P' with that at P changes nothing on the manifold. Thus, a bare manifold admits the most general topological transformation possible, and hence its symmetry is that of the group of all possible topological transformations.

We can formulate these ideas analytically by coordinatizing our manifold. If the coordinates of the point P are the set of numbers $\{x^\mu\}$ and the coordinates of the point P' associated with the point P are the set $\{x'^\nu\}$, we can express the association by giving the x''s as functions of the x's for each pair of associated points. Since the coordinatization is assumed to be continuous, at least over finite patches, we can express the entire mapping or transformation by the equation

$$x'^\mu = x'^\mu(\{x^\nu\}) \tag{69}$$

Any set of four functions $x'^\mu(\{x^\nu\})$ then serve to generate a topological transformation.

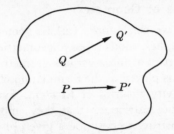

Figure 2-4   Infinitesimal mapping of the manifold onto itself.

In the case of an infinitesimal deformation or mapping, we can represent the mapping by means of a vector field over the manifold. The elements of this vector field are the vectors formed by connecting each point P to the infinitesimally displaced point P' with a short arrow leading from P to P' (Figure 2-4). We then say that the manifold admits a group of motions generated by this vector field. Since the mappings that leave the topology of the manifold unchanged are arbitrary except for the restrictions stated above, we see that any vector field on the manifold will generate a possible motion.

What happens to the symmetry properties of the space when we impose a geometrical structure, such as an affinity or a metric tensor, on it? When we perform our mapping of points of the manifold onto other points, we must always compare the geometric structure at each of the two associated points. Only if they are identical can we say that the mapping is an invariant mapping and represents a symmetry of the space.

It is clear that, whenever we impose a geometric structure on our manifold, we automatically reduce the symmetry group from that of all possible topological mappings to some subgroup. Thus, the imposition of a Lorentz metric on the manifold reduces the symmetry group to that of the Lorentz transformations. For some other type of metric there may be no symmetry group at all.

Since, in the future, we shall be dealing almost exclusively with metric geometries, we shall only talk about their symmetry properties, although similar arguments can be carried through for the case of affine and projective geometries. We then seek the general conditions under which a mapping or transformation of the manifold leaves unchanged the metric structure imposed upon it. To simplify the discussion, we shall consider only the case of an infinitesimal motion of points into new points. Since every finite transformation can be built up from a sequence of infinitesimal transformations, this restriction will not limit the generality of our considerations.

Let the vector field $\xi^\mu(x)$ carry the point P with coordinates $\{x^\mu\}$ over to the point P' with coordinates $\{x^\mu + \xi^\mu(x)\}$. Since the metric is taken to be a tensor, it transforms as

$$g'_{\mu\nu} = \frac{\partial x^\rho}{\partial x'^\mu} \frac{\partial x^\sigma}{\partial x'^\nu} g_{\rho\sigma} \tag{70}$$

In this case the x''s are the coordinates of the point P' so that

$$x'^\mu = x^\mu + \xi^\mu(x) \tag{71}$$

Since the ξ's are assumed to be infinitesimal quantities, the inverse transformation is

$$x^\mu = x'^\mu - \xi^\mu(x') \tag{72}$$

Thus, the metric to be assigned to the point P' under this transformation is

$$g'_{\mu\nu} = g_{\mu\nu} - g_{\mu\rho}\xi^\rho{}_{,\nu} - g_{\rho\nu}\xi^\rho{}_{,\mu} \tag{73}$$

where all quantities appearing on the right-hand side of this equation are to be evaluated at the point P.

The original metric at the point P' can be expressed in terms of quantities evaluated at point P by making a Taylor expansion of the metric about the point P:

$$g_{\mu\nu}(x + dx) = g_{\mu\nu} + g_{\mu\nu,\rho}\xi^\rho \tag{74}$$

The difference $\overline{\delta g}_{\mu\nu}$ between these two metrics $g'_{\mu\nu}$ and $g_{\mu\nu}(x + dx)$ is thus given by

$$\overline{\delta g}_{\mu\nu} = - g_{\mu\rho}\xi^\rho{}_{,\nu} - g_{\rho\nu}\xi^\rho{}_{,\mu} - g_{\mu\nu,\rho}\xi^\rho \tag{75}$$

The necessary and sufficient condition that the motion generated by the vector field $\xi^\rho(x)$ leave the geometry unchanged is that the two metrics given by Eqs. (73) and (74) be the same:

$$\overline{\delta g}_{\mu\nu} = 0 \tag{76}$$

The equation for the ξ's implied by Eq. (76) can be written in the compact form

$$\xi_{\mu;\nu} + \xi_{\nu;\mu} = 0 \tag{77}$$

This equation is known as Killing's equation, and any vector field that satisfies it is known as a Killing vector field. One can obtain similar conditions on a vector field that serves to generate a motion which leaves the affine geometry of a space invariant. Since Eq. (77) contains only geometric objects (the vector ξ) and geometric operations (covariant differentiation), it is a geometric equation and is independent of any particular coordinatization of the manifold. The Killing vectors, being the generators of infinitesimal invariant motions of the space, determine the symmetry properties of the space. Similarly, the symmetry properties determine the infinitesimal generators. Since an arbitrary vector field will not, in general, satisfy Eq. (77), we see that this space has a much smaller symmetry group than a bare manifold.

We can best illustrate these ideas for the case of the flat space-time geometry of special relativity. There, if one introduces cartesian coordinates, the metric takes the form given in Eq. (50) for all points of the manifold. [One need not use Cartesian coordinates for the determination of the Killing vectors; any coordinate system will do. However, Killing's equation (77) is greatly simplified when one uses these coordinates.] For the case of flat space and Cartesian coordinates, the covariant derivatives appearing in Eq. (77) can be replaced by ordinary derivatives. In that case, the most general solution can be written

$$\xi_\mu = \epsilon_{\mu\nu} x^\nu + b_\mu \tag{78}$$

where $\epsilon_{\mu\nu}$ is an arbitrary constant antisymmetric matrix and the b's are arbitrary numbers. It is evident that the ξ's thus found serve as the generators of infinitesimal inhomogeneous Lorentz transformations.

Similarly, one can find the Killing vectors associated with other metrics. For the Schwarzschild metric, one Killing field represents translations in time. Hence, the Schwarzschild metric is time symmetric, thus static. A six parameter Killing field represents rotations in space, hence the Schwarzschild metric is also spherically symmetric. We emphasize again that the Killing vectors are geometric objects that represent an inherent symmetry of the space and are completely independent of any particular coordinatization of the underlying manifold.

The above material completes this brief survey of tensor analysis and differential geometry. We have not attempted to be complete or rigorous, but rather to emphasize the main ideas of these fields which play an important role in general relativity. For more detailed treatments of these topics, the reader is referred to the references that follow.

Suggestions for Further Reading

1. E. Schroedinger, *Space-Time Structure*, Cambridge University Press, Cambridge, 1960. Many of the derivations outlined in this lecture are carried out in detail in this short but beautifully lucid book.
2. H. Weyl, *Space-Time-Matter*, Dover, New York, 1950. This is still one of the great books of mathematical physics and contains one of the best and deepest discussions of relativity and geometry, even though it was first written in 1918. In many places we have been guided by Weyl's treatment.
3. W. Pauli, *Theory of Relativity*, Pergamon, New York, 1958. There is a succinct and beautiful technical discussion of Riemannian geometry contained in this excellent review of relativity.

4. L. P. Eisenhart, *Riemannian Geometry*, Princeton University Press, Princeton, N.J., 1926 (2nd ed., 1949). A standard text on the subject which is quite readable and contains much advanced material, but does not discuss the most recent work on the subject.

5. T. J. Willmore, *An Introduction to Differential Geometry*, Oxford, New York, 1959. Contains a readable treatment of many of the modern developments in the field.

6. P. Alexandroff, *Elementary Concepts of Topology*, Dover, New York, 1961. This book contains an excellent introduction to this subject. It succeeds in making the basic ideas of the subject intuitively clear, and there is no lack of diagrams to illustrate these ideas. In style, it is the antithesis of the abstract school of writing in mathematics.

3

Gravitation as geometry—I:
The geometry of space-time and
the geometrodynamical standard meter

Robert F. Marzke and John A. Wheeler

How Can the Idea of Curved Empty Space Have any Tangible Meaning?

Einstein's theory states that gravitation is a manifestation of the geometry of curved empty space. What idea could make one more uncomfortable! To conceive of curved space seems difficult enough. To speak of curved *empty* space seems preposterous. How can one possibly get any concrete hold on such an ethereal concept?

Illustration of the Geometry of a Curved Manifold

Consider a simpler situation where some of the same issues come to the fore. Let one be given a collection of city names. Let one also be given a table of the distances between these cities. How does one know that these cities belong on a curved surface rather than on a flat chart?

Consider, for example, major airports of the world: the Azores, Berlin, Bombay, Buenos Aires, ... We abbreviate these names: AZ, BE, BO, BA, ... We start tabulating the distances between these airports in a matrix labeled by rows and columns as in Table 3-1.

We have proceeded only a little along the way toward constructing a complete table when the wind picks up the scrap of paper and whirls it away. It falls in the midst of a group of students surveying outdoors with their instruments and plotting tables. One picks it up and studies it a while. He thumb tacks down onto his plane table a new sheet of paper. He marks a black dot with his pencil and labels it AZ. With his ruler, he

Table 3-1

Geometry Is Revealed by a Sufficiently
Extensive Table of Airline Distances

	AZ	BE	BO	BA	$\cdots$
AZ	0	2148	5930	5385	$\cdots$
BE	2148	0	3947	7411	$\cdots$
BO	5930	3947	0	9380	$\cdots$
BA	5385	7411	9380	0	$\cdots$
$\cdots$	$\cdots$	$\cdots$	$\cdots$	$\cdots$	$\cdots$

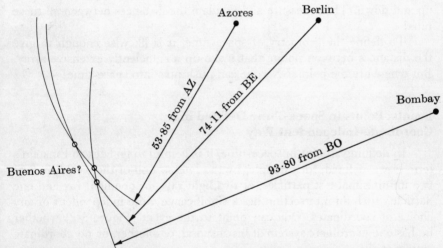

Figure 3-1 No position can be found on a flat surface for the fourth point, Buenos Aires, which will give correct distances from the three airports that have already been charted.

measures off 21.48 cm from this dot and puts down a second point BE. All goes well also with his third step: He marks down a point BO, which is distant 59.30 cm from AZ and 39.47 cm from BE. However, trouble arises when he comes to the last column in Table 3-1. Try as he will, the student can find no location for a fourth point BA that is compatible with the numbers in the last column (Figure 3-1).

While he is struggling to make sense out of the table of numbers on the piece of paper, and beginning to give up hope for a solution, a colleague comes along and hears about the situation. He suggests: "Why not try mapping these numbers on a curved surface?" After a little discussion, it is evident to both that this idea is reasonable. There is surely—they agree— a sphere of *some* radius on which all the distances can be fitted together into a consistent pattern. One of them is good at solid geometry and even calculates the radius of curvature required for consistency. He finds 39.60 cm. The other points out that the radius of the earth is about 4000 miles and argues then that the distances in the table must be given in miles. From here, it is only a step for the two to arrive at a complete understanding of the meaning of the table.

The implication of this example is clear enough. Geometry is specified as soon as the distance between every point and every other point has been given. For example, to characterize the geometry of a boat, first lay it on the ground hull up. Push pins into the hull every foot or so, left and right, up and down. Then measure and tabulate the distances between all these pins!

To define the geometry of space-time, it is likewise enough to give the distances between points that make up a sufficiently extensive array. But where are the points? No one can push pins into space-time!

Events: Points in Space-Time Defined in a Coordinate-Independent Way

In defining a point in space-time, it is helpful to go back to Einstein's term *event*, defined, for example, by the intersection of the world lines of two infinitesimal test particles, or two light rays, or one light ray and one particle. Such an intersection has a significance quite independent of any choice of coordinates. One can point to the event (Figure 3-2) whether he has one coordinate system at his disposal, or another, or no coordinate system at all.

The illustration shows only a limited number of world lines and events. A more detailed diagram would show a maze of world lines and of light rays and the intersections between them. From such a picture one makes the step to the idealized limit: an infinitely dense collection of light rays and of world lines of infinitesimal test particles. This collection is to be compared with a great stack of straws of hay. The points of contact between straw and straw correspond to the everywhere-dense set of intersections between world line and world line. The events defined in this way fill out all space-time. Each has a well-defined significance, no matter who the observer is.

Add to the idea of event the idea of distance between one event and

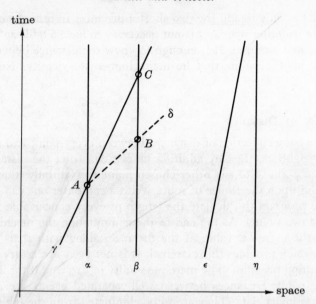

Figure 3-2 Sample world lines. The world lines α and β are crossed by another world line γ and by a light ray δ. The points of crossing define the events A, B, and C.

another. In this way come to the idea of establishing a giant notebook. This observational record is subdivided by rows and columns. Each row belongs to one point. Each column belongs to one point. The entry in a given row and column is the interval of proper time, or of proper distance, between one specified point and another. How this interval is to be measured is yet to be discussed. Grant that one somehow has come into possession of a method to make this distance measurement. Grant also that one has the patience to make sufficiently many such measurements. Idealize to an almost infinite number of rows and columns. The notebook will supply all the raw material that one needs to define the geometry of spacetime. It will be so heavy that it will have to be trundled about on a wheelbarrow. Therefore, the question arises: Is there not some simpler way to describe the information contained in this all-encompassing record?

Distances between Nearby Points Are Enough to Define the Geometry

Clearly, it is not necessary to know the distance from New York to San Francisco if one knows the distance from New York to Chicago, the distance from Chicago to San Francisco, and if one is assured, in addition, that Chicago lies on the airline connection between the two coastal cities.

Then one has only to add the two shorter distances in order to obtain the longer one. In other words, it is not necessary to have a table so extensive as the one just pictured. It is enough to know the distance between every point and all the points that lie in its immediate vicinity. No more is required.

Additivity of Distance

If one has a collection of distances between every point and all its immediate neighbors, then by addition he can construct the distance from any chosen point A to any other chosen point P. Naturally, this distance will depend upon the choice of route. With a computer one can set up an automatic program to calculate the length of every conceivable route between the two points. At the end of the computation the machine prints out only the extremal value of the distance, along with that "geodesic routing" which provides this extremal. It is not even necesssary to set up the computing program. The mere possibility of carrying it through illustrates the point. Distances between well-separated events are not to be ranked as primary data. They are to be eliminated from the table. This is simplification number one!

Cataloging of Points Simplified by Four Families of Coordinate Surfaces

Simplification number two is an improved method by which to catalog the points. One may have started by assigning a seven-digit telephone number to each event. However, these numbers will run out far too soon for one to finish the job. Therefore, introduce instead four one-parameter families of surfaces. One such family of surfaces may be compared with a pile of automobile fenders nested one above another and numbered serially. Imagine another family of surfaces intersecting and interpenetrating this first family after the manner of construction of an egg crate (but a very deformed and curvilinear egg crate!). In three-dimensional space, three such independent-interpenetrating families of surfaces give the means to catalog conveniently the position of each point. Three coordinates x, y, z or x^1, x^2, x^3 specify, respectively, the labels of the three intersecting surfaces that run through the point in question. In space-time, four families of coordinate surfaces are enough to tell the position of any given event.

Continuity and Independence the Only Requirements; No Preferred Coordinate System

Coordinate surfaces are introduced only for bookkeeping purposes. They run through the collection of events with due regard to continuity and to independence of each family from the others—but nothing more. The four families of surfaces provide one with a four-part "telephone number" (t, x, y, z) for each point that one wants to talk about. A new telephone number $(\bar{t}, \bar{x}, \bar{y}, \bar{z})$ will be attributed to the same point in an alternative cataloging system based on four quite different families of surfaces. The new numbering system—provided it too satisfies the requirements of continuity and independence—is just as good as the old one. Neither numbering system contains any information whatsoever about curvature. Without information on *distances*, the coordinates reveal no more quantitative information about the geometry of space-time than the letters AZ, BE, BO, BA,...—in and by themselves—tell about the curvature of the earth!

Coordinates as Catalog Numbers

Now that *a* coordinate system is available, it is possible to catalog the typical point P in the great haystack of events as an ordered set of four numbers (x, y, z, t). A nearby event P' is similarly cataloged by four nearby numbers $(x + dx, y + dy, z + dz, t + dt)$.

Simplification by Reason of Limited Dimensionality of Space-Time

There are indefinitely many points P', P'', P''' in the neighborhood of P. Therefore, it might appear that indefinitely many numbers are required to tell the distances between these points. This fear is unjustified, because space-time has a limited dimensionality.

The dimensionality reveals itself by the circumstance that the distances between nearby points are not independent of one another. For example, in two-dimensional space, it is possible to specify the three separations (12), (23), (31) between three points, 1, 2, 3, arbitrarily within the limits set by the triangle inequality. However, to tell where a fourth point is, it is only necessary to give the two distances (14) and (24). The third distance (34) is fully determined by the data already given, except for the freedom of choice of a $\pm$ sign in a square root. A like formula exists in spaces with higher number of dimensions. It is possible to prove from this circumstance that *the distance from any point to a nearby point depends bilinearly upon the coordinate differences between the two points*, according to the formula

$$(ds)^2 = g_{\alpha\beta} \, dx^\alpha \, dx^\beta \tag{1}$$

(See the Appendix to this chapter for a further discussion of this point.) Here, Einstein's summation convention is used, according to which, repetition of an index implies summation over that index. Each label independently goes over as many values as there are dimensions; thus, α, β = 0, 1,

2, 3. The *metric coefficients* in (1)—later also called *gravitational potentials*—can be defined without loss of generality in such a way as to be *symmetric* with respect to change of indices; thus,

$$g_{\alpha\beta} = g_{\beta\alpha} \tag{2}$$

In consequence of this symmetry, not 16 but only 10 distinct quantities are required—in addition to the coordinate differences dx^0, dx^1, dx^2, dx^3 themselves—to specify the distances between a typical point and the infinitude of points in its immediate neighborhood. What a fantastic decrease in the size of the notebook required to specify the geometry of space-time!

Of course, the metric coefficients $g_{\alpha\beta}$ will ordinarily depend upon position. In any empirical representation of the facts, one will have these numbers not everywhere, but only here and there at reasonably closely spaced intervals. The data thus recorded will be taken over by the computer staff operating on the top floor of the imaginary laboratory. They will translate from tables of values of the $g_{\alpha\beta}$ into curve-fitting formulas. They will give back analytical expressions for the $g_{\alpha\beta}$ as functions of the four coordinates. These ten formulas summarize in shorthand form all the raw material about the geometry of space-time. So much for the original enormous notebook—and how to condense it!

Now for the actual mechanism of determining the distance between one point in space-time and a nearby point.

Question about Clocks and Measuring Rods of Atomic Constitution

In older textbook discussions of relativity, clocks and measuring rods of atomic constitution were used to determine intervals of proper distance and proper time. In more recent times, the question has been raised whether any of the constants of physics change as the expansion of the universe proceeds. If so, there may be a variation with time in the masses of the elementary particles—and possibly also in the quantum of charge. Such changes will affect differently two familiar standards of length.

Take the platinum-iridium measuring rod that served as standard from 1889 to 1960. The length is specified by two scratches. They span some fixed number of atoms in the crystal lattice of the rod. The size of the lattice unit is some simple multiple of the size of the hydrogen atom. It depends on the same physical constants which determine the size of the hydrogen atom. To be sure, some other numbers come in—for example, the nuclear-charge numbers of the platinum and iridium atoms. The occurrence of these pure numbers does not change the conclusion: From fundamental atomic physics, we can say that the platinum-iridium meter

$$N_1(\hbar^2/me^2)$$

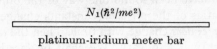

platinum-iridium meter bar

$$N_2(\hbar^3c/me^4)$$

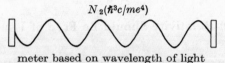

meter based on wavelength of light

Figure 3-3 Two standards of length that depend upon different combinations of the physical constants.

is some dimensionless multiple N_1 of the Bohr radius, $\hbar^2/me^2$ (Figure 3-3).

Since October 1960, the standard meter has been defined to be 1,650,763.73 wavelengths of orange-red light of the gas krypton 86.

This standard is governed by the same physical factors that determine the wavelength of the simplest lines of the hydrogen spectrum (apart from dimensional factors that depend on the charge of the krypton atom and the particular quantum numbers of the atomic levels that we are talking about). One will recall that, up to a numerical factor, the wavelengths of the lines in the hydrogen spectrum are governed by the factor $\hbar^3c/me^4$ (Bohr's theory of hydrogen). Therefore, the new standard meter can be expressed in the form $N_2\hbar^3c/me^4$, where N_2 is some pure number.

Ratio of Two Standards Changes if the Fine-Structure Constant Changes

The values of the two meters agreed at the time of switch of standards in 1960:

$$\frac{\begin{pmatrix}\text{meter based on}\\\text{krypton light}\end{pmatrix}}{\begin{pmatrix}\text{meter based on}\\\text{Pt-Ir bar}\end{pmatrix}} = \frac{N_2(\hbar^3c/me^4)}{N_1(\hbar^2/me^2)}$$

$$= (N_2/N_1)(\hbar c/e^2) \tag{3}$$

Moreover, the numbers N_2 and N_1 cannot change as time goes on. However, the ratio of physical constants,

$$\hbar c/e^2 = 137.037\ldots$$

may change with time as the expansion of the universe proceeds, if arguments that Dirac and Dicke have put forward are to be believed. It is not possible to take any final stand on this issue at this time. No conclusive argument appears to have been found one way or the other as to whether the dimensionless ratios of the physical constants change with time.

Suppose that $\hbar c/e^2$ *does* change with time. Then the ratio between the two standard meters will also vary. We shall be faced with a serious difficulty. Which meter is right? And, if one is wrong, how do we know that both are not wrong?

Classical General Relativity Should Be Free of Issues of Quantum Physics

Put the issue in other terms: Why should it be necessary to lean at all upon the atomic constitution of matter to define a standard of length? Why bring the quantum of action into the foundation of classical general relativity? Why found length measurements upon *either* $\hbar^2/me^2$ or $\hbar^3 c/me^4$?

Bohr and Rosenfeld[1] have discussed the general structure of physical theory. They have stressed that every proper theory should provide in and by itself its own means for defining the quantities with which it deals. According to this principle, classical general relativity should admit to calibrations of space and time that are altogether free of any reference to the quantum of action.

Weyl and Lorentz

The search for an intrinsic method of comparing lengths is marked by an interesting history. Weyl, in the early editions of his book *Space-Time-Matter*,[2] argued that it was enough to study the patterns of light rays to arrive at a way to compare an unknown interval CD between two nearby events anywhere in space-time with the interval AB between two fiducial events. Lorentz[3] then constructed a counter example: one space-time with the metric coefficients $g_{\alpha\beta}(x)$ and another with the metric coefficients $g'_{\alpha\beta}(x) = \lambda(x)g_{\alpha\beta}(x)$, where $\lambda(x)$ is an arbitrary function of position. He showed that the tracks of light rays—and therefore the pattern of their intersections—are identical in two spaces that evidently have different geometries. He concluded that the world lines not only of light rays but also of material particles are required if one is to have a well-defined way of comparing distances. Weyl corrected later editions of his book accordingly. However, neither investigator supplied the construction by which one can actually determine space-time intervals. This was given by Marzke in his Princeton A.B. senior thesis.[4]

Marzke's Method of Measurement

The construction of this thesis is recapitulated here because it is so central to the logical foundations of relativity. The discussion divides itself naturally into five parts: (1) idealizing to flat space, (2) constructing one world line parallel to another, (3) constructing a geodesic clock, (4) connecting the interval of interest with the time of ticking of a geodesic clock, and (5) extension to regions of space-time so large that curvature has to be taken into account.

Locally Flat Space-Time

(1) To be able to idealize to flat space requires that one should be able to tell when space-time is curved! In this connection, recall one way to tell that the earth's surface is curved. Stretch a string 100 km long from some point B to another point C. From B stretch another string, this time 1000 km long, to some point A so located that the string AB meets the base line CB in a right angle at B. Likewise, from C stretch a 1000-km string to a point D, so chosen that DC and BC meet perpendicularly at C. Does this construction produce a rectangle? No, the ends A and D have separation which is short of 100 km. The fractional discrepancy in length is

$$\frac{\begin{pmatrix}\text{change in}\\\text{separation}\end{pmatrix}}{\begin{pmatrix}\text{original}\\\text{separation}\end{pmatrix}} = \frac{BC - AD}{BC} = \frac{\begin{pmatrix}\text{length of travel}\\\text{perpendicular to}\\\text{original base line } BC\end{pmatrix}^2}{2(\text{radius of curvature})^2} \tag{4}$$

$$= \frac{(1000 \text{ km})^2}{2(6378 \text{ km})^2} = \text{one part in } 81$$

Take over these ideas to the analysis of space-time. Consider two particles that are free of the action of electromagnetic and all other forces except, possibly, gravitation, and that have negligible gravitational pull upon each other. Start them off with a specified separation and with zero relative velocity. See if their separation begins to decrease (Figure 3-4). If so, we say we have evidence for the curvature of space. It is even possible to dispense with distance measurement. To see qualitative evidence for the curvature of space-time, it is sufficient to look for a crossing of originally parallel world lines.

Will not the paths of the two test objects be perturbed by the collisions that they make with other matter? Thus, a satellite circulating the earth is impeded by the dust it encounters. It departs by a measurable amount from an ideal geodesic.

It is possible to secure an ideal geodesic by employing the windshield double satellite suggested by Schwarzschild. This object is composed of two concentric spheres—an inner *conscience* or ideal satellite, and an outer

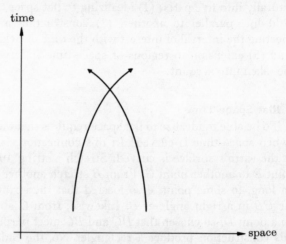

Figure 3-4 The crossing of two world lines that were originally parallel gives a qualitative means to estimate the curvature of space.

or *conscience-guided* satellite—equipped with vernier rocket jets so that it can respond to the dictates of its conscience regardless of the drag of cosmic dust. This type of test body is discussed in more detail in Chapter 1.

The distance from the starting point to the first crossing of the originally parallel trajectories gives a way to estimate the radius of curvature. Now limit attention to a region of space-time so small that, within it, all effects of curvature are negligible. More specifically, let one have an estimate for the effective radius of curvature of space-time, ρ. Let one be given instructions as to what accuracy is demanded of him. Then the fractional error in lengths is specified. Thus, we can determine from Eq. (4) in how small a region of space we must operate in order to keep the fractional error less than the specified amount. In other words, by restricting attention to a sufficiently small region of space-time, we can idealize space-time to be flat to any desired degree of precision.

Construction of a Parallel

(2) With ideal flatness now defined, proceed with the next step, to construct a parallel. The possibility of constructing parallels has already been assumed in the discussion of curvature. It remains to be seen how the construction of parallels is actually carried out.

In Figure 3-5, *ACDF* is the world line of one particle. PROBLEM: Find a world line parallel to *ACDF*. SOLUTION: (1) Find a test particle that

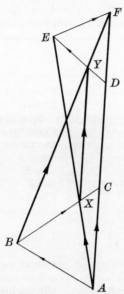

Figure 3-5 Construction of a world line XY parallel to a given world line AF. The thin lines are the tracks of light rays used in the construction.

will collide with the given particle (heavy line BF crossing $ACDF$ at F). (2) Let the first particle emit a flash of light at some point A on its world line. This light will be scattered by the second particle at a sharply defined point B and return to the first particle at a well-determined point C. (3) Thus, define the light ray BC and finish the first stage of the construction. (4) The second stage of the construction is centered on the world line of a third particle. It crosses the world line of the first particle at the already specified event A. In addition, it crosses the already well determined light ray BC at some arbitrary intermediate point X. By reason of the local flatness of space-time, this world line—continued—also crosses BF. (5) Let light flashes be emitted here and there along the track of the first particle. Let each pulse of radiation be scattered by the third particle and arrive back at the first particle. In this way, determine by trial and error and eventual success, a point D and light rays DE and EF. Again, because space-time is locally flat, the ray DE crosses the line BF at some point Y. (6) The two points X and Y are our two fiducial points. Consider, among all the different infinitesimal test particles going in various directions at various speeds, that particular one that will go from X to Y. It supplies the parallel XY to the original world line $ACDF$.

Table 3-2

Cartesian Analysis of the Construction of Figure 2-5, Showing That the
World Line XY as There Defined Is Parallel to the Given World Line $ACDF$

Event or line of events	(x, t)	Reason
A	$(0, 0)$	Choice of coordinate system
C	$(0, 2a)$	Choice of coordinate systems; definition of a
B	$(-a, a)$	Connected by light rays to A and C
E	$(-b, c)$	Definition of b and c
D	$(0, c - b)$	On axis, and connected by light ray to E
F	$(0, c + b)$	Same
AE	$bt + cx = 0$	Checks for A and E
BC	$t - x = 2a$	Checks for B and C
X	$\left(\dfrac{-2ab}{b + c}, \dfrac{2ac}{b + c}\right)$	Intersection of AE and BC
BF	$at + (a - b - c)x$ $= a(b + c)$	Checks for B and F
DE	$t + x = c - b$	Checks for D and E
Y	$\left(\dfrac{-2ab}{b + c}, c - b + \dfrac{2ab}{b + c}\right)$	Intersection of DE and BF
XY	$x = \dfrac{-2ab}{b + c}$ $t = \text{anything}$	Checks for X and Y

One can verify this construction by introducing a local Lorentz
reference system so that all world lines and light rays are straight lines.
Let the origin be chosen at the point A, and let the time axis be so selected
that the original particle $ACDF$ is at rest. Then the coordinates of the
points encountered in the construction are found by step-by-step analysis
(Table 3-2).

Local Inertial Reference System

The analysis just outlined depends upon the existence of an inertial
reference system— a system in which the world lines of all light rays and
all free particles appear straight. The existence of a gravitational field
above the earth's surface is no bar to setting up such a reference system
there. The tracks of free particles will appear straight when viewed from

a freely falling elevator. This is the lesson from the experiments of Eötvös and Dicke and from Einstein's equivalence principle. It is only required that the elevator be not too large. If two test particles are separated by a horizontal distance Δx in a freely falling elevator, they are drawn downward by accelerations that have the same magnitude $g = GM/r^2$. Here r is the distance to the center of the earth and $M(\text{kg})$ or $M^*(\text{m}) = GM/c^2$ is the mass of the earth. However, the accelerations differ in direction by the small angle $\theta = \Delta x/r$. Therefore, the two falling particles move toward each other with the acceleration $g\theta(\text{m/sec}^2)$; or

$$\frac{d^2(\Delta x)}{d\left(\begin{array}{l}\text{time in meters}\\ \text{of light travel}\\ \text{time}\end{array}\right)^2} = -(g/c^2)(\Delta x/r) = -\Delta x(M^*/r^3) \tag{5}$$

Here the quantity $M^*/r^3 = 1.71 \times 10^{-23}$ m^{-2} measures the curvature of space by the earth's gravitational field. In order that this curvature should produce fractional corrections in lengths less than one part in 10^8, the time of experimentation in the falling elevator should be restricted by the equation

$$1.71 \times 10^{-23} \text{ m}^{-2}(\text{time in meters of light travel time})^2 \lesssim 10^{-8} \tag{6}$$

implying a time less than 3×10^7 m, or a tenth of a second. This time limit is enormous compared to the time required to parallelize two world lines 5 m apart according to the construction of Figure 3-5. Therefore, the construction makes good sense at the laboratory scale of experimentation.

The Geodesic Clock

(3) Having two particles moving along parallel world lines, we can let a pulse of light be reflected back and forth between them. In this way we define a geodesic clock. It may be said to "tick" each time the light pulse arrives back at object number one. Whether the clock ticks rapidly or slowly is a matter of choice, based on whether the two objects are far apart or close together. In any event, questions of atomic constitution have nothing to do with the length of the tick!

Geometrodynamical Standard Meter; The Comparison of Intervals

(4) The geodesic clock is to be used to compare an unknown interval *CD* with a standard interval *AB*. The event *A* may be an explosion or a spark discharge that took place 50 years ago, and *B* may be a spark that came off just a little later. These two flashes are going to serve as the calibration points for the measurement of all other space-time intervals. They define what might be called the *geometrodynamic standard meter*. How

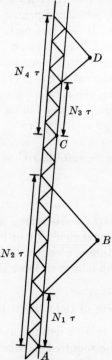

Figure 3-6 Use of a geodesic clock to compare the intervals CD and AB. One particle of the clock moves along a nearby and parallel world line. The sloping lines represent light rays. Marzke's analysis leads to the result $CD/AB = (N_3N_4/N_1N_2)^{1/2}$.

then can one express some unknown interval CD in terms of the standard interval AB?

Find a world line (Figure 3-6) that passes through A and C. We assume that this is possible. In other words, we assume that C lies inside the future light cone of A. Then, quite close to the world line AC find a parallel world line. The two world lines, together with a pulse of light going back and forth between them, constitute a geodesic clock. Denote by τ the time of one zig-zag track of light starting at AC and returning to AC. Now determine the ratio between the time of ticking τ of this geodesic clock and the standard interval AB of proper time. For this purpose, pick out from among all the events on the world line AC that one at which a sudden flash causes a pulse of light to reach B. This event occurs later than event A. Count off the number of ticks of time N_1 from A to this start of the

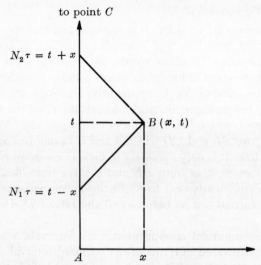

Figure 3-7 The light rays to and from B viewed in a frame of reference in which AC is at rest.

light pulse. Also observe the return of the light pulse from B to AC. Again count off the number of ticks from A, a number denoted this time by N_2. Then a simple analysis gives the interval AB:

$$AB = (N_1 N_2)^{1/2} \tau \tag{7}$$

For a proof of this result, go (Figure 3-7) to a Lorentz reference system in which the world line AC is at rest, and the event A lies at the origin. Denote by x and t (both in meters!) the coordinates of the event B in this frame of reference. Then the time of start of the pulse *toward B* is

$$N_1 \tau = t - x \tag{8}$$

and the time of *return* of this pulse to the geodesic clock is

$$N_2 \tau = t + x \tag{9}$$

Multiply (8) and (9) and take the square root to obtain the result (7).

In a similar way the interval CD is expressed in terms of the characteristic time of the clock by counting ticks: $CD = (N_3 N_4)^{1/2} \tau$. Finally, one determines this previously unknown interval in terms of the standard interval AB and the observable numbers N_1, N_2, N_3, N_4:

$$CD/AB = (N_3 N_4 / N_1 N_2)^{1/2} \tag{10}$$

More General Comparisons

A few comments are in order. It is not required that the intervals AB and CD should be time-like. For example, when AB is space-like, the number N_1 is negative. In other words, the pulse of light has to start toward B before the event A has taken place. Similar considerations apply to the sign of the number N_3. Consequently, an imaginary value for the ratio of Eq. (10) has a simple physical interpretation: Of the two intervals AB and CD, one is space-like and the other is time-like. Also, it is still possible to compare AB and CD when A and C *cannot* be connected by a time-like world line. It is only necessary to pick a new event E so far in the future, and so located, that both AE and CE are time-like, and to pick another event F sufficiently near to E. Then the comparisons EF/AB and EF/CD can be carried out as before, and the ratio CD/AB can still be found.

Still another comment is appropriate: All intervals, whether space- or time-like, are expressed in terms of the standard interval AB. There is no difference between the units used for intervals of distance and for intervals of time. The number 3×10^8 never shows itself. The importance of light rays and the light cone in the intrinsic geometry of physics comes more directly to the surface. The true function of the speed of light is no longer confused with the trivial task of relating two separate units of interval, the meter and the second, of purely historic and accidental origin.

Case of Curved Space-time

(5) Now for the comparison of intervals AB and CD separated time-wise by a great stretch of *curved* space-time! Find, as before, the track AC of an infinitesimal neutral test particle that will go freely from A to C. Find a second geodesic that is parallel to AC at A, as determined by the methods already outlined. Try to use the pair of geodesic as the centers to send a light pulse back and forth in order to define a geodesic clock. The construction does not serve its purpose. Owing to the curvature of space-time, the geodesics change their separation (Figure 3-8).

The clock changes its interval. For example, let the geodesics be pursued a distance d in a region of space where the effective radius of curvature is of the order R. Then the fractional change in the time between clock ticks will be of the order

$$\Delta\tau/\tau \sim (d/R)^2 \qquad (11)$$

The inaccuracy will be too large to tolerate if the geodesic clock is used without correction over the entire interval $d = L$ between AB and CD when L is comparable to the radius of curvature itself.

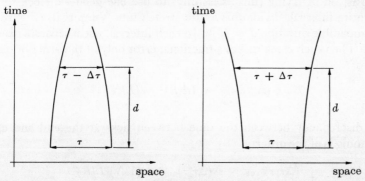

Figure 3-8 The change in the time between ticks in an uncorrected geodesic clock goes in proportion to the square of the elapsed time d in a region where the effective curvature differs from zero by a nearly constant amount. The converging geodesics on the left are in a region of positive curvature. The diverging geodesics on the right are in a region of negative curvature.

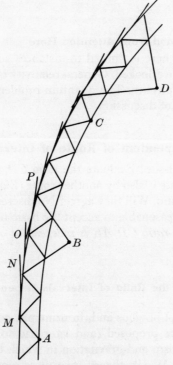

Figure 3-9 Many successive geodesics MN, OP, etc., stay parallel to the geodesic AC long enough to carry forward the time interval T with the desired precision.

Instead of trying (unsuccessfully) to use one geodesic clock to span the entire interval, divide this entire stretch into N intervals (Figure 3-9) of comparable duration $d = L/N$. In each interval, use a separate geodesic clock. Then each clock makes a fractional error only of the order of magnitude of

$$(\Delta\tau/\tau)_{\substack{\text{one} \\ \text{clock}}} \sim (d/R)^2 \sim (L/NR)^2 \tag{12}$$

The discrepancy between the time between ticks at the end and at the beginning is of the order

$$(\Delta\tau/\tau)_{\substack{\text{over-} \\ \text{all}}} \sim N(\Delta\tau/\tau)_{\substack{\text{one} \\ \text{clock}}} \sim (1/N)(L/R)^2 \tag{13}$$

This discrepancy can be made as small as one pleases by making the number N of geodesic clocks employed sufficiently great. Therefore, the curvature of space-time interposes no obstacles to the comparison of intervals at an arbitrary separation to an arbitrary degree of precision by the use of light rays and geodesics.

Quantum Effects Excluded from Attention Here

The analysis given here is limited to distances sufficiently great that quantum effects can be overlooked. General relativity is treated here within the context of classical physics. The quantum problem is also of interest, but it is not the subject of discussion.[5]

Distance Ratios Independent of Route of Intercomparison(?)

Now for a central issue! Evaluate the ratio CD/AB by one route of intercomparison. Evaluate it also by another route (Figure 3-10). Compare the two values for the ratio. Will they agree? No discrepancy has ever been found. Therefore, it is reasonable to accept the basic postulate of Riemannian geometry, that *the ratio CD/AB is independent of the choice of route of intercomparison.*

A Geometry in Which the Ratio of Intervals Depends on the Route of Intercomparison

This postulate is not obvious and, in principle, could even be wrong. For example, Weyl once proposed (and later had to give up) a unified theory of electromagnetism and gravitation in which the Riemann postulate was abandoned. In Weyl's theory, two measuring rods, cut to have identical lengths at a point A in space-time, and carried by different routes to a point C, will *differ* in length when they are brought together. The

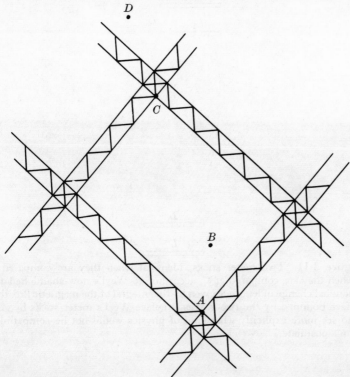

Figure 3-10 Two alternate routes for the intercomparison of the space-time intervals *AB* and *CD*. That the ratio *CD/AB* is completely independent of the choice of route is a basic postulate of Riemannian geometry.

fractional change in length (Figure 3-11)

$$\delta L/L = \ln(L_2/L_1)$$

is given in Weyl's theory by the expression

$$\delta L/L = C\Phi \tag{14}$$

Here *C* is a universal constant and Φ is the total flux of the magnetic field through the surface bounded by the pair of routes. This result definitely disagrees with the Riemann postulate.

The conceivability of alternative theories raises the question: How accurately has the Riemann postulate been tested? Evidently, there is no lack of predictions to test! Every interval *AB*, when compared with another interval *CD* by two different routes, opens the way to a check. It would be

Figure 3-11 Two meter sticks, identical when they are compared at A, differ when they are compared at C, according to Weyl's now-abandoned theory. The fractional change in length is given by the integral of the magnetic flux through the surface bounded by the two curves. Replace Weyl's meter sticks by geodesic clocks to see more explicitly what kind of physics would not be compatible with Riemann's postulate.

difficult to think of any theory that leaves itself more open to disproof if it is wrong—nor any important theory where the opportunity to make such checks has been less used.

Validity of Pauli Principle as Partial Evidence for Riemann's Postulate

If little has been done directly to compare *lengths*, perhaps the comparison of *masses* will do temporary service as evidence. If lengths change on being taken around a flux-bearing region and if lengths are correlated with masses by Bohr's formula for the radius of a hydrogen atom,

$$a = \hbar^2/me^2 \tag{15}$$

then electrons might be expected to show differences in mass according to their past histories. But a difference in electron masses would ultimately show up in a violation of the Pauli exclusion principle. It would be impossible to keep particles from occupying the same orbits if they had different masses. In other words, if the atomic electrons had different masses, they would all fall into the K orbit. Then iron atoms would be fantastically diminished in size, and the earth would collapse. This collapse has not taken place in 5×10^9 years. In this time, the L electrons of iron revolve in their orbits and turn through

$$(5 \times 10^9 \text{ years}) (3 \times 10^7 \text{ sec/yr}) (4 \times 10^{18} \text{ radians/sec}) \sim 10^{36} \text{ radians} \tag{16}$$

Assume that this is enough motion to bring to light—by a transition from the L level to the K level—a difference of mass as big as 1 part in 10^{36}, if such a difference should exist. Since such transitions have not taken place, it is reasonable to conclude that the masses of the electrons that have come together in the interior of the earth differ from each other by less than one part in 10^{36}. Argue then that the scales of length associated with different electrons have also changed relative to one another by less than 1 part in 10^{36} during the history of the earth. In this way, set an upper limit for Weyl's coefficient of length change C in Eq. (14). In each day, an electron near the earth's surface circumnavigates a flux of the order

$$1 \text{ gauss} \times 10^{18} \text{ cm}^2 \tag{17}$$

or in 5×10^9 years

$$\Phi \sim 10^{30} \text{ gauss cm}^2 \tag{18}$$

In contrast, an electron near the center travels in a route embracing a much smaller flux. Ultimately, we assume, the circulatory currents within the earth's interior bring the two electrons together for the mass comparison that we have already discussed. Therefore, we conclude that the observed stability of the earth against collapse imposes on the coefficient of Weyl an upper limit of

$$G = \frac{\delta L/L}{\Phi} < \frac{10^{-36}}{10^{30} \text{ gauss cm}^2} = 10^{-66}/\text{gauss cm}^2 \tag{19}$$

The assumptions and loopholes in this analysis should be emphasized. The upper limit given in Eq. (19) is not a hard, firm, upper limit. It would be desirable to have a more *decisive* experimental argument for the Riemannian postulate even at the cost of losing a number of those powers of ten which look so impressive in Eq. (19).

Summary

In summary, Riemann postulated, first, the existence of an interval between any two points and, second, a value for this interval (relative to some standard interval) that is well defined, regardless of one's choice of coordinates, and regardless even of whether one uses any coordinates at all. No experimental evidence or argument of principle has ever been sustained against this postulate that the ratio between two intervals is independent of the route of intercomparison. A way has been described by which this intercomparison of intervals can be carried through without any recourse to measuring rods or clocks of atomic constitution. This construction means that general relativity, in and by itself, provides its own means for defining intervals of space and time—relative to a certain geometrodynamic standard meter—independent of all questions whether such physical constants as m, M, e, and $\hbar$ change with time.

Concrete Proposal for Definition of a Geometrodynamic Standard Meter

One final question: Will measuring techniques ever develop in such a direction that one will be able to supersede the krypton-86 standard meter as well as the platinum-iridium standard meter by a geometrodynamic standard meter, based on the invariantly defined interval AB between two events A and B that occurred some time in the past? ANSWER: One is already at the point where he can define a geometrodynamic meter! The events A and B are the equinoxes that defined the beginning and end of the tropical year 1900.0. The interval is carried forward in time by the world line of the earth as it moves in its orbit, and as corrected for the influence of the other bodies in the solar system. The accuracy with which the interval can be carried forward would seem to be substantially greater than that with which the Kr[86] meter can be reproduced, in so far as one can judge from the number of figures cited in the two cases[6]

1 meter = 1,650,763.73 orange–red wavelengths of Kr[86]

1 second = (1/31,556,925.974) of tropical year 1900.0

Moreover, one can measure[7] the speed of light, or the factor of conversion from seconds to meters, to one part in 10^6,

$$c = (299793.0 \pm 0.3) \times 10^3 \text{ m/sec}$$

Therefore, one is at liberty here and now to *define the geometrodynamic standard meter to be the fraction*

$$1/(9.460546 \times 10^{15})$$

of the interval between the two "effective equinoxes" that bound the tropical year 1900.0.

In terms of this geometrodynamic standard of length, it is a well-defined question to ask whether the Kr[86] meter, or the Pt-Ir meter, or both, are changing with time by reason of slow changes in m, M, $\hbar$, and e.[8]

References

1. N. Bohr and L. Rosenfeld, *Kgl. Danske Videnskab. Selskab, Mat.-Fys. Medd.*, **12,** No. 8 (1933); *Phys. Rev.*, **78,** 794 (1950) (cited for discussion of the principle that every proper theory defines in and by itself the means to measure the quantities with which that theory deals).
2. H. Weyl, *Raum-Zeit-Materie*, 1st ed., Springer, Berlin, 1918 (for measurement by light rays; also for Weyl's proposed unified theory).
3. H. A. Lorentz, *Collected Papers*, Vol. 5, pp. 363–382, Nijhoff, The Hague, 1937 [proof that the geometry $g_{\alpha\beta}(x)$ and the geometry $\lambda(x)g_{\alpha\beta}(x)$ give the same light rays but not the same particle geodesics].
4. R. F. Marzke, *The Theory of Measurement in General Relativity*, A. B. senior thesis, Princeton, 1959, unpublished (the present paper is based upon and constitutes a publication of the results in this thesis).
5. E. Schroedinger, *Preuss. Akad. Wiss. Berlin Ber.*, 238 (1931); M. F. M. Osborne, *Phys. Rev.* **75,** 1579 (1949); J. L. Anderson, *Rev. Mex. Fis.*, **3,** 176 (1954); H. Salecker and E. P. Wigner, *Phys. Rev.*, **109,** 571 (1958) (early steps toward the solution of what in the end will presumably prove to be one of the deepest and most difficult questions ever encountered in theoretical physics: how to define, within the context of quantum theory and in the sense of Bohr and Rosenfeld, the procedures for measuring noncomplementary aspects of the geometry of space-time).
6. G. M. Clemence, *Science*, **123,** 567 (1958) (value of length of tropical year quoted in text and analysis of the accuracy of various existing standards of time and frequency).
7. J. W. M. Dumond and E. R. Cohen, in E. U. Condon and H. Odishaw (eds.), *Handbook of Physics*, McGraw-Hill, New York, 1958 (value of speed of light quoted in text).
8. P. A. M. Dirac, *Proc. Roy. Soc. (London)*, **A165,** 199 (1938); E. Teller, *Phys. Rev.*, **73,** 801 (1948); R. H. Dicke, *Rev. Mod. Phys.*, **29,** 363 (1957) (discussion of question whether physical constants change with time).

Appendix A

Criterion for Establishing that an Ensemble of $(N + 1)$ Points Defines an N-Dimensional Euclidean Space

Do the $(N + 1)N/2$ distances between $(N + 1)$ points define the generalization of a triangle and a tetrahedron, an N-dimensional simplex in a Euclidean space? Then the volume V of this figure will be nonzero. A familiar piece of reasoning about the value of this volume may be recalled. It appears to rest on the use of a particular coordinate system, but the result makes reference only to distances, not to coordinates. Let the points be denoted as $0, 1, 2, \ldots, N$. Let the point 0 be at the origin, and let the coordinates of the k-th point be called $k_s (s = 1, 2, \ldots, N)$. The area of a triangle is

$$(1/2) \begin{vmatrix} 1_1 & 1_2 \\ 2_1 & 2_2 \end{vmatrix}$$

The volume of a tetrahedron is

$$(1/6)\begin{vmatrix} 1_1 & 1_2 & 1_3 \\ 2_1 & 2_2 & 2_3 \\ 3_1 & 3_2 & 3_3 \end{vmatrix}$$

The volume of the N simplex is

$$V = (1/N!)\begin{vmatrix} 1_1 & \cdots & \cdots \\ \cdots & \cdots & \cdots \\ \cdots & \cdots & N_N \end{vmatrix}$$

Rewrite the equation transposing rows and columns. Multiply the two equations recalling that the product of two determinants is equal to the determinant of their product. The element in the ith row and kth column of the product is the scalar product of the vector $(0i)$ by the vector $(0k)$:

$$(0i) \cdot (0k) = \sum_{s=1}^{N} i_s k_s$$

In flat space this scalar product is given by the formula familiar from a triangle,

$$(0i) \cdot (0k) = (1/2)[(ik)^2 - (0i)^2 - (0k)^2]$$

Therefore, only *distances* are involved in the standard formula for the volume,

$$V = (1/N!)\begin{vmatrix} (01)^2 & (01) \cdot (02) & \cdots & \cdots \\ (01) \cdot (02) & (02)^2 & \cdots & \cdots \\ \cdots & \cdots & \cdots & \cdots \\ \cdots & \cdots & \cdots & (0N)^2 \end{vmatrix}^{1/2}$$

The formula applies as well in flat Lorentz geometry as in flat Euclidean geometry. Its vanishing for $N = 5$ or more provides (1) a way to check, in the case of nearby events, that the dimensionality is actually four; (2) a way to deduce that distances between nearby points can be derived from four coordinates and ten $g_{\alpha\beta}$; and (3) a way to show the presence of curvature when five or more points are not sufficiently close by (failure of the calculated V_5 to vanish, not because the dimensionality is 5, but because the curvature is nonzero!). (This note is in reference to the introduction of the metric coefficients in the text.) See S. Piccard, *Sur les ensembles de distances des ensembles de points d'un espace euclidien*, Gauthier–Villars, Paris, 1940, for an analysis of the conditions that an ensemble of real numbers shall be the ensemble of distances between an ensemble of points in a Euclidean space.

4
Gravitation as geometry—II

John A. Wheeler

Distinction between an Allowable Geometry and an Arbitrary Geometry

In Chapter 3 we explored the meaning of Riemannian geometry.[1] We found it possible to give a meaning to the structure of such a geometry by using the concept of events—and of distances between these events—without recourse to the notion of coordinates. A procedure was given for relating one distance, or invariant space-time interval, to another, using for the intercomparison only the paths of light rays and material particles. The geometry was determined by the totality of all such distances. One four-dimensional Riemannian geometry was treated as seriously as another. Nothing was said about any physical law that might rule out the one geometry as inadmissible and rate the other geometry as reasonable. The present chapter is therefore focussed on the question: What distinguishes an allowable geometry from an arbitrary geometry?

By way of putting this question in perspective, compare relativity with mechanics. The science of mechanics consists of two branches, kinematics and dynamics. Kinematics describes conceivable motions without asking whether they are allowed or forbidden. Dynamics analyses the difference between a physically reasonable and a disallowed history.

Physics as Equations of Motion Plus Initial-Value Data

The selection of allowed Riemannian geometries from among merely conceivable Riemannian geometries is accomplished by Einstein's field equations. The principle of selection is not sharp enough to give a unique

65

dynamic history. In this respect, Einstein's field equations are very like Newton's equations of motion. Newton's equations in and by themselves do not fully specify the motion of a particle. The history of the particle only becomes completely determinate when appropriate initial value data have been given—for example, the position and velocity of the particle at a specified time. Will physics ever take on a new character? Will it ever *give* us the initial-value data *as well as* the equations of motion? Or will it always require us to go back to *observation* to get this initial value data? This is a deep question to which no one today has an answer.[2] For the time being, all of physics has to be accepted as constructed along these lines— not only particle mechanics, but also the dynamics of the electromagnetic field and the dynamics of geometry, or "geometrodynamics," to adopt a descriptive word for general relativity.

Initial-Value Data for Electrodynamics

Electrodynamics provides useful guidance for thinking about geometrodynamics. When faced with an issue in relativity, it often helps to try (1) to translate it into a corresponding problem in electrodynamics; (2) to analyze this problem; (3) to translate the answer back into a corresponding statement about geometrodynamics; and (4) to check this tentative answer by direct analysis.

Along this line, it is appropriate to look at the initial-value data required (together with Maxwell's equations) to specify the entire history of the electromagnetic field. The data are often given in the following two steps: (1) Pick out a space-like hypersurface slicing through space-time. This choice is analogous to the selection of a specified initial time in mechanics. (2) On this hypersurface give everywhere the value of the magnetic field (the analog of coordinate in mechanics) and the electric field (the analog of momentum in mechanics). Check that these data are "acceptable" in this sense: Test whether the divergence of each of the two fields vanishes (in the case of empty space). Then the initial-value data are said to satisfy the initial-value conditions. They are enough to fix the entire future and past of the electromagnetic field.

Intrinsic Three-Geometry and Extrinsic Curvature of a Spacelike Hypersurface

Similarly, in geometrodynamics the appropriate initial-value data on a spacelike hypersurface are (1) the three-dimensional geometry "intrinsic" to—or internal to—this hypersurface (compare the magnetic field in electrodynamics!) and (2) the "extrinsic" curvature of this hypersurface—a statement about how it *is* curved (or is *to be* curved) with respect to the enveloping and yet-to-be-constructed four-dimensional space-time (compare to electric field). So much for a brief preview of how geometrodynamics is understood today!

Learned Late How to Formulate the Typical Problem in General Relativity

The historic order of winning a way into the subject was very different from what this account would suggest. It was not appreciated until recently (Stellmacher; Mme. Fourès-Bruhat; Lichnerowicz; Arnowitt, Deser and Misner; Baierlein, Sharp, and Wheeler[3,4]) that the initial-value problem of geometrodynamics has many points of similarity with the initial-value problem of electrodynamics. Only with this forward step has one learned "what relativity is all about." Until this advance had been made, one did not know which features of a four-geometry could be specified arbitrarily and which follow as consequences from the specified data. Therefore, it was not even clear how to *formulate* the typical dynamic problem, much less how to *solve* it. The advance in our understanding may perhaps be symbolized by the use of the word geometrodynamics instead of general relativity to describe the subject initiated by Einstein.

This Lecture Outlined

To spell out in a little more detail what geometrodynamics is all about, it is appropriate to take up in this lecture four topics:
(1) the physical basis for Einstein's field equations
(2) the initial-value problem
(3) the solution of the initial-value problem (and then of Einstein's field equations) for the particularly simple illustrative case of the "Schwarzschild geometry"
(4) the motion of a test particle in this geometry as it relates to tests of Einstein's theory.

The Derivation of Einstein's Field Equations

The principle of *correspondence* with Newtonian gravitational theory furnishes a natural way into Einstein's theory. Thus, postulate that every neutral test particle moves along a geodesic in a four-dimensional Riemannian geometry. Demand that the motion so obtained shall reduce—for low velocities and small departures from flatness—to the Newtonian predictions. In addition to this principle of correspondence between Einstein's geometry and Newton's gravity, require that *geometric means alone shall transmit the effects of the masses that curve space-time*. In other words,

Einstein's equations will give information about *geometry* as it is affected by mass. However, they will give no information at all about any *coordinates* in terms of which one or another bookkeeper might choose to *express* that geometry. In principle, it is possible to express this interaction between mass and geometry in a form that is free of all reference whatsoever to any coordinates (as in group theory one discusses the properties of the group in terms of its multiplication table, free of all reference to any particular representation in terms of matrices!). However, one has not made such progress in general relativity as in group theory toward a coordinate-free way of speaking about things (analogous to Faraday's "tubes of force"). Therefore, in practice, one has been in the habit of using coordinates to write out Einstein's equations. In terms of coordinates, the demand for a purely geometric connection between mass at one place and geometry at other places is stronger than the demand for *covariance* of the field equations.[5] It requires that the ten field equations of Einstein should *not* be sufficient to determine the ten unknown metric coefficients g ("principle of weakness of the field equations"; see Chapters 1 and 2). Why not? Because a knowledge of these ten quantities would amount to a specification not only of the geometry, but also of the *coordinates* in terms of which that geometry is expressed—contrary to the demand for a solely geometric content to the theory.

So much for the two principles central to Einstein's theory: *correspondence* to Newtonian theory, and a purely *geometric* content. Now, start spelling out the content of the correspondence principle by looking at the equation of a geodesic!

Geodesic as History of Extremal Proper Time

The concept of geodesic already shows itself in simple terms in the case of travel on the surface of the globe from one point A to another point B. One takes an arbitrary route connecting the two points. The route is made up of segments, each connecting one point with a nearby point, each having a length that is presumed known. Where one is along such a given route can be told by adding the total mileage from the starting point to the point in question. The analogous concept in the case of the world line in space-time is the elapsed proper time τ; thus,

$$\tau = \int_{\text{start}}^{\text{given point}} d\tau = \int (d\tau^2)^{1/2} = \int (-d\sigma^2)^{1/2} = \int (-g_{\alpha\beta} \, dx^\alpha \, dx^\beta)^{1/2} \quad (1)$$

In terms of this parameter, one can think of the world line in question as being described by the four functions

$$x^\alpha = x^\alpha(\tau) \quad (2)$$

Actually, any other parameter λ that increases monotonically along the world line is just as good as τ itself in telling where one is along the world line; thus

$$x^\alpha = x^\alpha(\lambda) \tag{3}$$

and

$$\tau = \int_{\lambda=0}^{\lambda} [-g_{\alpha\beta}(dx^\alpha/d\lambda)(dx^\beta/d\lambda)]^{1/2}\, d\lambda \tag{4}$$

So much for an arbitrary route. From among all the routes connecting a point A to a point B that route is singled out as an extremal which does not change to the first order in a small quantity ϵ when a change is made in the route that is of the first order in ϵ:

$$x^\alpha(\lambda) \rightarrow x^\alpha(\lambda) + \epsilon\delta x^\alpha(\lambda) \tag{5}$$

where

$$\delta x^\alpha(\lambda) = 0 \quad \text{at} \quad \begin{cases} \lambda = \lambda_A \\ \lambda = \lambda_B \end{cases} \tag{6}$$

Write the lapse of proper time on the varied route in the form

$$\tau_{AB} = \tau_{AB}^{(0)} + \epsilon\tau_{AB}^{(1)} + \epsilon^2\tau_{AB}^{(2)} + \cdots \tag{7}$$

Then $\tau_{AB}^{(1)}$ depends upon: first, the original route; and second, the variation $\delta x^\alpha(\lambda)$ made in this route. However, in the case when $x^\alpha(\lambda)$ is an extremal, then $\tau_{AB}^{(1)}$ vanishes for all choices of the four variations $\delta x^\alpha(\lambda)$ (provided they go to zero at A and at B!).

The Quantum Background of the Classical Extremum Principle

Why should the extremal route be the one favored by nature? How can the particle "feel out" alternative routes through space-time and pick out the one that extremizes the proper time? Quantum theory gives the answer—an answer most readily stated in Feynman's formulation of the quantum principle.[6] The "total probability amplitude to pass from the specified initial configuration (here, A) to the final configuration (here, B)" is the sum of contributions from every conceivable history H that connects the two configurations. The partial amplitudes are identical in *magnitude* for all histories. The phase of the contribution from any given history is given by the action integral I_H associated with that history divided by the quantum of angular momemtum $\hbar$. In the present case, the action integral is given by the expression

$$I_H = - mc\tau_{AB} \tag{8}$$

Thus, Feynman's transition amplitude has the form of the symbolic sum ("functional integral over all histories" with normalization factor $\mathcal{N}$)

$$
\begin{pmatrix} \text{probability} \\ \text{amplitude} \\ \text{to pass from} \\ A \text{ to } B \end{pmatrix} = \langle x_B^\alpha | x_A^\alpha \rangle = \mathcal{N} \sum_H \exp(iI_H/\hbar) \tag{9}
$$

However, histories that vary greatly from the classic extremal history do not contribute appreciably to this sum. The phase is so far different from the extremal phase that the contributions of these histories cancel out by destructive interference. The total amplitude in typical cases has practically the phase it would have had if the motion had followed exclusively the classical history. To see how nature *appears* to select the classical history as preferred and yet, in reality, treats all histories on the same footing is the great achievement of quantum theory. It is at last clear why extremal principles—of which the demand for motion in a straight line or on a geodesic is a special case—occur throughout physics. One sees how deep was the penetration of Newton when at the beginning of his *Principia* he stated, ". . . the description of right lines and circles, upon which geometry is founded, belongs to mechanics. Geometry does not teach us to draw these lines, but requires them to be drawn."

Euler–Lagrange Equations for the Geodesic

Turn from the physics behind the extremal principle to the consequences of the extremal principle. Put the integral to be varied in the form

$$
\tau_{AB} = \int_A^B L(x^\alpha(\lambda), dx^\alpha/d\lambda) \, d\lambda \tag{10}
$$

Then the Euler–Lagrange equations for the extremizing path are

$$
(d/d\lambda)\partial L/\partial(dx^\alpha/d\lambda) - \partial L/\partial x^\alpha = 0 \tag{11}
$$

Rewrite this equation employing the following notation:

$$
\Gamma_{\beta\gamma,\sigma} = (\tfrac{1}{2})(\partial g_{\gamma\sigma}/\partial x^\beta + \partial g_{\beta\sigma}/\partial x^\gamma - \partial g_{\beta\gamma}/\partial x^\sigma) \tag{12}
$$

and (with $g^{\alpha\sigma}$ the matrix reciprocal to $g_{\mu\nu}$)

$$
\Gamma^\alpha_{\beta\gamma} = g^{\alpha\sigma}\Gamma_{\rho\gamma\,\sigma} \tag{13}
$$

(Christoffel symbols; both nontensorial quantities). Also, re-express the derivatives in (11) in terms of the proper time τ rather than the more general parameter λ, thus:

$$
(d/d\lambda) = (d\tau/d\lambda)(d/d\tau)
$$

$$
= [-g_{\alpha\beta}(dx^\alpha/d\lambda)(dx^\beta/d\lambda)]^{1/2} \, d/d\tau
$$

Find thus the *differential equation for a geodesic* (see Chapters 1 and 2)

$$d^2x^\alpha/d\tau^2 + \Gamma^\alpha_{\beta\gamma}(dx^\beta/d\tau)(dx^\gamma/d\tau) = 0 \qquad (14)$$

Specialization to Low Velocity and Nearly Flat Space

In Eq. (14), 16 terms have to be summed to obtain even one component of the quantity $d^2x/d\tau^2$. However, specialize now to the case of a slowly moving particle in a region of space-time that is nearly flat ($g_{ii} \approx 1$; $g_{00} \approx -1$; $g_{\alpha\beta} \approx 0$ for $\alpha \neq \beta$). In other words, neglect

$$dx^i/d\tau \qquad (i = 1, 2, 3) \qquad (15)$$

(Latin indices for space components vs. Greek indices for space-time components!) in comparison with unity, and neglect the difference between $dx^0/d\tau$ and unity. Then the geodesic equation of motion simplifies to

$$d^2x^k/d\tau^2 + \Gamma^k_{oo} = 0 \qquad (16)$$

Further, specialize to the case of a geometry—like that around the sun—which is *static* in the chosen coordinates. Then it follows from Eqs. (12) and (13) that the equation takes the form

$$d^2x^k/d\tau^2 = (\tfrac{1}{2})(\partial g_{oo}/\partial x^k) \qquad (17)$$

Compare Einstein's geometry with Newton's mechanics, recalling that, for a slowly moving particle, proper time (τ, meters) and ordinary time (t_{sec}, seconds; or $ct_{\text{sec}} = t$, meters) can be identified:

$$
\begin{aligned}
d^2x^k/d\tau^2 &= (1/c^2)(d^2x^k/dt_{\text{sec}}^2) \\
&= (1/c^2)(-\partial/\partial x^k)(\text{gravitational potential}) \\
&= (\partial/\partial x^k)(Gm/c^2r) \\
&= (\partial/\partial x^k)(m^*/r)
\end{aligned}
\qquad (18)
$$

Here m(kg), or m^*(meters) $\equiv Gm/c^2$, is the mass of the sun or other center of attraction, and r is the distance from this center to the test particle. From comparing (17) and (18), conclude that the oo component of the metric tensor agrees with the Newtonian gravitational potential ϕ_G up to a multiplicative factor and an additive constant. The constant is fixed by the requirement that the geometry must reduce to the Lorentz flat-space value far from the center of attraction. Thus find

$$
\begin{aligned}
g_{oo} &= -1 + 2m^*/r \\
&= -1 + 2Gm/c^2r \\
&= -1 + 2\phi_G/c^2
\end{aligned}
\qquad (19)
$$

Connection between Time–Time Component of Metric and Sources of Mass–Energy

The *linearity* of the result (19) in the source strength (to the order of approximation considered here) gives warrant for using the same formula (19) to determine the effect on the geometry brought about by a large number of stationary or slowly moving sources, whether localized or distributed. Therefore, it is appropriate to describe the sources in terms of a density distribution of mass $\rho(\text{kg}/\text{m}^3)$. The connection between the mass distribution and the Newtonian potential is given by Poisson's equation,

$$\nabla^2 \phi_G = -4\pi G\rho \tag{20}$$

From this equation follows an equation for g_{oo}, the first of Einstein's ten gravitational potentials:

$$\nabla^2 g_{oo} = -8\pi G\rho/c^2$$
$$= -(8\pi G/c^4)(\text{density of mass–energy}) \tag{21}$$

The Vectorial Character of the Corresponding Source Term in Electrodynamics

The principle of correspondence with Newtonian gravitational theory has carried us this far. To go further, we have to respond to the demand for a purely geometric connection between geometry and energy-momentum-stress. In trying to formulate this idea in usable form, it is of some help to recall the example of electrodynamics. In the earliest days, one looked apart from any influence of *motion* upon the distant effects of an electric charge. The *density* ρ_e of electric charge was alone considered the source of these effects. The propagation of these effects was considered to be described fully by an electrostatic potential ϕ satisfying Poisson's equation

$$\nabla^2 \phi = -4\pi\rho_e \tag{22}$$

The existence of magnetic effects associated with charges in motion forced one to recognize the concept of a magnetic potential A^k. This potential is realized today to be the space part of a four-potential A^α:

$$A^\alpha = \begin{cases} A^o = \phi = \text{electrostatic potential} \\ A^k = \text{magnetic potential} \end{cases} \tag{23}$$

Similarly, the charge density is appreciated to be but one component of a four-vector ρ^α:

$$\rho^\alpha = \begin{cases} \rho^o = \rho = \text{density of charge (charge units}/\text{m}^3) \\ \rho^k = (1/c)\ (\text{current density in charge units}/\text{m}^2\ \text{sec}) \\ \quad = (\text{charge units}/\text{m}^2\ \text{of cross section and m of time}) \end{cases} \tag{24}$$

The appropriate generalization of Poisson's equation is known to be

$$\Box^2 A^\alpha = -4\pi\rho^\alpha \tag{25}$$

This equation equates one four-vector to another. It therefore has a meaning and content that is independent of the particular Lorentz reference system in which it happens to be expressed. Lying behind any happenstance components that the four-vectors have in any random frame of reference one can conceive of the two four-vectors themselves in some intrinsic and coordinate-free description, as, for example, by way of arrows endowed with magnitude and direction. A similar description is now required for the gravitational problem.

Tensorial Character of Source in Geometrodynamics

On the right-hand side of the approximate geometric field equation (21) stands the "density of energy." This quantity is not—like the source in electrostatics—the time component of a four-vector. Instead, it is the time-time component T^{oo} of a *tensor*

$$T^{\alpha\beta} = \left(\begin{array}{c|c} T^{oo} & T^{ok} \\ \hline T^{jo} & T^{jk} \end{array}\right) \tag{26}$$

with the following interpretation in a locally Lorentz frame of reference:

$$\left(\begin{array}{c|cc}
\text{(energy per m}^3\text{)} & \begin{pmatrix}\text{flow of energy per m of}\\ \text{light travel time in } k\\ \text{direction per m}^2 \text{ of area}\\ \text{normal to } k \text{ axis}\end{pmatrix} \text{ or } & \begin{pmatrix}\text{velocity of light times}\\ \text{density of momentum}\\ \text{directed in } k \text{ direction,}\\ \text{on a "per m}^3 \text{ basis"}\end{pmatrix} \\
\hline
\begin{pmatrix}\text{energy flux in}\\ j \quad \text{direction}\end{pmatrix} & \begin{pmatrix}\text{momentum directed in}\\ k \text{ direction flowing per}\\ \text{sec in } j \text{ direction across}\\ \text{a m}^2 \text{ of area normal to}\\ \text{the } j \text{ direction}\end{pmatrix} \text{ or } & \begin{pmatrix}\text{force in } k \text{ direction}\\ \text{exerted by electromag-}\\ \text{netic field and other}\\ \text{agencies at } x^j - 0 \text{ } on\\ \text{fields and agencies at}\\ x^j + 0 \text{ per m}^2 \text{ of inter-}\\ \text{face}\end{pmatrix}
\end{array}\right) \tag{27}$$

In the special case of a fluid at rest and in hydrostatic equilibrium, the familiar descriptive parameters are the density of mass ρ, the energy density ϵ, and the pressure p. In this illustrative example, the energy-momentum-stress tensor, *evaluated in a local Lorentz frame of reference*, has the value

$$T^{\alpha\beta} = T_{\alpha\beta} = \begin{pmatrix} \epsilon + \rho c^2 & 0 & 0 & 0 \\ 0 & p & 0 & 0 \\ 0 & 0 & p & 0 \\ 0 & 0 & 0 & p \end{pmatrix} \tag{28}$$

The tensor character of the *source* term is, happily, compatible with the tensor character of the *effect*, as evidenced in the gravitational potentials $g_{\alpha\beta}$. Therefore, no escape is evident from having to follow the model of the four-vector electromagnetic field equations (25) and generalize the single gravitational field equation (21) to a ten-component tensor equation of the form

$$\text{``}\square^2 g\text{''}_{\alpha\beta} = -(8\pi G/c^4)T_{\alpha\beta} \tag{29}$$

The quotation marks are meant to indicate that the operator "$\square^2$" as applied to a tensor is not yet well defined. We know only that, for nearly flat space and practically stationary sources, "$\square^2 g$"$_{oo}$ should reduce to $\nabla^2 g_{oo}$. We therefore insist that "$\square^2 g$"$_{\alpha\beta}$ should be a general second-order differential operator built out of terms like

$$\partial^2 g_{\mu\nu}/\partial x^\rho \partial x^\sigma \tag{30}$$

There are ten distinct potentials $g_{\mu\nu} = g_{\nu\mu}$. There are ten distinct second derivatives $\partial^2 \ldots /\partial x^\rho \partial x^\sigma$. There are, therefore, 100 terms of the form (30) to be combined to make up the ten expressions denoted "$\square^2 g$"$_{\alpha\beta}$. In other words, there are 1000 coefficients to be found out before one has a proper definition of the quantities "$\square^2 g$"$_{\alpha\beta}$! However, the circumstance that "$\square^2 g$"$_{\alpha\beta}$ must be tensorial in the indices α and β reduces the number of unknowns from 1000 to 2:

$$\text{``}\square^2 g\text{''}_{\alpha\beta} = \text{(constant)}_1 \, (g^{\mu\nu}\partial^2 g_{\alpha\beta}/\partial x^\mu \partial x^\nu + \text{terms that contain only first}$$
$$\text{derivatives of the } g_{\gamma\delta} \text{ and that are uniquely determined}$$
$$\text{by the principle of covariance)}$$
$$\tag{31}$$
$$+ \text{(constant)}_2 \, g_{\alpha\beta} \, g^{\sigma\tau}(g^{\mu\nu}\partial^2 g_{\sigma\tau}/\partial x^\mu x^\nu + \text{terms that contain only}$$
$$\text{first derivatives of the } g_{\gamma\delta} \text{ and that are uniquely deter-}$$
$$\text{mined by the principle of covariance)}$$

This result follows from an analysis more detailed than it is appropriate to give here. However, the result itself can be expressed in more geometric language through the Riemann curvature tensor $R_{\alpha\beta\gamma\delta}$ that Anderson discusses in Chapter 2.

The Curvature Tensor as the Geometrodynamic Analog of the Electromagnetic Field

Recall (Chapter 3) that the curvature tensor measures the physically significant part of the gravitational field in the following sense: We start with two nearby and initially parallel geodesics (world lines of neutral infinitesimal test particles) and observe how rapidly they deviate from parallelism:

$$(D/D\tau)^2 \eta^\alpha + R^\alpha_{\beta\gamma\delta}(dx^\beta/d\tau)\eta^\gamma(dx^\delta/d\tau) = 0 \tag{32}$$

The quantity η^α is the coordinate difference between points on the two world lines that go with corresponding values of the proper time parameter τ. $(dx^\beta/d\tau)$ is the unit vector tangent to the one world line. $D/D\tau$ means proper derivative, as corrected for the curvilinearity of the coordinate system itself. Thus, for any vector $A^\alpha(\tau)$ given along the world line,

$$DA^\alpha/D\tau \equiv dA^\alpha/d\tau + \Gamma^\alpha_{\beta\gamma}A^\beta \, dx^\gamma/d\tau \qquad (33)$$

By observing this difference for a sufficient number of pairs of world lines passing through the same region of space-time, we are in a position to find all 20 distinct components of the curvature tensor.[7] This analysis—working with *pairs* of neutral test particles—is the analogue for gravitation of what one does in electromagnetism—working with *individual* and *charged* test particles—to find the electric and magnetic fields in a given locality.[8]

Curvature for Two-Sphere and Three-Sphere

By way of illustration of the curvature tensor, consider the geometry of a two-sphere of radius a. Two geodesics that start at the equator going north $(dx^1/ds = 0, \, dx^2/ds = 1)$ draw closer to each other at a well-defined rate $(1/\eta^1)(d^2\eta^1/ds^2) = -(1/a^2)$ in a locally Euclidean coordinate system. Thus, one concludes

$$R^1_{212} = R_{1212} = 1/a^2 \qquad (34)$$

in a locally Euclidean coordinate system. Similarly, for a three-sphere of radius a:

$$R_{1212} = R_{2323} = R_{3131} = 1/a^2 \qquad (35)$$

$$R_{1223} = R_{1231} = R_{2331} = 0 \qquad (36)$$

Curvature of an Expanding Universe

Still more interesting is the case of four-dimensions—most simply a three-sphere universe whose radius a is an arbitrary function $a(t)$ of an appropriately normalized time-parameter t:

$$d\sigma^2 = -d\tau^2 = -dt^2 + a^2(t)[d\chi^2 + \sin^2\chi(d\theta^2 + \sin^2\theta \, d\phi^2)] \qquad (37)$$

Here the location of any point in the three-sphere is described by the three angles θ, ϕ and χ. The angles θ and ϕ are the familiar spherical polar angles. They tell in what direction we should go from the origin to get to the point in question. The angle χ determines how *far* one must go to get there. The product $ad\chi$ takes the place of the usual element of radial distance dr. At any point in the four-space, set up a local Lorentz frame of reference with axes 0, 1, 2, 3 along the directions of increasing t, χ, θ, and ϕ. Referred to this reference system, the components of the curvature tensor all vanish except those equivalent to the following:

$$R_{1212} = R_{2323} = R_{3131} = (1 + \dot{a}^2)/a^2 \tag{38}$$

$$R_{0101} = R_{0202} = R_{0303} = -\ddot{a}/a \tag{39}$$

The Interaction of Matter and Geometry

The Riemannian curvature tensor tells how one quantity—the separation between two nearby and nearly parallel geodesics—changes as proper time increases. In this sense it tells the response *of* matter *to* geometry.

What about the converse issue, the response *of* geometry *to* matter? How is one to translate into well-defined geometric terms the symbolic equation

$$\text{``}\Box^2 g\text{''}_{\alpha\beta} = (8\pi G/c^4)T_{\alpha\beta} \tag{40}$$

connecting the metric with the stress-energy tensor? In this equation, the left-hand side, containing terms linear in second derivatives of the metric coefficients, must be built linearly out of combinations of components of the Riemann curvature tensor.[9] Therefore, one asks for quantities that (1) are determined by the curvature, that (2) have a particularly simple geometric significance, and that (3) tie up simply with the physics. It is worthwhile to look first at a plausible but wrong quantity in order to see more clearly what distinguishes the right quantity!

The Volume Defined by a Cluster of Test Particles

Consider a cluster of test particles sufficiently numerous to mark out the boundary of an elementary volume element. Let the test particles be at rest with respect to each other at some initial instant. Then gravitational fields in the neighborhood will cause accelerations of these particles relative to each other. The volume element will suffer changes in shape proportional to the second power of the proper time τ. In a local Lorentz reference system, directions along the x axis will increase fractionally by the amount

$$-(\tau^2/2)R^1_{010} \tag{41}$$

similarly for the y and z dimensions of the elementary volume. Consider as an example a cluster of particles dropped toward the earth from a height of several hundred kilometers. The x and y dimensions of the cluster contract (focusing effect of the earth's attraction), but the z dimension is drawn out (pull on lower particles of cluster greater than that on the upper ones). Moreover, the rate at which the z dimension extends is shown by elementary analysis to be twice as great as that at which the x and y directions contract. The *volume* does not change to second order in time so long as the space is free of matter and energy.

Attraction of Matter Inside

Now let the cluster of test particles explore a region of space filled with dust or other sources of mass-energy. Then the matter *within* the cluster will draw the test particles together, whereas the matter outside will have no effect on the volume to the second order in time. In other words, the volume-contraction factor

$$R^1{}_{010} + R^2{}_{020} + R^3{}_{030} = R^0{}_{000} + R^1{}_{010} + R^2{}_{020} + R^3{}_{030} = R_{00} \quad (42)$$

will measure directly the density of mass energy T_{oo}. Moreover, Newtonian gravitation theory gives a simple and definite prediction for the fractional change in volume.[10] From this analysis, it follows that the contraction factor has the value

$$R_{00} = 4\pi(G/c^4)T_{oo} \quad (43)$$

If this result were correct, it would follow from arguments of tensorial invariance that the gravitational field equations have the form

$$R_{\mu\nu} = 4\pi(G/c^4)T_{\mu\nu} \quad (44)$$

Trouble with the First Try at the Gravitational Field Equation

What is wrong with (44)? One will immediately say an equation is wrong if it equates a scalar to a vector. He will also say that it is wrong if it equates a vector with a nonzero curl to a vector with a zero curl. Equation (44) equates a tensor $R_{\mu\nu}$, which, in general, has a nonzero covariant divergence, to a tensor $T_{\mu\nu}$, which has a zero covariant divergence!

Tensors of Vanishing Covariant Divergence

What does it mean to say that the covariant divergence of a tensor is zero? And what geometric construction modifies the contracted or Ricci curvature tensor $R_{\mu\nu}$ into a tensor with vanishing covariant divergence?

At a point P in space-time select a timelike direction $dx^\alpha/d\tau$. Consider an element of three-space

$$d^3\sigma_\alpha = (-g)^{1/2}[\alpha\beta\gamma\delta]\frac{\partial(x^\beta, x^\gamma, x^\delta)}{\partial(u, v, w)}\, du\, dv\, dw \quad (45)$$

orthogonal to this timelike direction.[11] Ask for the amount of energy and momentum in this three-volume; in energy units it is

$$T^{\mu\alpha} \, d^3\sigma_\alpha \tag{46}$$

Compare with the energy and momentum in a like region displaced ahead in time by the interval $d\tau$. The two four-vectors cannot be compared directly because they are located at different points in space-time. The comparison demands parallel transport to a common location. Accordingly, the alteration in the energy-momentum is governed not by the ordinary rate of change but by the covariant rate of change of $T^{\mu\alpha}$. Comparing this change in energy-momentum with that brought in at the boundaries during the time in question (also computed covariantly for parallel transport to the same common location) and equating the surplus to zero, one has the covariant transcription of the usual principle of conservation of momentum and energy,[12]

$$T^{\mu\alpha}_{\;;\alpha} = 0 \tag{47}$$

Cartan's Construction for Geometric Tensor of Vanishing Covariant Divergence

Cartan gives the following instructive prescription to construct the *geometric* quantity, which has the same tensorial properties as $T_{\mu\nu}$, including the same vanishing covariant divergence[13]:

1. Consider an elementary three-dimensional region.

2. Consider a portion $dS^{\alpha\beta}$, of the two-dimensional frontier of this region.

3. Transport a vector A^γ by parallel displacement around the one-dimensional boundary of this two-dimensional region. The vector undergoes the change

$$\Delta A^\gamma = R^\gamma_{\;\delta\alpha\beta} \, dS^{\alpha\beta} A^\delta \tag{48}$$

4. a zero result (and therefore nothing of geometric interest) will be found by adding these changes for all the elements $dS^{\alpha\beta}$ over the entire boundary of the three-dimensional region. The reason is simple: One of the two-dimensional elements of the frontier is separated from another by a one-dimensional boundary. This boundary is traversed twice, once in each direction. The resulting contributions to the rotation of the vector A^γ cancel completely. A similar result in elementary-vector analysis is familiar: the integral of curl B over the two-dimensional boundary of a three-dimensional region vanishes automatically:

$$\iint (\nabla \times \mathbf{B}) \cdot d\mathbf{S} = 0 \tag{49}$$

Here one is adding *scalars* and getting zero. In the case of curvature one is adding *vectors* ΔA^γ and getting zero. But the zero result is independent of the vector A^γ with which one starts. Therefore, one can conclude that the *geometric sum of the rotation matrices*

$$R^\gamma{}_{\delta\alpha\beta} \, dS^{\alpha\beta} \tag{50}$$

extended over the two-dimensional frontier of the three-element is zero. The term geometric sum carries with it the connotation that the rotation matrices are carried by parallel transport to a common point before they are added. Cartan shows, incidentally, how to deduce from this elementary argument the Bianchi identity: the result

$$R^\gamma{}_{\delta\alpha\beta;\sigma} + R^\gamma{}_{\delta\sigma\alpha;\beta} + R^\gamma{}_{\delta\beta\sigma;\alpha} = 0 \tag{51}$$

The Concept of Moment of Rotation

5. The matrix rotation (50) that is associated with a given bit of two-surface can be compared with a vector force in elementary mechanics. The vanishing of the sum of the rotations can be compared with the vanishing of the sum of the forces. But, in mechanics it is necessary to pay attention not only to the *vectors* associated with these forces, but also to the *line of action* of these forces. In other words, it is necessary to consider the *moments* of the forces. Similarly, Cartan invites one to consider a kind of *moment* of the rotation (50). Think of the rotation (50) as represented by a bivector or elementary two-surface. The direction of this two-surface— which may be different from the direction of the area element $dS^{\alpha\beta}$—tells the plane of the rotation, and its magnitude (radians; dimensionless) tells the amount of the rotation. Pick some point P with respect to which to compute the equivalent of a moment. *What* point is chosen does not matter. Neither does it make any difference in mechanics when the system of forces add vectorially to zero! The vector from P to the surface element together with bivector of rotation associated with the surface element together define an elementary parallelopiped. It is Cartan's moment.

Moment of Rotation Definable by a Scalar in a Three-Dimensional Manifold

6. In a three-dimensional world, this moment is described by a single number, its volume. The sum of these numbers for all the two-surface elements of the frontier of the three-volume in question is proportional to the magnitude of this volume. The constant of proportionality—up to a numerical factor—is the scalar curvature invariant $^{(3)}R$ of the three-dimensional manifold at the point in question.

Moment of Rotation gives a Vector in a Four-Dimensional Manifold

7. In four-dimensional space-time, a three-element of volume under investigation $d^3\sigma_\alpha$ may be represented by a four-vector normal to the three-volume. When the volume is pure spacelike ($dx\,dy\,dz$, for example), the four-vector is pure timelike:

$$d^3\sigma_\alpha = (d^3\sigma_0, d^3\sigma_1, d^3\sigma_2, d^3\sigma_3)$$
$$= (-g)^{1/2}(dx\,dy\,dz, 0, 0, 0) \tag{52}$$

Summing Cartan's "moment of curvature" over all two-elements that bound this three-element, one comes to a totalized "moment of curvature" that (1) is proportional to the size of the three-element; (2) has, itself, the character of a three-element; and (3) therefore can also be described by a vector, say, $d^3\omega_\alpha$. Cartan shows that *the vector that measures the moment of curvature is given in terms of the vector associated with the three-element under investigation by the formula*

$$d^3\omega_\alpha = (R_{\alpha\beta} - \tfrac{1}{2}g_{\alpha\beta}R)\,d^3\sigma^\beta \tag{53}$$

Density of Moment of Rotation Gives the Einstein Tensor

8. From the very geometry of the moment analysis Cartan can show that the tensor on the right-hand side of (52) automatically has zero-covariant divergence[14]—a property not enjoyed by either the first or the second part of the tensor individually. Therefore, this tensor has the same *geometric character* as the stress-energy tensor $T_{\mu\nu}$.

9. Einstein's theory of gravitation is therefore founded upon the tensor equation

$$R_{\alpha\beta} - \tfrac{1}{2}g_{\alpha\beta}R = 8\pi(G/c^4)T_{\alpha\beta} \tag{54}$$

Here the constant of proportionality is obtained from the demand that a static geometry around a spherically symmetric center of mass m should be describable in terms of a principal metric coefficient of the form

$$g_{oo} = -1 + (2Gm/c^2r) \tag{55}$$

10. Pick any point P in space-time. Let a test particle pass through this point with any arbitrary velocity. A co-moving Lorentz frame has its time axis along a certain unit vector $dx^\alpha/d\tau$. Orthogonal to this axis is a local spacelike hypersurface. In this hypersurface, *the density of moment of curvature* (units length/length^3) *is equal to the density of energy* (translated from units energy/length^3 to geometric units by way of the factor $8\pi G/c^4$). To make this statement,

$$(R_{\alpha\beta} - \tfrac{1}{2}g_{\alpha\beta}R)(dx^\alpha/d\tau)(dx^\beta/d\tau) = (8\pi G/c^4)T_{\alpha\beta}(dx^\alpha/d\tau)(dx^\beta/d\tau) \tag{56}$$

for every point P and for a three-parameter set of directions $dx^\alpha/d\tau$ is to summarize the entire content of Einstein's equations.

Hilbert's Argument for the Four Identities Connecting Einstein's Equations

The ten equations (54) have between them four identities—four equations that really put no conditions at all upon the geometry because they are *automatically* fulfilled *whether* Eqs. (54) are satisfied:

$$(R^{\alpha\beta} - \tfrac{1}{2}g^{\alpha\beta}R)_{;\beta} = 8\pi(G/c^4)T^{\alpha\beta}{}_{;\beta} \qquad (57)$$

Therefore there are really only six net equations on the ten quantities $g_{\alpha\beta}$. This circumstance at first drove Einstein away from the final form of the field equations,[15] so that his preliminary publication[16] put forward equations of the form (44). Hilbert pointed out[17] that the equations set up to determine the $g_{\alpha\beta}$ would be quite unacceptable if they really succeeded uniquely to determine them. What is really relevant—and what *should* be determined—is the geometry and curvature of space-time. What coordinates we use to describe that geometry should be immaterial. If the equations were completely to determine the ten $g_{\alpha\beta}$, they would tell us not only the geometry but also—unhappily—the coordinates in terms of which that geometry is expressed. However, we know that only the interval between one event and another (between one crossing of world lines and another, for example) has any real significance:

$$ds^2 = g_{\alpha\beta}\, dx^\alpha\, dx^\beta \qquad (58)$$

How one draws coordinate surfaces through space-time is a matter of paper work and bookkeeping, and has nothing to do with the real physics.

Freedom in Choice of Coordinates Shows Up in Metric Coefficients

The freedom in the choice of coordinates is expressed by the four free functions in the general coordinate transformation

$$x^\mu = x^\mu(\bar{x}^0, \bar{x}^1, \bar{x}^2, \bar{x}^3) \qquad (\mu = 0, 1, 2, 3) \qquad (59)$$

This freedom in the coordinates shows up in the metric coefficients themselves:

$$\bar{g}_{\sigma\tau} = g_{\alpha\beta}\frac{\partial x^\alpha}{\partial \bar{x}^\sigma}\frac{\partial x^\beta}{\partial \bar{x}^\tau} \qquad (60)$$

The difference between $\bar{g}_{\alpha\beta}$ and $g_{\alpha\beta}$ typifies the arbitrariness that does exist and must exist in the solution of any proper set of gravitational field equations, when regarded as equations for *metric coefficients*. However, when regarded as equations for *geometry*, the equations leave no room for any arbitrariness, provided the *initial conditions* are properly stated.

Initial-Value Problem for Electrodynamics and Geometrodynamics

A discussion of the initial-value problem for geometrodynamics is properly prefaced by a review of the same problem for electromagnetism. There one considers all of space at a certain time—or, more generally, a spacelike hypersurface. Throughout this three-dimensional region specify the electric field and the magnetic field. From this *initial-value data* Maxwell's equations allow one to determine the entire future development—and past history—of the field. For this purpose, it is only necessary that the initial-value data be *properly specified*; that is, they must satisfy (in the case of charge-free space) the *initial-value equations*

$$\text{div } \mathbf{B} = 0 \qquad (61)$$

$$\text{div } \mathbf{E} = 0 \qquad (62)$$

throughout the three-dimensional region.

The Intrinsic Geometry

In geometrodynamics there is a similar formulation of the initial value problem.[18]

1. Specify a three-dimensional space-like geometry $^{(3)}\mathscr{G}$, for example, by giving six metric coefficients $^{(3)}g_{ik}(i, k = 1, 2, 3)$ as functions of three coordinates x^1, x^2, x^3. This one act in geometrodynamics is analogous to what one does in electromagnetism in two steps: (1) choosing a space-like hypersurface and (2) specifying the magnetic field (the so-called field coordinate) upon this hypersurface. It only remains to specify the "field momentum"—the analog of the electric field—upon this hypersurface.

The Extrinsic Curvature

2. Specify the *extrinsic curvature* K_k^i of the hypersurface (the so-called second fundamental form[19]), telling how it is curved with respect to the yet-to-be constructed enveloping four-dimensional manifold. Recall, by way of illustration, that the two-geometry *intrinsic* to a sheet of paper is Euclidean, in whatever way the paper is curved. This curvature is entirely *extrinsic*, having to do with how the piece of paper is located in the enveloping three-space. To define the extrinsic curvature more precisely, erect timelike normals of proper length $d\tau$ at the points x^i ($i = 1, 2, 3$) and $x^i + dx^i$. Draw the vector from the tip of the first normal to the tip of the

second normal. Carry this vector by parallel transport back to the original hypersurface. It does not agree with the vector dx^i between the bases of the two normals. Instead, its components can be written

$$dx^i + K^i_k \, dx^k \, d\tau \tag{63}$$

This expression defines the extrinsic curvature tensor K^i_k. If, instead of following two test particles for the proper time $d\tau$, one follows a whole cluster of test particles, one can define the *fractional change in volume* of the cluster,

$$(K^1_1 + K^2_2 + K^3_3) \, d\tau = (\operatorname{Tr} K) \, d\tau \tag{64}$$

Here the symbol $\operatorname{Tr} K$ stands for the trace of the extrinsic curvature. A more sophisticated measure of the deformation taking place in the cluster of test particles as time advances is provided by the "second invariant of the extrinsic curvature," the quantity

$$K_2 = (\operatorname{Tr} K)^2 - \operatorname{Tr} K^2 = (K^i_i)^2 - K^i_k K^k_i \tag{65}$$

The Initial-Value Equations

3. When the intrinsic geometry of the hypersurface and its extrinsic curvature have been specified, Einstein's equations determine uniquely the entire past and future history of the geometry, *provided* that the initial-value data satisfy the *initial-value equations*

$$R_{oo} - \tfrac{1}{2} g_{oo} R = (8\pi G/c^4) T_{oo}$$

and

$$R_{oi} - \tfrac{1}{2} g_{oi} R = (8\pi G/c^4) T_{oi} \tag{66}$$

or, in an often more convenient $(3 + 1)$-dimensional form[20],

$$(K^k_i - \delta^k_i \operatorname{Tr} K)_{|k} = 2(8\pi G/c^4) \binom{\text{density of flow of}}{\text{energy in } i \text{ direction}}$$

and

$$^{(3)}R + K_2 = 2(8\pi G/c^4)(\text{energy density}) \tag{67}$$

Einstein Field Equations Summarized in Last Initial-Value Equation

Eq. (67) is the heart of general relativity. We shall be applying it as an initial-value equation, but it holds true at every point P in space-time. By analogy consider in electrodynamics the equations

$$\operatorname{div} \mathbf{E} = 0 \qquad \operatorname{div} \mathbf{B} = 0 \tag{68}$$

which state that lines of force never end. Pick any point P in space-time. Construct through it a spacelike hypersurface with any slope. Demand for every choice of slope that the lines of force within the resulting hypersurface will have no endings. *From this requirement that lines of force will never end, one recovers Maxwell's equations in their entirety.* Similarly, the single requirement (67) that *the sum of the intrinsic scalar curvature plus the second invariant of the extrinsic curvature must equal* $(16\pi G/c^4)$ times *the energy density*, required of every hypersurface through every point P, contains the full content of Einstein's field equations.

Why the Curvature of the Hypersurface Appears

In the case of electrodynamics the hypersurface through the point P had to be specified only to the extent of giving its *slope*. This circumstance corresponds to the fact that electromagnetic forces are definable by their action on a *single* test particle. In contrast, gravitational forces are defined by the changes they produce in the separation of a *pair* of test particles. Therefore, one has to specify the *curvature* of the hypersurface to which the world lines are normal as well as its slope.

Application to Special Case of a Time-Symmetric Geometry

Now to illustrate the machinery of general relativity at work! Pick an example as simple as possible. Let the original spacelike hypersurface have *zero* extrinsic curvature. The resulting four-geometry predicted by Einstein's equations will be *time-symmetric* in this sense: everything that happens to the geometry after the chosen instant will be the mirror image of what happened before this moment.[21] Then the extrinsic curvature K_i^k vanishes. Further, limit attention to a situation in which there is no "real" energy present. Three of the initial-value equations are then automatically satisfied; and the fourth [Eq. (67)] reduces to the requirement

$$^{(3)}R = 0 \tag{69}$$

Further Specialization to Spherical Symmetry and Freedom from Matter

In order further to simplify the problem, assume that the geometry of the initial surface has spherical symmetry and departs from Euclidean character by a correction factor ψ^4, which depends solely upon a radial coordinate r; thus,

$$ds^2 = \psi^4(r)(dx^2 + dy^2 + dz^2)$$
$$= \psi^4(r)(dr^2 + r^2 d\theta^2 + r^2 \sin^2\theta \, d\phi^2) \tag{70}$$

with

$$r^2 = x^2 + y^2 + z^2 \tag{71}$$

Then Eq. (70) takes the simple form

$$\nabla^2 \psi(r) = 0 \tag{72}$$

—this simplicity being the motive for writing the correction factor as ψ^4 rather than ψ^2 or ψ!

The Solution for the Initial Three-Geometry

The solution of Eq. (72) contains two disposable constants and can be taken to have the form

$$\psi(r) = 1 + (m^*/2r) \tag{73}$$

Here the first constant has been set at unity to normalize distance measurements far away to the familiar standard of Euclidean geometry. The other constant

$$m^* = Gm/c^2 \tag{74}$$

has the dimensions of a length and provides a geometrized measure of mass.

We have just determined the space dependence of the familiar Schwarzschild geometry surrounding a spherically symmetric center of attraction. This geometry is the heart and soul of the three famous experimental tests of general relativity.

To summarize, we have determined an *initial* three-geometry that satisfies the initial-value equations of geometrodynamics—the analog of finding in electrodynamics a vector function of *position* $\mathbf{B}(x, y, z)$ with vanishing divergence. We have not solved the *further* problem of the dynamical evolution of this Schwarzschild geometry with time.[22]

An Unexpected Topology

A closer look at the Schwarzschild geometry at the moment of time symmetry is appropriate. Consider a fixed value of r and set $\theta = \pi/2$ (equator!) and let ϕ go from 0 to 2π. The distance covered is the quantity

$$(\text{circumference}) = \int ds = 2\pi r \psi^2$$
$$= 2\pi r (1 + m^*/2r)^2 \tag{75}$$

This quantity increases as expected for large r. However, it also increases for small r. It has the minimum value

$$(\text{circumference of throat}) = 8\pi m^* \tag{76}$$

for a value of the radial coordinate r equal to $m^*/2$. For still smaller r

values, the geometry is the mirror image of the geometry at larger r values, as one sees most simply by introducing the new radial coordinate $\bar{r}$ defined by

$$r\bar{r} = (m*/2)^2 \tag{77}$$

The element of distance ds [Eq. (70)], rewritten in terms of $\bar{r}$ instead of r, has exactly the original form (70)!

It is striking that, starting with the simplest of problems in geometrodynamics, one has been led to a non-Euclidean topology[22]—a three-dimensional geometry made up of *two* asymptotically Euclidean spaces connected by a throat. No such result would have been obtained if we had admitted "real" matter at the center, as we would have done, for example, if we had been determining the geometry in the interior of the sun. But in the present case we have curved *empty* space manifesting gravitational attraction. At a distance there is no way to tell—from the pull it exerts—that this object is any different from any real mass. In other words, we have in the pure Schwarzschild geometry a particularly simple *geometrodynamic model for mass.*

The Scope of Geometrodynamics

It is also possible to construct a geometrodynamic model for mass that has the Euclidean topology—a *geon* composed of electromagnetic or gravitational radiation holding itself together by its own gravitational attraction. Out of pure geometry it is also possible, within the framework of Einstein's standard 1915 theory, to obtain a description for electromagnetism and for electricity, which makes no call on any "real" charge.

Unsolved Issues at Planck's Characteristic Distance

The kinds of classical mass and classical charge that come out of geometrodynamics have not the slightest direct connection with the charges and mass of the elementary particles. One does not yet know the relation between the extraordinarily rich model world of Einstein's theory and the real world. To investigate that relation is one of the tasks of the future. It has to do with physics at the very smallest scale of distances, set by the quantum of action,

$$L* = (\hbar G/c^3)^{1/2} = 1.6 \times 10^{-33} \text{ cm} \tag{78}$$

and makes unprecedented demands on theory[23]—not least because experiment would seem to be out of the question in that domain!

Tensor vs. Vector Field as Seen in Velocity Dependence of Deflection

There is, however, one interesting prediction of relativity at a more approachable scale of distances that would be interesting to see checked experimentally, because it would show up the difference between the vector field of electricity and the tensor field of gravitation. Consider the deflection of a *relativistic* test particle ($\beta = v/c \sim 1$) by a spherically symmetrical center endowed, in the one case, with electric charge and, in the other case, with gravitational pull. Define the impact parameter b of the particle as the perpendicular distance from the center of attraction to the continuation of the original line of approach. Also let the charges of the test particle and of the center of attraction be expressed in geometric units by way of the formula

$$q^*(\text{cm}) = (G^{1/2}/c^2)q(\text{esu}) \tag{79}$$

Then, for large values of the impact parameter, the calculated deflection is[23]

$$\theta = 2(q^*_{\text{test}}q^*_{\text{center}}/bm^*_{\text{test}})\beta^{-2}(1 - \beta^2)^{1/2} \tag{80}$$

in the case of electromagnetism; and, in the case of gravitation,

$$\theta = 2(m^*_{\text{center}}/b)(1 + 1/\beta^2) \tag{81}$$

The very different velocity dependence in the two cases seems not to have been remarked on so far.

Special Case of Deflection of Light by the Sun

One can, of course, say that he has roughly checked one point on the curve (81) by measuring the deflection of light by the sun. In this case, (81) leads to the famous factor of two by which the predictions of Einstein and Newton differ from each other. The relevant factors in this case are

m = (mass of sun) = 1.987×10^{33} g
m^* = (geometrized mass) = 1.475×10^5 cm
b = (impact parameter) = 6.94×10^{10} cm
θ = $4m^*/b$ = (Einstein prediction) = $1.751''$
θ (observed at 1947 eclipse) = $2.01'' \pm 0.27''$
θ (observed at 1952 eclipse) = $1.70'' \pm 0.10''$
The agreement is reasonable.

Notes and References

1. The term Riemannian geometry as employed in the text is understood, in the sense employed by Cartan and most physicists, as a geometry defined by a line element of the form $ds^2 = g_{\alpha\beta}\,dx^\alpha\,dx^\beta$, whether the "signature" of the

metric is $-+++$ (of locally Lorentz character) or $++++$ (of locally Euclidean character). However, most mathematical discussions consider the term as implying a positive definite signature because many theorems have been established only under the restriction of positive definiteness.

2. Regarding the question of initial-value data and where they are to come from if they are not specified by the dynamic equations of physics, the question has been raised whether there exist any constants of the motion at all for a properly closed universe. In other words, is a model universe characterized by a unique quantum state, *free* of all disposable initial-value data? See J. A. Wheeler, *Rev. Mod. Phys.*, **29**, 463 (1957); *Geometrodynamics*, Academic, New York, 1962, p. 75 (cited hereafter as *GMD*); and a paper, "The Universe in the Light of General Relativity," appearing in two places: *Monist*, **47**, 40 (1962) and *Proceedings of the 1962 Boulder Summer Conference on Theoretical Physics*, Interscience, New York, in press.

3. The equations that must be satisfied by the three-geometry intrinsic to a space-like hypersurface and by the "extrinsic" curvature of this hypersurface relative to the enveloping—and yet-to-be constructed—four-geometry, if these are to be *compatible* parts of the total initial-value data: K. Stellmacher, *Math. Ann.*, **115**, 136 (1937); A. Lichnerowicz, *Helv. Phys. Acta Suppl.*, **4**, 176 (1956); Y. Fourès-Bruhat, *J. Rational Mech. Anal.*, **5**, 951 (1956); Y. Bruhat, chapter on the Cauchy problem in L. Witten (ed.), *Gravitation: An Introduction to Current Research*, Wiley, New York, 1962; R. Arnowitt, S. Deser, and C. W. Misner, *Phys. Rev.*, **113**, 745 (1959); *ibid.*, **116**, 1322 (1959); *ibid.*, **117**, 1595 (1960); *ibid.*, **118**, 1100 (1960); and R. F. Baierlein, D. H. Sharp, and J. A. Wheeler, *Phys. Rev.*, **126**, 1864 (1962).

4. The "sandwich formulation" of the initial-value problem as a means to go about the solution of this problem and the relation of this solution to Mach's concept of the origin of inertia are treated by R. F. Baierlein, D. H. Sharp, and J. A. Wheeler, Ref. 3, and by J. A. Wheeler, Chapter 15.

5. Covariance is not enough. The field equation $R_{\alpha\beta} - \lambda g_{\alpha\beta} = $ constant times $T_{\alpha\beta}$ is covariant with respect to change of coordinates as is $R_{\alpha\beta} - (\frac{1}{2})g_{\alpha\beta}R = (8\pi G/c^4)T_{\alpha\beta}$. However, the first equation does not supply a purely geometric connection between geometry and mass-momentum-stress, whereas the second one does.

6. R. P. Feynman, Ph.D. Thesis, Princeton, University, 1942; *Rev. Mod. Phys.*, **20**, 367 (1948); *Phys. Rev.*, **76**, 769 (1949); "The Concept of Probability in Quantum Mechanics," in J. Neyman (ed.), *Proceedings of the Second Berkeley Symposium on Mathematical Statistics and Probability*, University of California Press, Berkeley, 1951, p. 533; *Phys. Rev.*, **97**, 660, 1955; Mark Kac, *Probability and Related Topics in Physical Sciences*, Interscience, New York, 1951, including especially an appendix by A. R. Hibbs; C. Morette, *Phys. Rev.*, **81**, 848 (1951); P. Choquard, *Helv. Phys. Acta*, **28**, 89 (1955); J. C. Polkinghorne, *Proc. Roy. Soc.* (*London*), **A230**, 272 (1955); Izuru Fujiwara, "The Correspondence Principle I," in *Proceedings of the Physics Seminar in Trondheim*, **No. 3**, Nordita, Copenhagen, 1962; and the survey and literature references in B. Kurşunoğlu, *Modern Quantum Theory*, Freeman, San Francisco, 1962.

7. That the number of independent components of the Riemann curvature tensor is 20 follows from the symmetry properties set forth in Eqs. (48) and (60) of Chapter 2. The number of independent components in a space of n dimensions is $n^2(n^2 - 1)/12$, a result due to Christoffel and derived in L. P. Eisenhart, *Riemannian Geometry*, Princeton University Press, 1926, p. 21.

8. How the geometry looks a little way off from the track of a chosen test particle has been investigated in the following: E. Fermi, *Atti. Accad. Naz. Lincei*, **31**, 21, 51 (1922); F. Manasse, *Distortion in the Metric of a Small Center of Gravitational Attraction due to its Proximity to a Very Large Mass*, Ph.D. Thesis, Princeton University, September 1961 (submitted for publication in two parts, the first part jointly by F. Manasse and C. W. Misner).

9. See W. Pauli, *Theory of Relativity*, trans. by G. Field, Pergamon, New York, 1958 (cited hereafter as *TR*); see section 17 for the literature on building tensors out of components of the Riemann curvature tensor.

10. J. A. Wheeler, *Rev. Mod. Phys.*, **34**, 873 (1962). From the all-too-plausible character of the quasi-Newtonian argument given in the text for the wrong field equations the reader will see the (not yet satisfied in the literature nor here) need for a quasi-Newtonian argument for the *right* field equations!

11. The symbol $[\alpha\beta\gamma\delta]$ has the value 1 when $\alpha = 0$, $\beta = 1$, $\gamma = 2$, $\delta = 3$, and changes sign on the interchange of any two indices.

12. For further discussion, see Chapters 1 and 2; also see *TR*, p. 177 (Reference 9) and especially L. Landau and E. Lifshitz, *The Classical Theory of Fields*, trans. by M. Hamermesh, Addison-Wesley, Reading, Mass., 1st ed., 1951, pp. 320–321. That the covariant divergence, not the ordinary divergence, vanishes means that the electromagnetic field can give out energy to the geometry and take back energy from the geometry. In principle, it is possible to have an electromagnetic wave converging from great distances in an otherwise flat space, imploding to a temporary configuration of great and rapidly changing energy density that radiates strong gravitational waves, and then spreading out once more to infinity with greatly reduced electromagnetic energy.

13. Élie Cartan, *Leçons sur la géométrie des espaces de Riemann*, Gauthier–Villars, Paris, 2d ed., 1951, Chap. 8 on the Bianchi identities.

14. For an alternative way to give geometric content to Einstein's tensor (which however does not have the depth of Cartan's analysis) see Pauli, *TR*, p. 47 (Reference 9).

15. A. Einstein, *Preussische Akad. der Wiss. Berlin, Sitzungsber*, p. 844 (1915).

16. A. Einstein, *Preussische Akad. der Wiss. Berlin, Sitzungsber*, p. 778 (1915).

17. D. Hilbert, *Gesell. der Wiss. Göttingen, Nachrichten*, p. 395 (1915).

18. See Ref. 3.

19. See, for example, L. P. Eisenhart, *Riemannian Geometry*, Princeton University Press, 1926, Sec. 43.

20. In Eq. (67), the subscript $|k$ signifies differentiation performed covariantly with respect to the k-th coordinate and with respect to the geometry of the three-dimensional manifold.

21. See H. Araki, *Ann. Phys.*, **7**, 456 (1959) and D. Brill, *Ann. Phys.*, **7**, 466 (1959) for an analysis of other time-symmetric problems.

22. The topology and time evolution of the Schwarzschild geometry are shown in schematic diagrams in R. W. Fuller and J. A. Wheeler, *Phys. Rev.*, **128**, 919 (1962).

23. For a discussion, see, for example, J. A. Wheeler, *Rev. Mod. Phys.*, **34**, 873 (1962).

5

Gravitational waves

J. Weber

The Possibility of Gravitational Radiation: An Unsolved Theoretical Problem

A gravitational wave can be thought of as a propagating gravitational field. Such a wave should exert forces on objects with mass, whether they are charged or not. The relativist speaks of a gravitational wave as the propagation of the curvature of space-time.

Gravitational waves have never been observed. Indeed, a small number of highly reputable physicists doubt their existence. So we must first discuss the basis for our present notions about gravitational radiation.

In 1916, Einstein[1] investigated the weak-field solutions of his equations and concluded that quadrupole radiation is possible. The problem Einstein considered was that of a rod which spins about one of its axes (Figure 5-1).

He found the radiated power to be given by

$$P = \frac{32GI^2\omega^6}{5c^5} = 1.73 \times 10^{-59}I^2\omega^6 \text{ ergs/second} \tag{1}$$

I is the moment of inertia of the rod about the axis of spin, and ω is the angular velocity. G is the gravitational constant, and c is the speed of light. The frequency of the radiated wave is 2ω because of the symmetry of the rod. From this we find that a rod about 1 m long, spun at such a speed that it is on the verge of breaking as a consequence of the stress piling up at the center, would radiate perhaps 10^{-30} erg per sec. The characteristic time for radiation damping is roughly 10^{35} years. Because of the small rate of

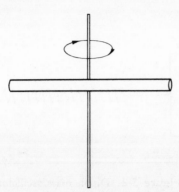

Figure 5-1 Spinning rod as a gravitational wave source.

energy radiation, there have been no experimental observations of this. Indeed, the experimental outlook has not been particularly encouraging.

It may be noted that the smallness of the radiation is in part due to the fact that quadrupole radiation is the lowest mode possible. This can be understood in simple terms as a consequence of momentum conservation. Suppose we have an isolated system composed of a large mass and a small mass coupled by a spring as shown in Figure 5-2. The total momentum of such an isolated oscillating system is a constant that we take to be zero.

$$m\dot{x}_m + M\dot{X}_M = 0 \tag{2}$$

Differentiating this with respect to time gives

$$m\ddot{x}_m + M\ddot{X}_M = 0 \tag{3}$$

This sum of mass times acceleration corresponds to charge times acceleration in electrodynamics. We know that a summation of charge times acceleration gives rise to dipole radiation. So the gravitation analog to electromagnetic dipole radiation vanishes as a consequence of momentum conservation.

This is only an approximation. In the next order, we would have to consider retardation effects. The contribution associated with the large mass would not quite cancel that resulting from the small mass at large distances. From this starting point, we conclude that the lowest order of gravitational radiation from a system cannot be dipole but must be quadrupole radiation.

Einstein's development of gravitational radiation is based on the weak-field solutions of his field equations. The strong-field solution requires exact treatment of the field equations, and this has never been carried out.

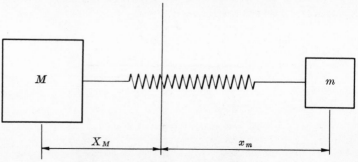

Figure 5-2   Dipole mass oscillator.

To undertake such a program one must start with Einstein's field equations:

$$R_{\mu\nu} - \tfrac{1}{2}g_{\mu\nu}R = \frac{8\pi G}{c^4}T_{\mu\nu} \qquad (4)$$

In empty space, the curvature scalar and the stress tensor vanish:

$$R = 0$$
$$T_{\mu\nu} = 0 \qquad (5)$$

Einstein's field equations reduce to

$$R_{\mu\nu} = 0 \qquad (6)$$

Then, to establish rigorously that there are gravitational waves, one must show that there are solutions of these highly nonlinear equations which asymptotically look like spherical waves; these solutions should not exhibit singularities. In addition, one must show that there are solutions of Eq. (4) in the region of the source which join smoothly onto the solutions of Eq. (6).

Such a program was not even carried out for electromagnetic waves until 1941. It was not until then that Schelkunoff[2] succeeded in getting a complete solution of Maxwell's equations satisfying the boundary conditions at the antenna and joining properly to solutions exhibiting spherical wave propagation. In view of the difficulty of obtaining rigorous solutions even in electromagnetic theory, it is quite clear why the theoretical problem is so very difficult in gravitation theory.

Weak-Field Wave Solutions of Einstein's Equations

Now I shall discuss the weak-field solutions. We obtain these by supposing that the space is almost flat, and that an almost-Lorentz metric is appropriate. Then we can write the metric tensor as a Lorentz metric, plus a small quantity of the first order:

$$g_{\mu\nu} = \delta_{\mu\nu} + h_{\mu\nu} \tag{7}$$

We may define an additional quantity ϕ^ν_μ:

$$\phi^\nu_\mu = h^\nu_\mu - \tfrac{1}{2}\delta^\nu_\mu h^\alpha_\alpha \tag{8}$$

where h^α_α is the trace of h. It is possible to show that this first-order quantity ϕ^ν_μ satisfies a familiar wave equation:

$$\Box\phi^\nu_\mu = -\frac{16\pi G}{c^4}\tau^\nu_\mu \tag{9}$$

provided that we impose the subsidiary condition

$$\phi^\nu_{\mu\ \nu} = 0 \tag{10}$$

$\Box\phi^\nu_\mu$ is the d'Alambertian of ϕ^ν_μ. τ^ν_μ is the lowest order part of T^ν_μ.

These are the equations with which Einstein, and later Eddington, dealt. They are formally the same as those of electrodynamics. Hence, we expect the stress-energy tensor to play the same role in gravitation theory as the four-current does in electromagnetic theory. It should be the source of the gravitational field, and hence the source of gravitational waves.

In 1939, a similar set of equations were obtained by Pauli and Fierz from quite different considerations. Pauli and Fierz were investigating the relativistic wave equations for particles of spin higher than $\tfrac{1}{2}$. They discovered that the appropriate relativistic wave equations for particles of spin 2 and rest-mass zero were the following:

$$\begin{aligned}\Box\phi^\nu_\mu &= 0 \\ \phi^\nu_{\mu,\nu} &= 0\end{aligned} \tag{11}$$

These are the same as Eqs. (9) and (10) for the vacuum case. This coincidence is hardly surprising. For spin-2 particles, a 10-component wave function is needed, five components for the spin and a doubling for the positive and negative energies. A second-rank symmetric tensor has 10 independent components, and hence is a suitable representation of a 10-component wave function.

Since, for the vacuum case, the two sets of equations [(9), (10), and (11)] are formally the same, it follows that the particles of the gravitational field, the gravitons, will have spin 2. Since the gravitational field has infinite range, it follows also that the rest-mass of the graviton is zero.

The Polarization of Gravitational Waves

Returning to Eq. (4), we may ask how many parameters are used to describe the polarization of a gravitational wave for a given direction of propagation. We can answer this by studying the structure of the curvature tensor $R^k_{\alpha\beta\gamma}$, which satisfies the vacuum-field equations

$$R^\nu_\mu = 0 \tag{12}$$

Here, R^ν_μ is the contracted $R^{\mu\nu}_{\alpha\mu}$. If the coordinate system is appropriately chosen, only three variables are needed to describe a gravitational wave going in a particular direction. For a gravitational wave propagating in the x^1 direction, the variables are g_{22}, g_{33}, and g_{32}. Of these, g_{22} and g_{33} are not independent. For a plane wave,

$$g_{22,00} + g_{33,00} = 0 \tag{13}$$

The fact that the gravitational wave exhibits these two degrees of freedom can be understood in a simple way. We may ask ourselves: What is the effect of the gravitational wave on a test particle? A discussion of this will bring us to the second part of my talk, which concerns how we might observe gravitational waves.

Consider the interaction between a gravitational wave and a single test particle that is set into oscillation by the wave. If we observe this interaction at the same position as the particle, then, in consequence of the equivalence principle, we shall oscillate in the same manner as the particle and will observe nothing (Figure 5-3).

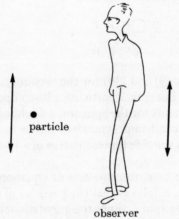

Figure 5-3　Single-particle motion due to a gravitational wave.

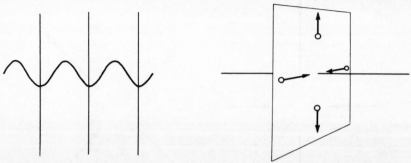

Figure 5-4   Relative motion of four particles due to a gravitational wave.

But this situation changes if we have a second particle at some distance from the first particle. Because of phase-retardation effects, the second particle would move relative to the first particle. Perhaps a careful observer might see the spacing of these two particles undergoing some sort of periodic change for a sinusoidal gravitational wave.

However, in addition to the accelerations induced by the wave, the effect of the varying metric on the separation of the particles must be considered. For the case of two particles aligned along the direction of propagation of the wave, these two effects precisely cancel each other—a not unexpected result in this field.

But, if we take two particles transverse to the direction of propagation, the geometry of space effect persists, and the differential particle motion is real. In this case, we observe relative displacements in the direction transverse to the wave.

Now suppose that four particles are arranged in a plane perpendicular to the direction of wave propagation as shown in Figure 5-4. An observer might see two of the particles moving apart and two moving together. This is characteristic of quadrupole oscillation.

In electromagnetic theory, for each direction of propagation there are two polarizations for a plane wave. One may be obtained from the other by a 90-degree rotation. In case of the gravitational wave interacting with four particles arrayed as in Figure 5-4, a 90-degree rotation produces no change. But a 45-degree rotation, as shown in Figure 5-5, does produce an independent state of polarization of the wave. The two degrees of freedom we discussed previously thus correspond to these two independent states of polarization.

This result appears nicely when the general theory of relativity is written down in the Hamiltonian form, in the weak-field approximation.

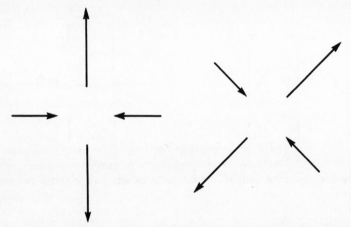

Figure 5-5 The two states of polarization of gravitational radiation.

The Hamiltonian form is

$$H = \sum \frac{\pi_k^{12}\pi_{-k}^{12}}{2} + \frac{k^2 h_{k12} h_{-k12}}{2} + 2\rho_k\rho_{-k} + \frac{k^2 q_k q_{-k}}{8} \qquad (14)$$

where

$$q_k = h_{k11} - h_{k22} \qquad (15)$$

The h_k's are Fourier coefficients. They satisfy the relations

$$h_{k12} = h_{-k^*12} \qquad (16)$$

The π's are the momenta canonically conjugate to these h's. One degree of freedom associated with the diagonal polarization (Figure 5-5) is characterized by the field variables and the canonical momentum densities π_{k12}. The other degree of freedom associated with up and down and horizontal polarization is characterized by the field variables q_k, which are related to the h_{k11} and h_{k22} as given in Eq. (15).

So, either by starting from a Hamiltonian form of gravitational theory or by starting with the Einstein weak-field conditions on the Riemann tensor, we conclude that, for each direction of propagation k (which is determined by boundary conditions), there are two degrees of freedom.

This is the formal structure with which we must deal. In the last 30 or 40 years quite a bit of theoretical work has been expended in attempts to prove or disprove the existence of these waves, because it was realized that the experimental problems were so enormous. One of the issues has been concerned with the equations of motion. General relativity differs from some other theories in that the equations of motion of bodies are contained within the field equations. So, it is appropriate to ask: Do the equations of motion allow particles to move in such a way that they will radiate?

This has been a subject of disagreement. Infeld, in Warsaw, among others, believes that objects moving under purely gravitational forces will not radiate. This would imply that a planet rotating about the sun does not radiate gravitational waves.

Whether this is the case is not the crucial issue because our interest is not restricted to systems involving purely gravitational forces. In fact, the forces with which we deal in our laboratory are very much stronger than gravitational forces. There is no reason to believe that particles moving under the influence of electromagnetic forces or nuclear forces will not radiate. Consider, for example, two masses coupled by a spring. These masses move partly under the influence of gravitational forces and partly under the influence of elastic forces, which are electromagnetic in origin. The nongravitational forces play a decisive role in methods for detection and generation of gravitational waves, which I shall describe next.

The Problem of Detecting Gravitational Radiation

What sort of experiments would we like to do in the field of gravitational radiation? The classic example of radiation experiments was that of Hertz. He was able to generate and detect electromagnetic waves in the same laboratory, to show that they were polarized, and to show that they exhibit interference and diffraction phenomena. These are experiments that we should very much like to do with gravitational waves.

Another type of experiment involves the detection of natural gravitational radiation. Suppose there are sources generated outside the earth, or even outside the solar system. Is there any way that we could detect the existence of gravitational waves incident on earth from some cosmic source? Is it possible that such sources exist?

If the universe were created with an enormous bang, there might have been a lot of gravitational radiation generated initially. If we calculate the absorption cross section for these waves by ordinary matter, we find it is incredibly small. Consider, for example, a microwave graviton incident on a molecule with a large moment of inertia, say ammonia. If the graviton frequency is resonant with ammonia and has a line breadth of $\sim 10^4$ cycles, the absorption cross section is roughly 10^{-60} cm^2.

So these gravitational waves are not easily absorbed by atomic and molecular particles. If such waves were generated at the time of the creation, and if the universe is really finite and unbounded (closed), there is

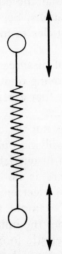

Figure 5-6 Simple harmonic-oscillator resonant detector.

some reason to believe that these waves would still be with us. Wheeler has estimated that the interstellar gravitational radiation could be as high as 10^{-29} to 10^{-28} grams/cm³ and still be consistent with present data on the expansion of the universe. Its Fourier transform would be peaked at 1 cycle per million years. Hopefully there is a high-frequency tail that might be detectable. There is, then, some motivation for searching for gravitational waves of cosmological origin.

How do we go about constructing a detector for gravitational waves? I have discussed the relative motions of particles in a gravitational field. If we have a plane-gravitational wave and two test particles, the spacing of the particles will change under the influence of the wave. If we want to get a larger effect, we might couple these two masses by a spring and thus make use of resonance (Figure 5-6). In this manner, we can obtain a much-larger absorption cross section. It is possible to show[1] that the behavior of this detector is that of a harmonic oscillator, which is driven by the curvature tensor.

The equation of motion for the relative displacement ξ^μ is given by

$$\frac{d^2\xi^\mu}{dt^2} + \frac{D}{m}\frac{d\xi^\mu}{dt} + \frac{k\xi^\mu}{m} = -c^2 R^\mu{}_{0\alpha 0}\, r^\alpha \qquad (17)$$

where we have chosen a convenient coordinate system. The $R^\mu{}_{0\alpha 0}$ are what DeWitt calls the electric components of the curvature tensor. r^α is the position vector of one particle relative to the other.

The absorption cross section for such a detector depends on how it is built. In contrast to this, in electromagnetic theory it is known that the absorption cross section averaged over all orientations for a radio antenna properly matched to its load is independent of the details of the antenna. An antenna is matched to its load if the reactance is tuned to zero and the load is equal to its own radiation resistance. In this case the absorption cross section σ is determined by the wavelength λ:

$$\sigma = \lambda^2/4\pi \tag{18}$$

A corresponding result can be obtained in gravitation theory. We can show that the absorption cross section for such a matched antenna does not depend on the kind of antenna. Indeed, it is even independent of the gravitation constant as long as the antenna is only damped by a resistance comparable with its radiation resistance. Unfortunately, the radiation damping for gravitational waves is about 34 orders of magnitude smaller than the radiation damping for electromagnetic waves. So there is no hope of matching such an antenna to its load. The internal irreversible processes will always be many orders larger.

The absorption cross section for such an antenna, considering the fact that it is not matched to its load, turns out to contain the constant of gravitation. It is

$$\sigma = 15\pi Gm|r|^2(Q\beta^2/8\omega c) \tag{19}$$

$m|r|^2$ is the quadrupole moment of the antenna. Q is the electrical engineer's notation for π times the number of oscillations that the free oscillator undergoes before its amplitude decays by a factor of e. ω is the angular frequency and c is the speed of light. β is determined by the gravitational wavelength

$$\beta = 2\pi/\lambda \tag{20}$$

This cross section approaches a maximum when the spacing of the two masses $|r|$ approaches an acoustic wavelength rather than a wavelength of light. This is a consequence of the fact that the restoring forces in the antenna are propagated with the speed of sound in the spring rather than with the speed of light.

In practice, a large cylinder or a sphere excited in its normal modes provides a more convenient detector than masses coupled by springs. If gravitational radiation can somehow couple to the normal modes of a large cylinder, this would be a detector of gravitational radiation.

A Laboratory Gravitational-Wave Detector

Such a detector is being built at the University of Maryland by Zipoy, Forward, and myself. This is part of an experimental program to

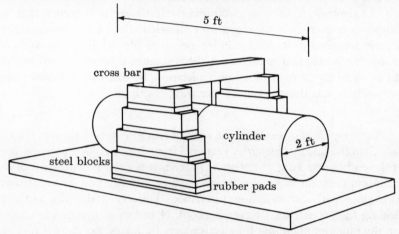

Figure 5-7 Resonant-cylinder detector.

measure the curvature tensor and search for gravitational waves. The detector that we are constructing consists of a 1.5-ton aluminum cylinder which is suspended in a large vacuum chamber, 10 ft long and 7 ft in diameter. The cylinder is suspended by a wire wrapped around it at the center. The wire is held by a cross-bar, which, in turn, is supported by a sequence of acoustic filters (Figure 5-7).

With such a device, we are limited in principle by the Brownian motion of the normal modes of the cylinder itself. This corresponds to an energy of kT in each resonant mode. This thermal energy is distributed over the 1.5 tons of aluminum. So it corresponds to an exceedingly small relative end-face displacement of roughly 10^{-14} cm. This displacement is of the order of 0.01 of a nuclear diameter.

This seems a phenomenally small number. Of course, the oscillations executed by the individual atoms on the end faces are very much greater than this. 10^{-14} cm is just the statistical average fluctuation for all the atoms.

The detection of such motion poses an interesting problem. The displacement is 10^{-10} of the wavelength of light, so optical methods for detecting are not promising. Instead, we have secured a number of quartz strain gauges to the central section of our cylinder (Figure 5-8). These strain gauges convert the normal-mode oscillations of the cylinder to a voltage. This voltage is fed to a very sensitive radio receiver whose output is recorded (Figure 5-9). The radio receiver is tuned to 1657 cps, the frequency of the normal mode that we are using. This corresponds to a

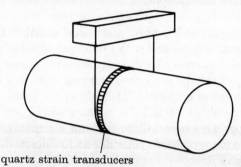

quartz strain transducers

Figure 5-8 Strain gauges for detecting vibration of resonant cylinder.

wavelength of the gravitational wave of about 10^7 cm. The radio receiver
has a noise performance much better than a maser. The noise temperature
is better than 1 degree Kelvin. The reason for this astonishingly good
noise performance of a low-frequency radio receiver is that the noise
resistance of the amplifier corresponds to about 6000 ohms, and the impe-
dance looking into the amplifier is about 10,000 megohms.

I should not dwell too much on the instrumentation except to note
that it is highly influenced by a theorem attributed to Dayhoff that a simple
experiment cannot be done without several racks full of electronic apparatus.
And what could be more simple than a cylinder suspended in a vacuum?

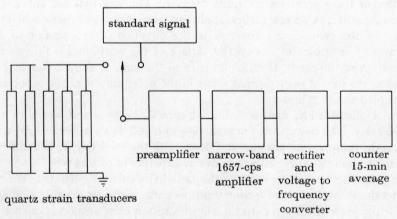

quartz strain transducers

Figure 5-9 Block diagram of electronics for gravitational wave detector.

Many considerations complicate the instrumentation. The gain of the radio receiver is surely going to change with time. So, every 15 min we disconnect the detector, and connect a standard signal to the input. The input standard signal is compared with the output suitably attenuated and the difference used to control a servosystem which readjusts the gain of the receiver. The output voltage is rectified and converted to a frequency that is measured by means of a counter. The gain of the radio receiver before and after it was recalibrated and the counter output, are automatically recorded on a tape. This tape will be fed into a computer for a Fourier analysis of the data for periods of a solar day and a sidereal day. Most of the instrumentation was done by Forward.

An issue that was raised early in our investigation was whether we would ever really achieve the sensitivity we want to have without introducing extraneous background noise generated, for example, by passing trucks or students marching around the campus. A mount with acoustical filters was designed by Zipoy. The acoustic filters worked quite successfully. The required isolation is achieved. The isolation is so good that we must strike the vacuum chamber with a hammer to excite the normal modes.

However, some other difficulties which we did not anticipate now become apparent. Unfortunately, the isolation of the amplifiers and the input circuits will have to be improved. The input circuits, which are immersed in liquid helium, contribute more noise of mechanical rather than thermal origin. We shall minimize these effects by moving the apparatus to an isolated location.

Suppose there is gravitational radiation emitted by the sun. How do we detect it? The aluminum-bar detector is an antenna designed to receive a signal resulting from a fourth-rank-tensor field. We are familiar with antennas that receive a second-rank (electromagnetic) tensor. We know some of these antennas are quite directive. Our gravitational antenna is also directive, as we saw earlier. It obtains its maximum response when the axis of the cylinder is transverse to the direction of propagation of the waves. The apparatus sits on the surface of the earth, and it follows the rotation of the earth. If radiation is from the sun, or some other part of space, we should see a diurnal effect in the noise output of the amplifiers coupled to the cylinder.

Unfortunately, man is a diurnal animal; he lives and works by the solar day. The power-line fluctuations go up and down with the solar day, and the temperature goes up and down with the solar day. It is a difficult task to eliminate these effects from any experiment of this type.

Another way is to increase the sensitivity of our apparatus. We see that the absorption cross section is proportional to the quadrupole moment. For the present 1.5-ton detector, the absorption cross section is calculated to be roughly 1 square Bohr radius (10^{-16} cm^2). This is a fairly small cross section, but enough to get started. To obtain a larger cross section, we can increase the moment of inertia of the antenna. There is a difficulty of size, because the present apparatus is already 10 ft long and 7 ft in diameter.

The Earth and Moon as Gravitational-Wave Detectors

However, we can use the earth itself as a detector.[1] The earth is a large object, and it is close by. At least in principle, we can instrument it. Its quadrupole moment is many orders larger than the quadrupole moment of this cylinder.

The normal modes of the earth were identified during the Chilean earthquake by the California Institute of Technology seismology group and by others. We are able to take the Cal. Tech. seismology data on the oscillations of the earth's normal modes and convert these into a limit[3] on the flux of gravitational radiation.

Ideally, what we would like to get from earth-strain data is the following: The earth has many modes of oscillation. Some have the correct symmetry to be excited by the gravitational waves, and some have not (i.e., modes with spherical symmetry will not be excited by gravitational waves). Thus we would like to have information about the amplitude of oscillation of modes with wrong symmetry and of modes with the right symmetry. If such information is available, we can find with sufficient assurance that gravitational waves are present.

However, the data show a large level of noise. This is not thermal noise, because the amplitude of thermally excited oscillations of the earth's crust is far too small. This noise is due to winds on the earth's surface. These winds give a large strain-noise background. The only thing we can do is to observe the noise level and calculate from that an upper limit for the gravitational-radiation flux. However, we must be careful in interpreting the data in terms of radiation from the sun because of the long integration time of the earth. An earth mode with a period of 1 hour and a Q of roughly 400 has a decay time of about 400 hours.

With these difficulties in mind, we can set limits on the power spectrum of the curvature tensor from the earth seismic data. The limit on the power spectrum is less than 5×10^{-76} cm^{-4} rad^{-1} sec^{-1}. It is difficult to appreciate the meaning of a number like this. It is enough to say that if the local radius of curvature of space resulting from the presence of such a wave were smaller than roughly 1 light year, it would have shown up in such an experiment. The earth, then, is not as good a detector as we might have hoped.

One way of getting around the problem of the wind noise is to use the moon as a detector. It has a big cross section of the order of hundreds of square meters. This is assuming that the moon's modes have a Q

of about 400. There should be no winds on the moon and, hopefully, not much seismic activity. If the moon is actually a quiet place, it should be an excellent detector for gravitational waves. We have been calculating what limits are imposed by earth and sun motions on the use of the moon as a detector for gravitational waves. In order to use the moon in this way, we envisage instrumenting a satellite probe with a gravimeter, landing it on the moon's surface, and telemetering back information on the motions of the lunar surface.

We might also use the moon's motion around the earth as a detector. There are peculiarities of the moon and planetary motions that have never been accounted for. These could possibly be effects of gravitational waves. But data on these anomalies is not well enough understood at present to make this interpretation.

Generation of Gravitational Radiation

There are large-scale astronomical motions of matter that could generate appreciable gravitational energy flux. The most obvious ones are double stars, especially when both stars are dwarfs.[4,5] These stars rotate with respect to each other at fantastic speeds.* We do not have any idea how many there are in the universe. Another possible source is the collision of neutral matter.

These are some of the possible sources of cosmic gravitational radiation that we wish to detect. Next I wish to discuss the possibility of generating gravitational waves in the laboratory.

I have mentioned previously the use of spinning rods as a source of gravitational radiation. However, there are other, better ways of making use of the stress tensor as a source. One way is to use an acoustic resonator. In a spinning rod, the stress accumulates at the center, and, as a consequence, the rod breaks. In the case of an acoustic resonator, the stresses build up over planes. With the stresses distributed in this manner, it is possible to have a much-larger integrated stress tensor, which is the real source. For this reason an acoustic resonator is better than a rod.

How large should such a resonator be? One may think that the block of material subject to acoustic stresses ought to be of the magnitude of a

---

* A white-dwarf binary star with a period of approximately 100 sec and a mass roughly equal to that of the sun would radiate about 2×10^{37} ergs/second. This is 5000 times the sun's optical luminosity. Most of the radiation would be essentially monochromatic, at twice the rotation frequency. A binary neutron star has the possibility of even greater output of gravitational radiation. For a pair of stars with separation $\sim 10^6$ cm the orbit has a period of 5 milliseconds, and the radiation is 2×10^{52} ergs per sec. The loss of energy would bring them together in about 2 sec. Recently, a double star (Nova Sagittae) was discovered, with a period of 1 hour 21 min.

gravitational wavelength. This is about 100,000 acoustic wavelengths. However the device is actually an assembly of quadrupoles with each of the quadrupoles oscillating out of phase relative to its nearest neighbor. The combined effect is essentially that of radiation from a single quadrupole.

Although the first-order effects do seem to cancel in this way, we can show that the higher-order effects do not. In addition, in a piezoelectric crystal, charges build up on the end faces, and certain components of the electromagnetic stress tensor in the crystal do not reverse sign every $1/2$ acoustic wavelength. By driving a piezoelectric crystal off resonance, we can build up a region of the order of a gravitational wavelength with stress corresponding to the breaking stress of the material. In this way, at a fixed frequency we can improve on a spinning rod by about 40 orders of magnitude.

Our contributions to this field have consisted in development of the theory and apparatus for measurement of the Riemann tensor. The use of nongravitational restoring forces and resonance effects has resulted in about a 10-order improvement in sensitivity for measurement of the dynamic curvature tensor. Present apparatus is sufficiently good to warrant search for gravitational waves. The 40-order improvement in source strength over a spinning rod is still about 15 orders short of enabling a wave-zone experiment to be done in a small laboratory.

References

1. For bibliography and detailed analysis of results presented here see J. Weber, *General Relativity and Gravitational Waves*, Interscience, New York, 1961, Chaps. 7 and 8.
2. S. A. Schelkunoff, Proc. IRE, **29,** 493, (1941).
3. R. L. Forward, D. Zipoy, J. Weber, S. Smith, and H. Benioff, *Nature*, **189,** 473, (1961).
4. R. L. Forward, Gravity Research Foundation Prize Essay, 1962.
5. F. J. Dyson, Gravity Research Foundation Prize Essay, 1962.

6

Mach's principle and experiments on mass anisotropy

V. W. Hughes

Mach's Principle and Possible Anisotropy of Inertial Mass

An old conceptual problem in physics is that of a preferred coordinate system or an inertial frame of reference in empty space. Related to this problem is the question of whether any meaning can be assigned to the inertial mass of an isolated body. Mach suggested the viewpoint, which has become known as Mach's principle,[1] that an inertial frame of reference is determined by the mass distribution in the universe, that the inertial force on a body is the gravitational interaction of distant matter on the body, and that the inertial mass of a body is determined by all the matter in the universe. In the framework of this view, one can ask whether an anisotropic distribution of matter in the universe has the consequence that inertial mass itself has a directional dependence, that is, is anisotropic.

In this chapter, I shall discuss possible observable effects of an anisotropy of inertial mass, if it exists, and experiments that have been carried out in search of such effects. My discussion of the possible observable effects is based largely on the work of Coconni and Salpeter.[2,3]

Figure 6-1 shows a body of mass m and an additional bit of mass ΔM in the universe at a distance r from m. Coconni and Salpeter[2] propose that the contribution Δm to the inertial mass m by the mass ΔM is given by

$$\Delta m \propto \frac{\Delta M}{r^{\nu}} \tag{1}$$

in which

$$0 < \nu < 1$$

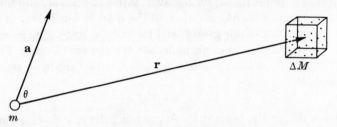

Figure 6-1 Body of inertial mass m accelerated relative to a bit of distant matter of mass ΔM.

Suppose that the direction of acceleration of body m is at an angle θ with respect to the direction $\mathbf{r}$ from body m to body ΔM. The question of interest is what dependence can we assume for Δm on the angle θ. We can take the view that Mach's principle applies so that the inertial mass of the body is determined by all the matter in the universe, but nevertheless that there is no θ dependence. However, the more interesting approach is to assume some angular dependence and to attempt to detect its consequences. The angular dependence must be an even function of θ and must have the same value for $\theta = 0$ and $\theta = \pi$. These requirements can be understood by considering the elementary cases of simple harmonic motion and uniform circular motion; physically unattractive discontinuities in kinetic or potential energy or velocity and the loss of the conservative character of ordinarily conservative forces occur if these requirements are not fulfilled. If the angular dependence is expressed as a series of Legendre polynomials, the simplest allowed anisotropic term then is $P_2(\cos \theta) = (3 \cos^2\theta - 1)/2$, so that

$$\Delta m \propto \frac{\Delta M}{r^\nu} P_2(\cos \theta) \tag{2}$$

More generally, the usual Newtonian law,

$$\mathbf{F} = m\mathbf{a} \tag{3}$$

in which the mass m is a scalar quantity is replaced by

$$F_i = m_{ij}a_j \tag{4}$$

in which the mass m_{ij} is a tensor quantity. Because of the even dependence of mass on angle, m_{ij} is a symmetric tensor. The generalized kinetic energy is then

$$T = P_iP_j/2m_{ij} \tag{5}$$

in which P_i, P_j are components of momentum.

Consider a simple model for the distribution of mass around the earth, as shown in Figure 6-2. Assume that all the mass in our galaxy is located at the center of mass of our galaxy, and that all the rest of the mass in the universe is distributed with uniform density throughout all space. Principal axes can be chosen as indicated in Figure 6-3, so that the mass tensor will be diagonal. If

$$m_{zz} = m_0 + \Delta m \qquad (6a)$$

where Δm is due to the point mass M_0 of our galaxy, and m_0 is due to all the rest of the mass in the universe, then

$$m_{xx} = m_{yy} = m_0 - \frac{\Delta m}{2} \qquad (6b)$$

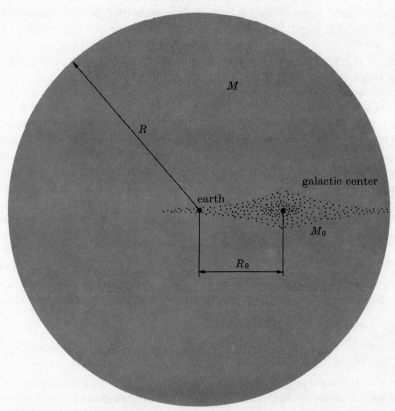

Figure 6-2   Model for mass distribution in the universe. Mass distribution is uniform throughout a spherical universe of radius R except for the mass in our own galaxy M_0, which is regarded as a point mass located at the center of mass of our galaxy.

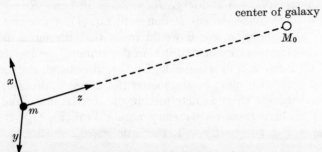

Figure 6-3 Principal axes for inertial mass tensor for model of mass distribution shown in Figure 6-2.

From Eq. (5) the kinetic energy can be written:

$$T = T_0 - \frac{\Delta m}{m_0} T_0 P_2(\cos\theta) \tag{7}$$

in which

$$T_0 = \frac{(P)^2}{2m_0}$$

and the term involving Δm is a correction term resulting from mass anisotropy. We shall apply this expression in quantum mechanical calculations and consider T_0 to be the conventional quantum mechanical kinetic energy operator and the second term in Eq. (7) to be a perturbing term in the Hamiltonian.

An evaluation of $\Delta m/m_0$ can be made with reference to Figure 6-2 and Eq. (1). The mass M of the universe outside our galaxy is assumed to be uniformly distributed around the earth out to the radius of the universe R, and the mass M_0 of our galaxy is located at a distance R_0 from the earth. Hence

$$m_0 \propto \int_0^R \frac{4\pi r^2 \rho \, dr}{r^\nu} = \frac{4\pi\rho R^{3-\nu}}{3 - \nu} \tag{8}$$

in which ρ = density of mass in the universe, and

$$\Delta m \propto \frac{M_0}{(R_0)^\nu} \tag{9}$$

The ratio is

$$\frac{\Delta m}{m_0} = \frac{M_0}{(R_0)^\nu} \frac{(3 - \nu)}{4\pi\rho R^{3-\nu}} \tag{10}$$

Take the values[4] $M_0 = 3 \times 10^{44}$ g, $R_0 = 2.5 \times 10^{22}$ cm, $R = 3 \times 10^{27}$ cm, and $\rho = 10^{-29}$ g/cm³. In connection with Eq. (1), it was stated that $0 < \nu < 1$. The condition $\nu < 0$ would mean that the more distant a particular mass the more influential it is in determining the inertial mass of a body, and hence it is unreasonable. On the other hand, the condition $\nu > 1$ would imply that quite nearby matter (for example, the sun) would have the predominant effect in determining the inertial mass, and hence it is contrary to observations on planetary motion. From Eq. (10), if $\nu = 0$, then $\Delta m/m_0 = 3 \times 10^{-10}$; if $\nu = 1$, then $\Delta m/m_0 = 2 \times 10^{-5}$.

Experimental Tests for Mass Anisotropy

On the macroscopic level, several systems could exhibit the effects of mass anisotropy. One system is the simple pendulum whose period is given by

$$T = 2\pi \sqrt{\frac{L}{g}} \sqrt{\frac{m}{m_g}} \qquad (11)$$

in which m is the inertial mass, m_g is the gravitational mass of the pendulum bob, L is the length of the pendulum, and g is the gravitational acceleration. The period is independent of mass if the inertial mass and the gravitational mass are equal. However, if the inertial mass has an anisotropy, but the gravitational mass does not, the period could depend on the orientation of the pendulum.

Another macroscopic dynamical system capable of exhibiting the effect of mass anisotropy is the piezoelectric quartz crystal oscillator. During a day, the orientation of the quartz crystal and hence of the piezoelectric vibrations changes with respect to the direction to the galactic center resulting from the rotation of the earth. The constancy of the frequency of a quartz crystal oscillator with respect to the hyperfine structure transition frequency of the cesium beam Atomichron has been studied. The latter frequency cannot exhibit any mass anisotropy effect, as will be discussed later. These studies[5] have exhibited no mass anisotropy effect and establish an upper limit to the anisotropic contribution to the mass $\Delta m/m_0$ of about 1 part in 10^9.

Salpeter and Coconni[2] suggested that the effect of mass anisotropy on the atomic Zeeman effect (or fine structure) may be measured with great sensitivity. An atomic electron with nonzero orbital angular momentum will move in different directions with respect to an external magnetic field in different magnetic substates, and, hence, if the mass depends on the direction of motion, the energy difference between different magnetic substates will depend on the mass anisotropy. For concreteness and simplicity, we consider an atom with a single electron in a p state. In the

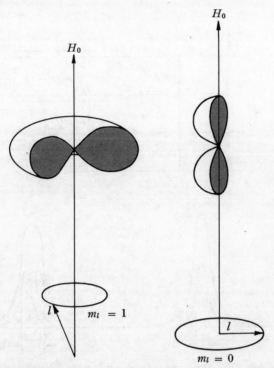

Figure 6-4 Spatial distribution of a p electron ($l = 1$) in different magnetic substates m_l relative to a z axis in the direction of an external field H_0.

$m_l = 0$ magnetic substate, the angular part of the wave function is

$$Y_{1,0} = \sqrt{\frac{3}{4\pi}}\cos\theta$$

and the electron moves predominantly along the direction of $\mathbf{H}_0$ as shown in Figure 6-4. In the $m_l = \pm 1$ magnetic substates, the angular wave functions are

$$Y_{1,\pm 1} = \sqrt{\frac{3}{8\pi}}\sin\theta\, e^{\pm i\phi}$$

and the electron moves in the plane perpendicular to $\mathbf{H}_0$ (Figure 6-4). The expectation value of the perturbing term in the Hamiltonian equation

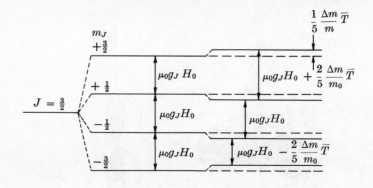

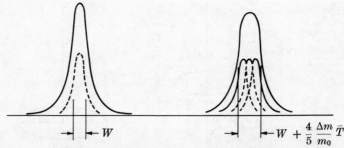

Figure 6-5 Zeeman energy levels and resonance lines for a $P_{3/2}$ electron as perturbed by mass anisotropy. The width of a normal Zeeman line is noted as W, and the width of the unresolved lines associated with mass anisotropy is $W + (4/5)\,(\Delta m/m_0)\overline{T}$. This figure is also applicable to the nuclear energy levels and resonance lines for a nucleus with spin $I = 3/2$.

(7) gives the contribution of the mass anisotropy to the energy of a particular magnetic substate:

$$\Delta E = -\frac{\Delta m}{m_0}\overline{T}\,\overline{P_2(\cos\theta)} \tag{12}$$

where $\overline{T}$ is the mean kinetic energy of the electron and $\overline{P_2(\cos\theta)}$ is the expectation value of $P_2(\cos\theta)$ in a particular magnetic substate. The perturbing energy term of Eq. (12) is like an electric quadrupole interaction term.

The perturbed Zeeman levels for a $P_{3/2}$ state are shown in Figure 6-5. Normally there would be a single Zeeman line, but in the presence of the mass anisotropy term there will be three different lines in the Zeeman spectrum as shown in this figure. If the effect of mass anisotropy were present but were too small to be resolved, the three lines would appear as a single broadened line, with an increased width

$$\Delta W = \frac{4}{5} \frac{\Delta m}{m_0} \overline{T} \tag{13}$$

The above results are obtained under the assumption that the direction of the magnetic field is toward the galactic center. If the magnetic field points at some angle β with respect to the galactic center, then we must replace $\overline{P_2(\cos \theta)}$ in Eq. (12) with $\overline{P_2[\cos(\theta - \beta)]}$. By a simple spherical-harmonic addition theorem:

$$\overline{P_2[\cos(\theta - \beta)]} = \overline{P_2(\cos \theta)}P_2(\cos \beta) \tag{14}$$

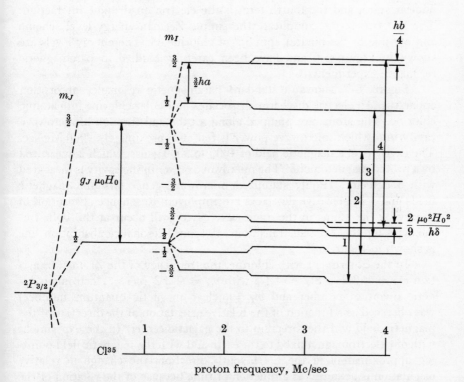

Figure 6-6 Energy levels of the ground $^2P_{3/2}$ state of the Cl^{35} atom in an external magnetic field H_0. The energy shift proportional to H_0^2 arises from perturbation due to the neighboring $^2P_{1/2}$ level. Energy levels associated with $m_J = -1/2, -3/2$ are not shown. Under strong-field conditions, the transition $(m_J, m_I) = (3/2, 3/2) \leftrightarrow (1/2, 3/2)$ is observed. δ is the fine structure separation between $^2P_{3/2}$ and $^2P_{1/2}$ levels.

The Zeeman effects of two atoms—oxygen in the ground ^3P state and chlorine in the ground $^2P_{3/2}$ state—have been studied by the method of paramagnetic resonance absorption in a test for mass anisotropy. Chlorine is the simpler theoretically because the electronic configuration has an almost-closed shell and so can be represented as a single hole, whereas oxygen has four $2p$ electrons. The relevant part of the Hamiltonian for chlorine is given as

$$\mathcal{H} = \mu_0 g_l \mathbf{L} \cdot \mathbf{H}_0 + \mu_0 g_s \mathbf{S} \cdot \mathbf{H}_0 + a\mathbf{I} \cdot \mathbf{J} + b\mathcal{H}_a \tag{15}$$

The first two terms give the interaction of the orbital magnetic moment and the spin magnetic moment of the electron with the external magnetic field $\mathbf{H}_0$ in which μ_0 = Bohr magneton, and g_l and g_s are the orbital and spin g-values. The third term is the magnetic hyperfine interaction of the electronic magnetic moment with the nuclear magnetic moment (I = nuclear spin), and the fourth term is the electric quadrupole interaction. The last two terms complicate the simple Zeeman energy level scheme and are due to the nuclear spin 3/2 of chlorine 35. The energy levels are shown in Figure 6-6 and have been carefully studied in paramagnetic resonance experiments.[6,7]

Figure 6-7 shows a standard paramagnetic resonance absorption apparatus. An electric discharge dissociates molecular chlorine into atomic chlorine. The atoms are pumped along a tube and through a microwave cavity into which microwave power is fed at approximately 9000 Mc/sec. The cavity is in a magnetic field of 4000 to 5000 gauss, which is measured by a proton magnetometer. The microwave power in the cavity is measured with a detector. Highly stabilized microwave generators and magnetic fields and very sensitive detectors are employed. Resonance absorption of energy by the atoms in the microwave cavity will occur at the Bohr frequencies for the Zeeman transitions. A typical resonance absorption line is shown in Figure 6-8.

In the experiment with chlorine, the frequency of the Zeeman transition $m_J = +3/2 \rightarrow m_J = +1/2$ with $m_I = +3/2$ (m_J = electronic magnetic quantum number and m_I = nuclear magnetic quantum number) was observed as a function of the relative orientation of the direction of the magnetic field and the direction to the galactic center. In the experiment with our electromagnet fixed to the earth and with the magnetic field pointing approximately in the north-south direction, the change in relative orientation is achieved as a function of time because of the rotation of the earth. In New Haven, at 41° latitude, at a certain time in the sidereal day, the south direction in the horizontal plane points within 22 degrees toward the center of our galaxy; 12 hours later this same direction along the earth's horizontal plane points 104 degrees away from the galactic center. It is important, of course, that the frequency standard with respect to which the

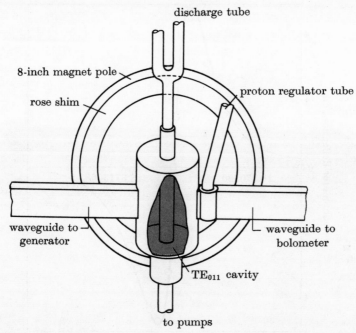

discharge tube

8-inch magnet pole

rose shim

proton regulator tube

waveguide to generator

waveguide to bolometer

TE_{011} cavity

to pumps

Figure 6-7 Schematic diagram of paramagnetic resonance absorption apparatus.

Zeeman transition frequency is compared will itself exhibit no mass anisotropy effect. Most Zeeman transition frequency measurements, such as those quoted by Cocconi and Salpeter, have been referred to crystal oscillator secondary standards calibrated occasionally against the signal from WWV, and hence, because of possible mass anisotropy effects in the crystal oscillator, are not suitable for the present purpose. In our experiment, a frequency derived from the cesium atomic frequency standard (National Company Atomichron) was used. The transition $(F, M_F) = (4, 0) \leftrightarrow (3, 0)$ used in this frequency standard[8] will not exhibit any mass anisotropy effect. The magnetic field is maintained constant with a proton-resonance probe whose resonance frequency is compared with the Atomichron frequency. For a constant magnetic field, the proton resonance frequency will exhibit no mass anisotropy effect. The transition $m_J = +3/2 \leftrightarrow m_J = +1/2$ with $m_I = +3/2$ in the $^2P_{3/2}$ state of Cl^{35} was observed over a 12-hour period. No variation with time of the Zeeman transition frequency occurring at about 9190 Mc/sec in a magnetic field of 4730 gauss was observed within the experimental error of 30 kc/sec. If the electronic

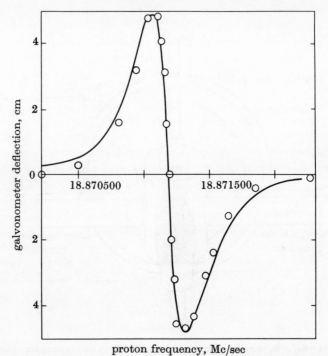

Figure 6-8   Typical paramagnetic resonance absorption line in chlorine for the transition $(m_J, m_I) = (3/2, 3/2) \leftrightarrow (1/2, 3/2)$.

structure of chlorine is treated as a hole moving in a Coulomb potential resulting from the nucleus and electrons, the upper limit to $\Delta m/m_0$ of 10^{-10} is obtained.

A second method is to observe the frequencies of two Zeeman transitions where the intervals would be affected differently by any mass anisotropy. It is only necessary to observe the two transitions at the time at which the direction to the galactic center is such as to maximize the mass anisotropy effect. Simple experimental data of this type are available from the Zeeman transitions $\Delta M_J = \pm 1, \pm 2$ in the $^3P_2$ state of atomic oxygen.[9] From these data, it can be deduced that $\Delta m/m_0 < 10^{-10}$.

The reason that such high sensitivity can be obtained in the atomic paramagnetic resonance experiment is that we are observing a Zeeman transition with high energy resolution, and the Zeeman energy difference is only a small fraction of the total electronic binding energy. On the other hand, any mass anisotropy will contribute to the kinetic energy of the electron, which is enormously larger than the Zeeman energy. Thus our resolution for the determination of the Zeeman splitting represents an extremely small fraction of the total electronic kinetic energy, and hence a very small fractional mass anisotropy can be observed.

Coconni and Salpeter pointed out in their second paper[3] that higher sensitivity in the search for mass anisotropy could be achieved by studying nuclear energy levels as compared with atomic energy levels because the kinetic energy for a nucleon in a nucleus is much larger than the kinetic energy for an electron in an atom. Typically, a nucleon in a nucleus has a kinetic energy of the order of 10 Mev, whereas an electron in an atom has a kinetic energy only 10^{-6} times as great. In particular, they proposed use of the Mössbauer effect, which gives a very high fractional energy resolution, to search for mass anisotropy effects in the energy levels of Fe^{57}. There is a 14-kev transition from an upper nuclear state with $I = 3/2$ to the ground state with $I = 1/2$. The virtue of the Mössbauer effect is that a very narrow gamma ray line can be obtained when the iron nucleus is bound in a crystal lattice so that the recoil for a nuclear gamma ray emission is absorbed by the crystal lattice as a whole. The question is whether there are any mass anisotropy effects on the energy levels or line widths. A group from Illinois[10] studied the width of the Mössbauer line as a function of time as the angle between a magnetic field direction and the direction to the galactic center changed, and found that the width was constant within the experimental accuracy. The natural line width of the Mössbauer resonance ($\sim 10^{-8}$ ev), which is determined by the lifetime of about 10^{-7} sec of the excited nuclear state, provides the limit to the experimental accuracy. This line width is much larger than the line width in the atomic Zeeman resonance, which was some 10^4 cps, but the kinetic energy term $\overline{T}$ is much larger as well, and there is therefore a net gain in accuracy over that from the atomic Zeeman effect. The Illinois group concluded that

$$\frac{\Delta m}{m_0} < 5 \times 10^{-16}$$

A much more sensitive test for mass anisotropy can be obtained from an ordinary nuclear magnetic resonance experiment. To test for mass anisotropy what is really needed is the smallest observable frequency uncertainty; the Mössbauer effect does not provide this, because of the short lifetime of the nuclear excited state. On the other hand, in the case of ordinary nuclear magnetic resonance, line widths of the order of 1 cps can be obtained, and one can still take advantage of the large nucleon binding and kinetic energies.

Hence we performed a standard nuclear magnetic resonance experiment[11] of the type that Bloch and Purcell first initiated in the late 1940s.[12] Other nuclear magnetic resonance experiments could be interpreted as providing an upper limit to possible mass anisotropy. However, no one had taken the trouble to observe a resonance systematically through a sidereal day. Also no care had been taken to specify properly the frequency standards.

Our experiment was done on the Li^7 nucleus in its ground state, which has a nuclear spin of $3/2$. This nucleus has one extra proton outside of closed shells. According to the shell model, this odd proton is in the $P_{3/2}$ state, and, since the shell model is quite successful in predicting the nuclear magnetic moment, we have confidence in the applicability of the shell model to Li^7. In contrast, Fe^{57}, which was used in the Mössbauer experiment, has the disadvantage of a more complicated shell model interpretation.

In a magnetic field, the Li^7 nucleus will have four energy levels corresponding to the allowed values of the magnetic quantum number M_I. In the absence of any mass anisotropy, adjacent levels are equally spaced, and a single nuclear resonance line will be observed. If the mass anisotropy effect is present, there will be three different intervals that will lead to a triplet nuclear resonance line, if the structure is resolved, or to a single broadened line if the structure is unresolved (see Figure 6-5). Over a 12-hour period, the resonance line for Li^7 was observed in a $1\ N$ water solution of $FeCl_3$ saturated with $LiCl$. The magnetic field of about 4700 gauss was stabilized against the proton resonance frequency with the Atomichron as a frequency standard. A narrow line was obtained by use of homogenizing coils on the electromagnet and by spinning the nuclear sample. Only a single line was observed with a width of 1.2 cps, which is determined in part by inhomogeneity of the magnetic field and in part by the thermal relaxation time associated with magnetic dipole interactions between the Li nuclei. The line width changed by less than 0.2 cps over a sidereal day. The expected line broadening resulting from mass anisotropy is

$$\Delta W = \frac{4}{5} \frac{\Delta m}{m_0} \overline{T} P_2(\cos \beta) \tag{16}$$

[see Eqs. (13) and (14)]. Using 10 Mev as the average kinetic energy $\overline{T}$ of the Li^7 nucleon, we obtain[13] the limit $\Delta m/m_0 < 10^{-22}$.

A similar experiment has been done by Drever[14] with the result

$$\frac{\Delta m}{m_0} < 5 \times 10^{-23}$$

Interpretation of Experiments

The upper limit of $\Delta m/m_0 < 10^{-22}$ is very much less than the limit of 3×10^{-10} predicted from the model of Salpeter and Coconni by setting

$v = 0$, and, hence, in the framework of their theory, we can say that there seems to be no mass anisotropy with regard to direction in our own galaxy.

As a matter of aesthetic completeness, we intend to improve our experiment in several ways. The resolution can be improved and use of a rotatable magnet will allow us to orient the field in all directions in space. The experiment should also be done with nuclear spins greater than $3/2$ so that we can test for other than a $P_2(\cos \theta)$ dependence on angle.

The atomic electron experiment and the nuclear experiment could give different answers in the spirit of the arguments of Coconni and Salpeter. In the case of the electron, the binding force is the electromagnetic force. For the nucleus, it is a nuclear force. It is conceivable that one of these could exhibit anisotropic properties that would balance out a mass anisotropy, whereas the other might not. Hence it is useful to have tests for the several types of known forces.

As a final point in the interpretation, we note that, although Coconni and Salpeter use Mach's principle to argue for a possible inertial mass anisotropy, Dicke has pointed out that Mach's principle may actually imply that there can be no observable anisotropy,[15] and hence the null result in the experiments provides support for Mach's principle. Dicke's conclusion is essentially that, according to Mach's principle, all particles and fields must exhibit the same anisotropy, and thus there can be only null results in the experiments considered.

In another theoretical paper, Epstein[16] emphasized that the viewpoint of Coconni and Salpeter allows for anisotropy only in the kinetic energy term. Epstein pointed out that one can generalize to allow for anisotropy in the potential energy term also, and, if this is done in a certain way, there will be exact cancellation of any anisotropic effects. He argued that one would expect anisotropy in the potential energy term because the electromagnetic potential involves an exchange of photons, and one should assign anisotropy effects to the photon field as well. The theoretical interpretations of Dicke and Epstein are consistent with the view that the null results of these experiments show that mass anisotropy is universal in accordance with Mach's principle, the same for all particles and fields.

The more conventional interpretation—that the negative result of the mass anisotropy experiments "provides strong support for the present formulation of the general theory of relativity and no support for a strong form of Mach's principle"—is given by Weber.[17]

References

1. See Chapter 7 of this volume by R. H. Dicke.
2. G. Cocconi and E. E. Salpeter, *Nuovo Cimento*, **10**, 646 (1958).
3. G. Cocconi and E. E. Salpeter, *Phys. Rev. Letters*, **4**, 176 (1960).
4. C. W. Allen, *Astrophysical Quantities*, The Athlone Press, London, 1955.

5. L. Essen, J. V. L. Parry, and J. McA. Steele, *Proc. Inst. Elec. Engrs.*, **107B**, 229 (1960).
6. V. Beltran-Lopez and H. G. Robinson, *Phys. Rev.*, **123**, 161 (1961).
7. J. S. M. Harvey, R. A. Kamper, and K. R. Lea, *Proc. Phys. Soc. (London)*, **76**, 979 (1960).
8. P. Kusch and V. W. Hughes, *Encyclopedia of Physics*, Springer-Verlag, Berlin, 1959, vol. 37, part I.
9. H. E. Radford and V. W. Hughes, *Phys. Rev.*, **114**, 1274 (1959).
10. C. W. Sherwin, H. Frauenfelder, E. L. Garwin, E. Lüscher, S. Margulies, and R. N. Peacock, *Phys. Rev. Letters*, **4**, 399 (1960).
11. V. W. Hughes, H. G. Robinson, and V. Beltran-Lopez, *Phys. Rev. Letters*, **4**, 342 (1960).
12. A. Abragam, *The Principles of Nuclear Magnetism*, Oxford, New York, 1961.
13. V. Beltran-Lopez, H. G. Robinson, and V. W. Hughes, *Bull. Am. Phys. Soc.*, **6**, 424 (1961).
14. R. W. P. Drever, *Phil. Mag.*, **6**, 683 (1961).
15. R. H. Dicke, *Phys. Rev. Letters*, **7**, 359 (1961).
16. S. T. Epstein, *Nuovo Cimento*, **16**, 587 (1960).
17. J. Weber, *General Relativity and Gravitational Waves*, p. 162, Interscience, New York, 1961.

7

The many faces of Mach

R. H. Dicke

Two Historical Viewpoints: Absolute Space and Relativistic Space

It is rather interesting that, as far as I know at least, only two pictures of physical space have ever been proposed. Even going back to the ancient Greeks, there has not appeared any other than these two pictures. One employs the idea of absolute space. This is the notion that a physical space has a structure of its own. From ancient times to the twentieth century, this was usually taken to mean that space was filled with a medium of some kind. This idea appeared in Descartes' philosophy. The medium, which he called a plenum, was presumed to carry the planets around the sun as ships floating in a gigantic vortex in the ethereal sea. This accounted for the motions of the planets, and in a completely quantitative way, provided one made the right assumptions about the vortex, namely, that it moved in just the way the planets are observed to move.

Newton's ideas concerning an absolute space are well known. His law of gravitation seems to imply an "action at a distance" in a vacuum. After a visit to England, Voltaire wrote in 1730, "A Frenchman who arrives in London will find philosophy like everything else very changed there. He left the world a *plenum* and now he finds a *vacuum*." However, Newton seems to have had an ether- (or plenum-) filled space in mind when he constructed his theory of gravitation. At one time[1] he said:

> That one body may act upon another at a distance through a vacuum without the mediation of anything else . . . is to me so great an absurdity that I believe that no man, who has in philosophical matters a competent faculty for thinking, can ever fall into it.

121

It is interesting that the other picture of space is also an old one, going back at least to the early eighteenth century. It seems to have first appeared in some statements made by the great British philosopher, Bishop Berkeley. This is the idea of a relativistic space. According to this idea, the only meaningful concepts of physical space are concepts that relate the position of matter relative to other matter. From this point of view empty space is devoid of sign posts, and the only properties space possesses are properties derived from the matter in the space.

I quote from Berkeley's writings as they appear in Sciama's book, *The Unity of the Universe.*[2] Similar statements can be found in *The Principles of Human Knowledge*, by Berkeley.[3]

> If every place is relative then every motion is relative, and as motion cannot be understood without the determination of its direction which in its turn cannot be understood except in relation to our or some other body. Up, down, right, left, all directions and places are based on relations and it is necessary to suppose another body distinct from the moving one.

That is a very clear statement of the principle of relativity. Berkeley further elaborates on it:

> Let us imagine two globes, and that besides them nothing else material exists, then the motion in a circle of these two globes round their common centre cannot be imagined. But suppose that the heaven of fixed stars was suddenly created and we shall be in a position to imagine the motion of the globes by their relative position to the different parts of the heaven.

Thus we have this rather early statement of the idea of relativity, which was later formulated independently by Mach and has become known as Mach's principle.

Mach's statement follows[4]:

> For me only relative motions exist....When a body rotates relatively to the fixed stars, centrifugal forces are produced; when it rotates relatively to some different body not relative to the fixed stars, no centrifugal forces are produced. I have no objection to calling the first rotation as long as it be remembered that nothing is meant except relative rotation with respect to fixed stars.

This is the idea that rotation of a body relative to the fixed-star system is equivalent to a rotation of fixed stars about the body. They both represent the same relative motions.

Then we come to some remarks of Einstein on the role of Mach's principle in physics[5]:

> But in the second place the theory of relativity makes it appear probable that Mach was on the right road in his thought that inertia

depends upon a mutual action of matter. For we will show in the following that, according to our equations, inert masses do act upon each other in the sense of the relativity of inertia, even if only very feebly. What is to be expected along the lines of Mach's thought?

Einstein has a list of three effects that he would expect to exist if Mach's principle were valid:

1.   A body must experience an accelerating force when neighboring masses are accelerated, and, in fact, the force must be in the same direction as that acceleration.

In other words, suppose we imagine a body inside a hollow spherical mass shell. If one were to accelerate the shell suddenly, this acceleration of nearby matter would, on a miniscule scale, be somewhat like an acceleration of the whole universe relative to the body. As a consequence, an inertial force might be expected to act on the body and to produce an acceleration of the body in the same direction as the acceleration of the shell. This inertial force ought to appear under these conditions as a direct effect of Mach's principle. Einstein showed that this effect exists in the formal structure of general relativity.

2.   A rotating hollow body must generate inside of itself a "Coriolis field," which deflects moving bodies in the sense of the rotation, and a radial centrifugal field as well.

We may give a qualitative argument for this point. Rotating a hollow spherical shell is in some sense the same as rotating the whole universe with all the matter it contains. Furthermore, a universe rotating relative to some "fixed" coordinate system, from the viewpoint of Mach, is completely equivalent physically to a rotation of the coordinate system relative to a fixed universe. We know that, in the latter case of the rotating coordinate system, Coriolis and centrifugal forces appear. So in the former case, in the same sense, a mass shell rotating relative to a fixed coordinate system should produce something like a Coriolis and a centrifugal field in this fixed system inside the shell. This effect was discussed by Thirring and Lense[6] within the framework of general relativity.

3.   The inertia of a body must increase when ponderable masses are piled up in its neighborhood.

Einstein seems to have been mistaken about this effect appearing in his theory of general relativity. The equations that Einstein exhibits to illustrate this effect[5] have their particular form as the result of the selection of a particular coordinate system, and the effect is simply a coordinate effect, occurring for a particular coordinate system only. This choice is arbitrary and there are no observable effects to be observed in a laboratory from matter piled up in a spherically symmetrical way about the laboratory. Brans has examined Einstein's discussion of this effect.[7]

Thus, effects 1 and 2 are present in general relativity but 3 is not. We shall encounter more evidence for the profound influence of the ideas of Mach on Einstein's thinking about gravitation. Traces of Mach's principle appears all through general relativity.

On the other hand, I would contrast the previous antediluvian quotations from Bishop Berkeley concerning the meaning of relativity with a modern statement appearing in Synge's book, *Relativity*, *The General Theory*.[8] In the preface he writes:

> I am much indebted to the well known books of Pauli, Eddington, Tolman, Bergmann, Möller and Lichnerowicz, but the geometrical way of looking at space-time was constructed from Minkowski. He protested against the use of the word "relativity" to describe a theory based on an "absolute" (space-time), and, had he lived to see the general theory of relativity, I believe he would have repeated his protest in even stronger terms. However, we need not bother about the name, for the word "relativity" now means primarily Einstein's theory and only secondarily the obscure philosophy which may have suggested it originally. It is to support Minkowski's way of looking at relativity that I find myself pursuing the hard path of a missionary. When in a relativistic discussion I try to make things clearer by a space-time diagram, the other participants look at it with polite detachment and, after a pause of embarassment as if some childish indecency had been exhibited, resume the debate on their own terms.

Having thus rejected the relativity of Mach and Berkeley, he goes on to deny another familiar principle of gravitation theory.

> The Principle of Equivalence performed the essential office of midwife at the birth of general relativity, but, as Einstein remarked, the infant would never have got beyond its longclothes had it not been for Minkowski's concept. I suggest that the midwife be now buried with appropriate honours and the facts of an absolute space-time faced.

We have, in this very modern point of view of an outstanding expert in relativity, the return to the idea that we are dealing with an absolute space-time. From the viewpoint of Synge, general relativity describes the geometry of an absolute space. According to him, certain things are measurable about this space in an absolute way. There exist curvature invariants that characterize this space, and one can, in principle, measure these invariants. Bergmann has pointed out that the mapping of these invariants throughout space is, in a sense, labeling of the points of this space with invariant labels (independent of coordinate system). These are concepts of an absolute space, and we have here a return to the old notions of an

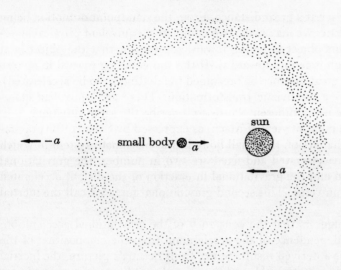

Figure 7-1 A simple model of the universe with a small body gravitating toward the sun. The rest of the matter in the universe is represented by a shell of matter at a great distance. It is possible to view the small body as accelerated relative to fixed matter at a distance and a nearly fixed sun or to view the matter at a distance and the sun accelerated relative to a fixed small body.

absolute space. According to this point of view, the chief difference between this absolute space and the one of Newton is that this space is four-dimensional and Riemannian, and we do not feel any necessity for filling it with a medium. Furthermore, the geometric properties of the space are influenced by the matter contained therein.

Sciama's Simplified Model for Interpreting Mach's Principle

The quotations we have presented indicate the extreme variety of the viewpoints of the experts in this field, including the giants of the past. It is this variety that motivated my choosing for a title of this lecture, *The Many Faces of Mach*. The face of Mach that I shall first present is that due to Sciama.[9] It is a greatly oversimplified picture, which discusses gravitation as a type of vector interaction. Similar discussions have been given by others. Recently, Weisskopf has based a similar discussion on the tensor interaction.

Imagine that we have a sun and some small test body falling toward it (Figure 7-1). We examine this in the framework of a universe with a large amount of matter at a great distance. From the standpoint of motion being purely relativistic, we may make two completely equivalent physical statements: that this object is falling toward the sun, or that the object is at rest and the sun is falling toward it. If the sun is falling toward it, so also may matter at great distance be presumed to fall (that is, to be accelerated). This is simply a relativistic transformation. These are equivalent statements. We are using different words to describe the same situation.

From the point of view of Mach, as expressed by Sciama, the gravitational forces that act on the small body in the coordinate system in which the body is unaccelerated and fixed are two in number, the gravitational pull of the sun and the gravitational interaction of the distant accelerated matter in the universe. This second gravitational force we call the inertial reaction.

Sciama suggests that the constancy of the gravitational acceleration, that is, the independence of the acceleration from the composition of the falling body, is a derived result. Since, from Sciama's picture, the inertial force is actually gravitational, and the special coordinate system is one for which the inertial (gravitational) force is balanced by the direct (gravitational) pull of the sun, this net force is zero and remains zero when some other test body is substituted. Thus, lead and aluminum weights would be expected to both remain at rest in this coordinate system and fall with the same acceleration in some other coordinate system.

According to Sciama, in this coordinate system the gravitational wave is radiated by the distant accelerated matter in such a way that the total force acting on the body is zero.

If one believes that this gravitational force can be interpreted as an ordinary force field that is propagated as a wave from great distance, there is a time retardation in this wave, similar to that which appears in the electromagnetic field of an accelerated charged particle. With such a wave phenomenon, the strength of the inertial reaction is expected to fall off as $1/r$, as one would expect from any time-retarded (radiation) effect.

According to Sciama's model, the inertial force on the small body shown in Figure 7-1, resulting from the acceleration of distant matter relative to it, is proportional to the mass of the small body m, the mass of the distant accelerating matter M, the value of the acceleration a, and the reciprocal of the distance to the accelerating matter:

$$F \approx \frac{GmMa}{rc^2} \tag{1}$$

The masses appear only in first order, since Sciama's formalism is linear. The r^{-1} dependence is resulting from the interpretation of this inertial field as a radiation resulting from the acceleration of distant matter. We should also include an inertial term having its origin in the accelerated sun, but this is very small compared with the contribution of matter at great distances.

This interpretation of Mach's principle implies a number of properties for the gravitational field.

First, one notes that, from this point of view, distant galaxies play an active role as the source of the inertial reaction and are not simply beacon lights to tell us where a "real" absolute space is. (One might say parenthetically that a difficulty with describing acceleration relative to an empty physical space is that one cannot discern sign posts in this absolute space. One way of getting around this objection is to simply distribute in space luminous dust of negligible mass. These luminous objects would permit us to see where the "real underlying absolute space" is.)

It should be noted that, in talking about a physical space as simply being illuminated with signposts of negligible mass, I am dealing with an absolute space as described by Synge. On the other hand, the picture of Berkeley, Mach, Einstein, and Sciama would suggest a much more direct physical relation between the inertial force and the presence of large amounts of matter at great distance. If one were to remove this matter, then according to Mach, the inertial force would disappear. If one were to reduce the matter to negligible proportions, there would be striking changes in local inertial effects. To summarize, according to Mach's point of view, we should interpret inertial effects as a consequence of interactions of matter at great distances in the universe with accelerated bodies in the laboratory. If we observe a gyroscope in the laboratory and this gyroscope continues to point to some particular distant galaxy, this is more than just an accidental correspondence. There are fields produced by matter at great distance, which interact with the gyroscope in the laboratory in such a way as to keep pointing in a direction fixed with respect to distant matter.

The model of Sciama is not a completely satisfactory framework for expressing Mach's principle. By selecting a particular coordinate system (with the test body at rest) for a discussion of gravitational effects, he has lost the advantage of general covariance. In attempting to express inertial forces as vector forces, the obvious difficulty encountered is that such forces are not acceleration-dependent. Thus, inertial effects must be described in Sciama's scheme of things in special coordinate systems where the test body is not accelerated. Also it is well known on other grounds that a vector theory of gravitation is unsatisfactory. For example, a vector interaction (such as an electromagnetic force) acts on a conserved quantity (such as charge), and the resulting accelerations depend upon the binding energy of a system of particles. Thus, in a vector theory, gravitational accelerations are not independent of the composition of the bodies.

Whereas Sciama's model of inertial effects does not provide a proper (coordinate-independent) theory of gravitation, it does provide a simple physical picture for the origin of inertial forces.

Limitations of General Relativity

As we saw from the statements of Synge, Einstein's theory is not relativistic in the Machian sense. In his theory, space has physical properties and constitutes a physical structure even in the absence of all matter. Motion of a massless test body is referred to as an absolute geometry.

On the other hand, it is remarkable how much of Mach's principle does permeate Einstein's general relativity. This will be discussed in detail later. Here we simply note that, by describing gravitational effects as resulting from a tensor field, Einstein was able to exhibit the inertial force, proportional to the acceleration of a particle, as one of the force terms derived from the tensor field. Nonetheless, general relativity does not appear to describe Mach's principle properly. This can be seen by noting that, in the absence of all matter, the metric tensor describes a flat space and that this flat space possesses inertial properties. Even Schwarzschild's famous solution is unsatisfactory, from the viewpoint of Mach. As one moves to infinity, and the mass source (the source of inertial forces according to Mach) disappears in the distance, the space becomes flat and continues to possess inertial properties in contradiction with the expectations of Mach.

It should be remarked, however, that a theory requires more than a set of differential equations. Boundary-value conditions, or initial-value conditions, are required before the theory is specified completely. Wheeler and others have remarked that the difficulties of general relativity *vis-à-vis* Mach's principle may be connected with boundary-value conditions, not field equations (see Chapter 15).

A Catalog of Long-Range Fields—Fermion Fields

As Mach's principle implies that distant matter exerts an influence on the laboratory, it is important to examine all the long-range fields with which we are familiar. These are the fields that could be the instruments through which such Machian interactions could take place.

Long-range interactions are caused by fields that, in the language of quantum-field theorists, represent zero-rest-mass particles. These fields can be cataloged as either boson or fermion fields asssociated with particles of integral or half-integral spin. To be of interest, these particles must be massless and chargeless.

Massless particles of half-integral spin such as neutrinos, do not provide a particularly promising way of getting gravitational effects. This

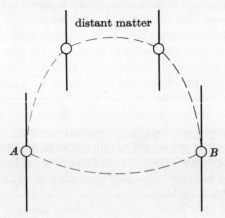

Figure 7-2   Feynman diagram of a four-neutrino exchange coupling bodies *A* and *B* and involving distant matter.

is because of the complexity resulting from the fact that at least two neutrinos are necessary in every static interaction. Neutrinos and anti-neutrinos must be paired properly.

Feynman, a few years ago, managed to obtain a $1/r^2$ force from an interchange of four neutrinos in the following way: A neutrino from body *A* is absorbed by a distant body; this body interchanges a neutrino with another distant body; a neutrino from this body is absorbed by body *B*; and, finally, a fourth neutrino is emitted from body *B* to body *A* completing the link (Figure 7-2). This leads to a $1/r^2$ force, between *A* and *B*, in a nice way.

Furthermore, there are some Machian ideas in this approach, because matter at great distance does play a role. There is a difficulty however. It turns out that nearby matter is more important than distant matter. Inertial effects are certainly not due mainly to the earth. We know that a gyroscope is observed to precess as the earth rotates. The interchange of four neutrinos does not seem to be a particularly promising approach to gravitation and to Mach's principle.

Long-Range Boson Fields—The Vector Field

The class of fields that appears to offer the most interesting possibilities for describing gravitational and inertial effects are long-range boson fields associated with neutral, zero-mass particles of integral spin. This class includes the scalar, vector, tensor, and higher-rank interactions. On the general grounds that nature although not simple is not vicious, I shall not consider boson fields beyond the second-rank tensor.

First, I shall discuss the vector field. We are familiar with a zero-mass vector field in the form of the electromagnetic interaction between matter. This is not the only possibility for a vector field. There could be other vector fields of importance in cosmology and in gravitation. For example, Lee and Yang[10] suggested some years ago that a zero-mass vector field might be responsible for baryon conservation. Such a field would be associated with a very weak interaction between nucleons. In the Lee–Yang theory, two neutrons (or hydrogen atoms) would repel each other as though they were equally "charged" particles; a neutron and an anti-neutron would attract each other.

One may ask if a vector-field interaction between particles of the same charge could be important on the scale of the universe. The answer seems to be that, if the hypothesis of a uniform and isotropic universe is valid and if the vector field is gauge-invariant, that is, if it obeys Maxwell-like equations, then, for large enough space averages, such a vector field cannot have important cosmological effects.[11] The reason for this is the following:

The antisymmetric tensor that represents electromagnetic fields (or the Lee–Yang vector field) has six nonzero components. These can be grouped into two sets of three components, both of which transform under proper rotations like ordinary spatial three-vectors and, in the electromagnetic case, are the electric and magnetic fields. If, in some coordinate frame, the universe appears isotropic in sufficiently large volume averages, there can be no net three-vector field averaged over such a volume. An "electric" or "magnetic" field would define a direction and destroy the isotropy. The electric and magnetic fields, when averaged over large volumes, must both be zero. Then all the components of the antisymmetric field tensor are zero, and, from the Maxwell-like equations these fields obey, the net charge and current densities must both average to zero over that volume.

$$F^{ij}{}_{;j} = J^i = 0 \qquad (2)$$

This charge-current density is a four-vector. Hence, if its components are all zero in the special coordinate system that exhibits isotropy, they are zero in any coordinate system.

This is a quite general conclusion. If the assumption of isotropy and uniformity of the universe is a valid one, there can be no net "charge" or "current" over large-volume averages. If the Lee–Yang field were to exist, nucleons and antinucleons must be present in equal numbers over large volume averages. This seems unlikely. If it were the case, collisions between matter and antimatter would have generated a substantial amount of gamma radiation, which would contribute to the present cosmic-ray flux. Such a γ-ray flux has not been observed.

This argument does not rule out the Littleton–Bondi suggestion concerning a charge excess in the universe, since their theory involves a breakdown of Maxwell's equations and is not gauge-invariant. Nor does it deny the possibility of obtaining baryon conservation from a gauge-invariant vector theory. For instance, Schwinger, in a recent paper,[12] pointed out that it is possible to have gauge-invariant vector fields with nonzero rest mass. One cannot say anything about such short-range forces on the basis of the arguments we have made. My conclusion is that, with the usual assumption of isotropy, large sections of the universe cannot interact with each other through vector interactions obeying Maxwell-type (gauge-invariant) equations in a uniformly isotropic universe.

There is a more general result in the case of a closed universe if we deal with a vector interaction involving charge of only one sign. In this case, it is not necessary to assume isotropy or uniformity. In any closed universe, a gauge-invariant vector interaction that interacts with matter, all assumed to be of the same sign of charge, cannot exist. There can be no net charge in such a universe because there is no place for a net outward "electric" flux to go. All flux lines must terminate on an equal number of charges of the opposite sign. But the existence of equal numbers of opposite charges is contrary to our assumption that all matter is a source for this field of the same charge. Hence there cannot be a vector field that depends on all matter in a closed universe being a source of the same sign. From this and the previous argument, I conclude that the vector field does not provide a promising approach to an expression of Mach's principle.

The scalar and tensor fields do appear to be capable of providing long-range gravitational effects of importance to cosmology and Mach's principle. Next, I shall describe some of the properties of the scalar interaction; properties that are not as well known as might be expected.

The Scalar Field: Some Unfamiliar Properties

I shall introduce a scalar-field variable that is generated by the matter in the universe and that varies from point to point. A four-force on matter is given by the gradient of that scalar:

$$F_i = \phi_{,i} \tag{3}$$

It is rather remarkable that such an interaction of a scalar field with a particle treated relativistically cannot occur unless the mass of the particle is a function of the scalar. One can see this in the following physical way: One would expect the rate of change with respect to proper time of the three space components of the momentum of a particle interacting with a scalar field to satisfy the following equation:

$$\frac{\partial}{\partial \tau} P_\alpha = F_\alpha = \phi_{,\alpha} \tag{4}$$

The components $\phi_{,\alpha}$ are the spatial derivative of the scalar field and P_α are the corresponding momentum components.

Now consider the corresponding four-vector equation in the special case where the scalar field is a static scalar and the coordinate system is stationary so that the only nonzero components of the gradient are space-like. Then the rate of change with respect to the time component is equal to zero.

$$\phi_{,4} = 0 \tag{5}$$

This means that the energy of the particle is equal to a constant [Eq. (4)].

$$E = m/\sqrt{1 - v^2/c^2} \tag{6}$$

On the other hand, Eq. (4) implies that, if the spatial derivatives are non-zero, the particle is accelerating. We have a situation in which the velocity of the particle is changing while the kinetic energy remains constant. Equations (5) and (6) can be satisfied only if the mass of the particle is changing. This appears to be a very general result. The interaction of a scalar field with a particle leads to a variation of the mass of the particle as a function of the scalar field.

Note, for example, that the obvious variational principle for obtaining equations of motion with a scalar interaction is

$$0 = \delta \int \left[\tfrac{1}{2} m u^i u_i + \phi \right] d\tau \tag{7}$$

where u^i is the four-velocity, m is the mass of the particle, assumed constant, and ϕ is the scalar-field variable. However, the Euler equation of motion obtained from this variational principle,

$$\frac{d}{d\tau}(m u_i) = \phi_{,i} \tag{8}$$

is not a correct equation. This can be seen by multiplying Eq. (8) by u^i and making use of the relation

$$u^i u_i = -1 \tag{9}$$

and the assumption that the mass is constant, to obtain the expression

$$u^i \frac{d}{d\tau}(mu_i) = \frac{1}{2}\frac{d}{d\tau}(mu^i u_i) = -\frac{1}{2}\frac{d}{d\tau}(m)$$

$$u^i \frac{d}{d\tau}(mu_i) = u^i \phi_{,i} = \frac{d\phi}{d\tau}$$

(10)

Therefore,

$$\frac{1}{2}\frac{d}{d\tau}(m) = -\frac{d\phi}{d\tau}$$

(11)

But Eq. (11) is inconsistent with the assumption that the mass is constant. A correct variational principle consistent with Eq. (9) is obtained by dropping the assumption that the mass is constant and making the variation subject to Eq. (9) as a constraint. Alternatively, it can also be obtained from the variational principle:

$$0 = \delta \int m\sqrt{-u^i u_i}\, d\tau$$

(12)

In either case the equation of motion is

$$\frac{d}{d\tau}(mu_i) + \frac{dm}{d\phi}\phi_{,i} = 0$$

(13)

and the mass of the particle is a function of the scalar field.

The scalar field leads to some other interesting effects. Since it is a boson field, one can simply sum all the effects of matter at great distance. Let me imagine the following simplified equation, something like a wave equation, satisfied by a scalar field. The source of this field is some scalar measure of the mass density in the universe ρ, multiplied by an interaction constant A:

$$\Box\phi = \nabla^2\phi - \frac{1}{c^2}\frac{\partial}{\partial t^2}\phi = -4\pi A\rho$$

(14)

We use a model of the universe consisting of a single shell of mass M and radius R. With the boundary conditions that ϕ goes to zero as R approaches infinity, the solution to Eq. (14) is

$$\phi = A(M/R)$$

(15)

for the interior of the mass shell.

It should be recognized that these equations are greatly oversimplified. The effects of space curvature are not included, and the matter density ρ has not been carefully specified. As the field ϕ is a scalar, the matter density must be a scalar, and a suitable measure is provided by the contracted energy-momentum tensor of matter. It is interesting to note that the virial theorem can be used to show that the time-averaged integral over a stationary localized body of the contracted energy-momentum tensor is equal to the total energy of the body. Thus, as in the case of the gravitational field, the scalar field is determined essentially by the total mass of the body under those conditions when gravitation is important. If we consider the interaction of some nearby matter through the scalar interaction, we see that the scalar will be a function of two terms, the effect of some nearby bit of matter, plus the contribution of matter at great distance.

Another interesting property of a scalar interaction is that it leads to an attraction between two bits of matter. Also, the strength of this interaction is of the order of magnitude of the gravitational interaction. It is very difficult to get a strong interaction with a scalar field because the sum over all the matter in the universe is enormous compared with the effect of the nearby object. The distant-matter term tends to dilute the effect of nearby matter, so that nearby matter has a relatively weak effect. One can show that, independent of the form, and independent of any preconceived ideas we have about how strong the coupling to the scalar is, the interaction strength turns out to be that of the gravitational interaction, within perhaps a factor of ten.[13]

The scalar field leads to an attraction that has about the right strength for gravitation. Also it exhibits one of the features of Mach's principle—namely, the inertial mass of a particle at a particular point depends upon the distribution of matter about that point (Einstein's third property). But the scalar field alone cannot represent gravitation. Other things are wrong. The scalar-field theory generally leads to the wrong perihelion rotation of Mercury. Also, light is not deflected by the scalar field as it goes by the sun; we cannot construct a theory of gravitation from a scalar field alone.

The Tensor Field: A Bridge from Mach's Principle to Geometry

The tensor field exhibits more or less those properties that we would expect to be associated with Mach's principle. We should examine how many of these come about.

First, if we desire a theory in which only the relation of matter to other matter is important, we would expect to express this theory in generally covariant equations. Explicit coordinate systems that might represent some intrinsic properties of space itself should not be used.

A second point is that, if we consider the laws of physics in two coordinate systems, one accelerated locally relative to the other, then what is an inertial force in one coordinate system can be a gravitational force in the other. There is an interplay between inertial and gravitational forces. They are two manifestations of the same thing. Because of this, we may eliminate the following tempting generalization of classic laws:

In classic mechanics, we write a variational principle as

$$\delta \int [\tfrac{1}{2}mv^2 - \text{p.e.}] \, dt = 0 \tag{16}$$

We would be tempted, perhaps, to generalize this for the laws of motion of a particle in a gravitational field with two kinds of terms, a term that would lead to the inertial effects and a term that would lead to the gravitational field effects:

$$\delta \int [I + G] \, d\tau = 0 \tag{17}$$

This is just the approach that is wrong from the standpoint of Mach's principle. One ought to be able to shuffle inertial forces and gravitational forces back and forth with simple coordinate transformations. But, if the integrand in Eq. (15) is an invariant (assuming generally covariant equations) integrated along some invariant measure of time along the path, a transformation from one coordinate system to another will not mix the two terms I and G in the integrand. The division between inertial and gravitational effects will be permanent if we write the equations this way.

This suggests that, to get Mach's principle into the theory in such a way that what is inertial force for one coordinate system is a gravitational force for another, we must obtain both forces from a single invariant. If inertial forces are to be connected with accelerations, it is clear that this invariant must be quadratic in velocities. The simplest such invariant is one that involves a tensor field and is given by $g_{ij}u^i u^j$. It is not obvious at this point that g_{ij} has anything to do with the metric tensor. The g_{ij} may be any non-skew-symmetric tensor field. From this invariant, we can form a variation principle for which both inertial and gravitational forces come from the same term:

$$\delta \int g_{ij}u^i u^j \, d\tau = 0 \tag{18}$$

In this form, a coordinate transformation will transform one type of force into the other.

This suggests that gravitation should have something to do with tensors and tensor fields. Otherwise, we are in trouble with the interchange and interplay between inertial and gravitational effects.

If we have only a single tensor-field entry in our equations for the motion of all particles, it is a simple step to call this tensor the metric tensor and define the geometry of the space in such a way that this is the metric tensor of that geometry. This, from one point of view, is an arbitrary definition of what we mean by the geometry. It is a geometry in which the gravitational trajectories of structureless particles are defined to be geodesics. That is, these paths are given by the variational principle:

$$0 = -\delta \int g_{ij} u^i u^j \, d\tau \tag{19}$$

with

$$-d\tau^2 = g_{ij} \, dx^i \, dx^j = ds^2 \tag{20}$$

and

$$u^i = \frac{dx^i}{d\tau}$$

Thus

$$0 = \delta \int ds \tag{21}$$

In the case of a particle of zero rest mass, we have

$$ds = 0 \tag{22}$$

and

$$\int ds = 0 \tag{22a}$$

Such trajectories are called null geodesics of the geometry.

This definition of the geometry is possible only if the motion of (essentially point) particles in a gravitational field are uniquely given independent of their composition by equations of the form of Eq. (19). If one bit of matter (e.g., a neutron) moves on a certain path, and another (say, a hydrogen atom) starting from the same initial conditions departs from this path, it would be impossible to define both paths as geodesics. In this case it would not be possible to determine a unique geometry from the gravitational motions of particles.

From the point of view of Mach's principle, we do expect a unique space-time to be associated with gravitation. We have given a rough but not conclusive argument for this in terms of Sciama's model. The uniqueness of the gravitational acceleration, in other words, the space-time (geodesic) path, is something that one might expect as a result of the application of Mach's principle.

Thus, we are led in a more or less straightforward way from considerations of Mach's principle to the ideas that we have unique space-time paths for the motion of matter in a gravitating field, that we may represent this motion by equations involving a tensor field, that we get the equations of motion from a variational principle of the form of Eq. (18), and that we may define this tensor field to be the metric tensor of our geometry.

There remains the question whether meter sticks would really measure the distances given by this geometry, because we have defined the distances simply in terms of the space-time motion of particles. The following argument indicates that meter sticks do properly measure distances in this geometry.

Equation (18) represents a generalization of the corresponding equation from special relativity, the Minkowski metric tensor being replaced by the generalized symmetric tensor g_{ij}. If the classic equation of motion, obtained as an Euler equation from the variational principle, is to be consistent with a quantum-mechanical formulation of the same problem, the wave equation must be derived from a Lagrangian density, with the Minkowski tensor again replaced by g_{ij}. If all the field equations, including Maxwell's, are generalized in this way, Minkowski's metric tensor disappears completely, being replaced by g_{ij}.

It is always possible to choose a coordinate system such that g_{ij} is Minkowskian and has zero first derivatives at a point. As long as second and higher derivatives are sufficiently small and the measuring rod is sufficiently small, the equations of motions of all the particles and fields comprising the measuring rod are identical (for this coordinate system at this particular point) with those of special relativity. Thus it measures a space-like length interval correctly. Being an invariant measure of this interval, this measure holds for other coordinate systems also. We conclude, therefore, that under these conditions, meter sticks and clocks made of ordinary matter, that is, constructed of particles interacting with the strong interactions, and for which gravitational interaction self-energies are rather small, do, in fact, measure this geometry in a proper way.

It is concluded that the tensor field is essential for expressing the laws of gravitation in a manner compatible with Mach's principle. We have also seen that the long-range scalar field could have important cosmological effects and play an important role in relation to Mach's principle.

Manifestations of Mach's Principle by the Scalar Field

We consider now the problem posed by the Schwarzschild solution in general relativity. Any localized mass distribution, in a space otherwise empty, determines a gravitational field that describes a flat space asymptotically. No other reasonable boundary conditions have been found. But, such a flat space, with no nearby matter, has absolute inertial properties.

This paradox could be avoided if space were to close about any localized mass distribution. Such space closure might be achieved if a scalar field were present, in addition to the tensor field.

With masses of particles varying inversely as some positive power of a scalar field λ and the boundary condition $\lambda \to 0$ asymptotically for an open space (or $\lambda = 0$ somewhere inside a closed space), one has a mechanism for closing the space. A particle could not move into a region with $\lambda \to 0$, for its energy would go to infinity. This suggests therefore that a scalar field with

$$m = m_0 \lambda^{-n} \tag{23}$$

is a possible way of achieving space closure.

Because of the great accuracy of the Eötvös experiment, it is necessary to assume the same λ dependence for all particles. Otherwise, a constant gravitational acceleration independent of composition would not be achieved.

Another feature of the scalar field is also useful for more fully incorporating Mach's principle into a relativistic theory of gravitation. As we have seen, the ideas of Berkeley, Mach, and Sciama lead us to believe that the gravitational acceleration of a body should depend upon the mass distribution about the body. We have noted (page 126) that Sciama's expression for the inertial force is

$$F \sim \frac{GMma}{Rc^2} \tag{24}$$

where, in this case, we take M to be the total mass of the universe to its visible limits and R to be a suitable measure of the radius of the universe. This equation agrees with the more usual expression

$$F = ma \tag{25}$$

only if

$$\frac{GM}{Rc^2} \sim 1 \tag{26}$$

This relation is also obtained from a consideration of the Lense–Thirring effect of general relativity. Inside a hollow massive shell, of mass m and radius r, rotating about an axis with angular velocity ω_1, a gyroscope would be expected to precess relative to distant matter in the universe at a rate

$$\omega_2 = \left(\frac{8}{3}\right)\frac{Gm}{rc^2}\omega_1 \tag{27}$$

If Mach's principle is applicable, ω_2/ω_1 should depend upon the mass distribution in the universe:

$$\frac{\omega_2}{\omega_1} = f\left(\frac{m}{M}, \frac{R}{r}\right) \tag{28}$$

where M and R are again suitable measures of the mass and radius of the observed portion of the universe. For $(m/M) \ll 1$ and $(m/r)(R/M) \ll 1$, the above equation, (27), due to Thirring and Lense, suggests that the appropriate lowest order expansion of the function f is

$$\frac{\omega_2}{\omega_1} = \gamma \frac{m}{M} \frac{R}{r} \tag{29}$$

where γ is a dimensionless number of the order of unity. Note that, when combined with Eq. (27), this gives

$$\frac{GM}{Rc^2} \sim \gamma \tag{30}$$

From a slightly different orientation and from the viewpoint of Mach the Coriolis forces appearing in a rotating coordinate system may be considered due to a Lense–Thirring rotation induced by the whole universe rotating about the point in question. If one were to naively apply the Lense–Thirring formula to this situation (for which it is not valid because it was derived from the weak-field solution) one would obtain

$$\omega_1 \sim \frac{GM}{Rc^2} \omega_1 \tag{31}$$

again implying that

$$\frac{GM}{Rc^2} \sim 1 \tag{32}$$

If an equation such as (32) is to be considered the prototype of a proper equation to be formulated exactly someday, either: (1) The mass distribution M/R is fixed by the field equation and/or by boundary conditions on the field equations or, (2) the gravitational constant is variable, being a function of the mass distribution.

Consider the first alternative. If Einstein's field equation is valid, the gravitational constant is fixed. If this be assumed, Eq. (32) can be incorporated into gravitation theory by introducing a scalar field. A scalar field, generated by all the matter in the universe and acting on the particles in the universe, could conceivably affect all their masses in such a way as to keep M/R constant. It should be noted that this would not represent a limitation upon the number of particles in the universe, but rather that, through the intercession of the scalar field, the masses of the particles would adjust themselves appropriately, in such a way as to give M/R the appropriate value.

It is as though the universe is a giant servosystem, continuously and automatically adjusting particle masses to the value appropriate to the feed-back condition

$$\frac{GM}{Rc^2} = 1 \tag{33}$$

In this connection, it should be remarked also that this effect of a long-range scalar field provides a ready explanation for the great weakness of gravitation, as expressed by the small size of the gravitational coupling constant compared with atomic coupling.

$$\frac{Gm_p^2}{\hbar c} \sim 10^{-40} \tag{34}$$

According to this explanation, this number is so small because m_p, the mass of the proton, has been reduced to very small value through the effect of the scalar field generated by the enormous amount of matter in distant parts of the nucleus.

In this connection, it should be remembered that, expressed in proton mass units, the mass of the universe is roughly

$$\frac{M}{m_p} \sim 10^{80} \tag{35}$$

and that the radius of the universe in Compton wavelengths is roughly

$$\frac{Rm_p c}{\hbar} \sim 10^{40} \tag{36}$$

The fact that

$$\frac{Gm_p^2}{\hbar c} \sim \left(\frac{m_p}{M}\right)^{1/2} \sim \frac{\hbar}{Rm_p c} \tag{37}$$

suggested to Dirac[14] that, as the age of the universe $\sim R/c$ changes, M and G change in such a way as to preserve this relation. In terms of the effect of an ordinary scalar field, we would say that m_p would change rather than G.

The author has argued[15] that the two relations given by Eq. (37) may be obtained from Eq. (32), which is implied by Mach's principle and a consideration of the conditions necessary for the existence of the solar system.

It is suggested that general relativity may be made compatible with the requirements of Mach's principle if a long-range scalar field exists in addition to the tensor field of Einstein's theory.

Such a scalar field could serve to close the space about a localized mass distribution and to so adjust particle masses as to satisfy the Machian condition

$$\frac{GM}{Rc^2} \sim 1 \tag{32}$$

Also, in accordance with Einstein's 3rd requirement discussed above, an effect not present in ordinary general relativity, a scalar field of the type to be described and generated by matter piled up about a laboratory serves to increase inertial effects. The chief observable effect of these increased inertial forces is a reduction in locally induced gravitational accelerations. (That is, because of increased inertial reactions gravitational accelerations are less.)

In Chapter 8, I shall indicate that the appropriate scalar theory is one for which particle masses vary as $\lambda^{-1/2}$, and that the theory may be transformed, with a unit transformation, in such a way that particle masses are constant but that the gravitational "constant" is variable. In this form of the theory, the gravitational coupling constant $Gm_p^2/\hbar c$ varies as a result of G varying. m_p, $\hbar$, and c are all constant. With this form of the theory, the Einstein field equation is not valid. Instead, one has an equation that is essentially one of the Jordan equations. This point will be discussed more in detail in Chapter 8. In Chapters 8 and 12, I shall consider the implications for astrophysics and geophysics of the scalar field, should it be found eventually to exist.

In summary, we have seen that there are many faces of Mach, almost as many as there are people who have written on the subject. Grounded as it is in philosophical matters of deep significance, the principle is *anschaulich* and difficult to raise (or lower, depending upon your point of view) to the status of a quantitative theory. It is suggestive that Einstein was lead to his very elegant theory of gravitation by hints derived from this principle. It may still contain much of value to future physicists.

References

1. I. Newton, *Principia Mathematica*, 2nd ed., Motte-Cajori, London, 1713.
2. D. W. Sciama, *The Unity of the Universe*, Doubleday, New York, 1961, pp. 97–98.
3. B. Berkeley, *The Principles of Human Knowledge*, A. Brown & Sons, London, 1937.
4. E. Mach, *The Science of Mechanics*, 5th English ed., LaSalle, Ill.,1942, Chap. 1.
5. A. Einstein, *The Meaning of Relativity*, Princeton University Press, Princeton, N.J., 1955, p. 100.
6. H. Thirring and J. Lense, *Z. Physik.*, **19,** 156 (1918).
7. C. Brans, *Phys. Rev.*, **125,** 2194 (1962).
8. J. L. Synge, *Relativity, The General Theory*, North-Holland, Amsterdam, 1960, pp. ix–x.
9. D. W. Sciama, *Roy. Astron. Soc. Monthly Notice*, **113,** 34 (1953).
10. T. D. Lee and C. N. Yang, *Phys. Rev.*, **98,** 1501 (1955).
11. R. H. Dicke, **126,** 1580 (1962).
12. J. Schwinger, *Phys. Rev.*, **125,** 1043 (1962).
13. R. H. Dicke, *Phys. Rev.*, **126,** 1875 (1962).
14. P. A. M. Dirac, *Proc. Roy. Soc. (London)*, **165A,** 199 (1938).
15. R. H. Dicke, *Nature*, **192,** 440 (1961).

8

The significance for the solar system of time-varying gravitation

R. H. Dicke

Mach's Principle—A Guide for Modifying Einstein's Theory

In Chapter 7 I discussed a number of general features of gravitational theory. Two of these features furnish the starting point for this chapter.

1. The requirements that a theory of gravitation be expressed in generally covariant equations and that inertial and gravitational forces both be obtained from a single invariant lead to the representation of gravitational effects by a tensor field. Einstein's theory is a particular example of a tensor theory in which the tensor field is the only field exhibiting gravitational effects and the geometry is so defined that this tensor is the metric tensor of the geometry.

2. Einstein's general theory of relativity is not relativistic in the Machian sense. That is, this theory is not limited to a description of the relations between positions of matter. Rather, properties such as fixed directions are ascribed to empty space in the complete absence of matter, and motion is referred to a preferred, or absolute, geometry.

In this lecture, I shall discuss how Einstein's theory can be modified to overcome, at least in part, its absolute space-time character by introducing a second field quantity into the equations. Then, I shall go on to relate this modification to some of the problems connected with geophysics and astrophysics.

I anticipated some of the characteristics of this modification in Chapter 7 with the discussion of Sciama's model. Sciama's equations seem to suggest that it is possible to incorporate Mach's principle more completely into general relativity by introducing a gravitational "constant" that is a function of some field variable.

This possibility has also been raised in connection with a time-varying gravitational constant. The suggestion of a time-varying gravitational constant may have first appeared in physics in connection with Milne's ideas of cosmology. Later, Dirac[1] suggested that certain numerical coincidences of large cosmological numbers might imply time-varying gravitation, that is, a gravitational constant which is not truly a constant, but a function of time. Still later, Jordan[2] attempted to put Dirac's ideas into a proper field-theoretic form by making the gravitational "constant," a function of a scalar.

I shall approach this matter in a slightly different way, by pointing out explicitly that, in addition to the gravitational field which is connected with the geometry of space, one can have long-range matter-type fields. We are already familiar with one of these, the electromagnetic field. Two charged particles can interact with each other over a long distance through electromagnetic fields. In Chapter 7, I showed that this kind of vector field appears to be ruled out for producing long-range effects of cosmological importance. Large sections of the universe cannot interact with each other through vector interactions obeying Maxwell-type (gauge-invariant) equations in a uniformly isotropic universe.

A Second Tensor in Gravitational Theory: An Unpromising Innovation

Within the framework of relativity, there are two other fields that might play important roles in cosmology. One is a scalar long-range field, and the other is a tensor long-range field, that is, a second tensor field, in addition to the metric tensor that is associated with gravitation in Einstein's theory. I shall take these in inverse order, discussing the tensor field first.

It is possible to have a tensor interaction in addition to the metric tensor of space. But it would be very difficult to incorporate into the theory another such long-range tensor field. A second tensor field would be expected to lead to queer results in some experiments such as the ones that Hughes and his associates performed. Hughes, and independently Drever, were able to demonstrate the isotropy of space to a very high precision. This experiment is discussed in detail in Chapter 6.

The reason the tensor field is expected to run into difficulty with the Hughes experiment was first discussed quantitatively by Peebles and Dicke.[3,4] Their argument is the following: Assume there is some second tensor field. We may choose a coordinate system for which the metric tensor is locally Minkowskian. Then, generally speaking, the second tensor will not be locally Minkowskian but will have some form for which the spatial parts of this tensor exhibit an anisotropy. If there are forces associated with this second tensor field, it would be expected that this spatial anisotropy would appear in the results of the Hughes experiment.

If we should happen to find isotropy simultaneously for both tensors in a particular coordinate system, we could simply transform to a moving coordinate system. If the tensors are not identical, we can always, by moving, obtain a lack of spatial isotropy in one of the tensors. I believe that, because of the tremendous precision and sensitivity of the experiment, this is a compelling argument against the second-tensor interaction. I see no very obvious way of getting an appreciable interaction through a second long-range tensor field.

The Remarkable Properties of the Scalar Field

The case for the scalar field is more promising. I shall summarize its properties, which were mentioned in Chapter 7. It is remarkable that, for the little we know about this interaction in an observational way (in fact, even its existence is in doubt), we can delineate its properties so well. This is because the interaction is so simple that a couple of observations and the requirement of Lorentz invariance are sufficient to specify fairly completely its properties. The properties of a long-range scalar interaction (a neutral, scalar, massless field) are the following:

1. The scalar field leads to an attractive force between bodies.

2. The scalar field can only be weak. Its strength must be of the order of the gravitational interaction.

3. The scalar field does not interact with photons or other particles moving with the velocity of light.

4. The scalar force weakens as the particle speed increases, varying as $\sqrt{1 - v^2/c^2}$.

5. The interaction of a scalar field with a particle cannot occur unless the mass of the particle is a function of the scalar.

This means that work must be done on the particle to move it in a nonconstant scalar field. This implies an extra force, which acts on matter by virtue of its interaction with the scalar. We express this in the form of an equation by

$$\frac{d}{d\tau}(mu_i) - \tfrac{1}{2}mg_{jk,i}u^ju^k + m_{,i} = 0 \tag{1}$$

where

$$u^i = \frac{dx^i}{d\tau}$$

$$u^iu_i = -1$$

$$d\tau^2 = -g_{ij}\,dx^i\,dx^j = -ds^2 \tag{2}$$

and

$$m_{,i} = \frac{dm}{d\phi}\phi_{,i} \tag{3}$$

The great accuracy of the Eötvös experiment imposes the requirement that, if there is such a scalar interaction, all particles must suffer essentially the same type of scalar interaction. Otherwise, there would be anomalous accelerations. In other words, if the mass of the proton plus electron varied with the scalar with some different functional dependence than the mass of the neutron, then, generally speaking, a neutron would fall with a different acceleration from that of an ordinary hydrogen atom. So we face the requirement that the functional dependence of the mass on the scalar-field variable should be equal to some constant times some standard function that is the same for all particles.

$$m(\phi) = m_0 f(\phi) \tag{4}$$

The assumption that the mass of a particle is a function of a scalar leads to some rather strange effects. In particular, the gravitational coupling "constant," then, is not really constant. The gravitational constant can be given as a dimensionless number, a coupling constant, in terms of atomic constants as

$$\frac{Gm_p^2}{\hbar c} \simeq 10^{-40} \tag{5}$$

where m_p is the mass of the proton. But, if the mass of the proton varies from one place to the other, this ratio will also vary so that the gravitational interaction expressed in atomic units is not constant.

Normally, the dimensionless coupling constants of physics, such as

$$\alpha = \frac{e^2}{\hbar c} \simeq \frac{1}{137} \tag{6}$$

and

$$\frac{Gm_p^2}{\hbar c} \sim 10^{-40} \tag{7}$$

are regarded as *fait accompli* of nature, numbers preordained and unrelated to other physical dimensionless numbers. However, if the gravitational coupling constant is variable and is determined as a function of some scalar-field variable, in turn determined by the matter distribution in the universe, it becomes possible to understand the extraordinary value of this number. In my opinion, the number 10^{-40}, contrary to what Eddington thought, would not be expected to appear in a formalism as a pure number of simple mathematical origin. However, with the above interpretation,

$Gm_p^2/\hbar c$ may be considered small because the universe has so many particles ($\sim 10^{80}$). This large amount of matter, at great distances in the universe, generates a local value of m_p such that the gravitational coupling constant is small.

There is another remarkable feature associated with varying particle masses. If the masses of atoms vary, so also do their periods and diameters and, as a result, the lengths of meter sticks and the periods of clocks. These are all affected by the value of the scalar field. A meter stick at one place has a different length than a meter stick somewhere else (Figure 8-1) because the geometry that I have been using to describe these effects is not the geometry that is measured by meter sticks and clocks but that given by the metric tensor of Einstein's field equations. That is, it is the geometry for which the unit of length is $(G\hbar/c^3)^{1/2}$, the unit of time is $(G\hbar/c^5)^{1/2}$, and the unit of mass is $(\hbar c/G)^{1/2}$.

We have a problem then of redefining the geometry, if we wish, in such a way that the length of a meter stick does not change. That is, we may define the unit of length everywhere to be that length measured by a meter stick that is transported from place to place (Figure 8-2). If I redefine the geometry in this way, such that meter sticks and clocks do behave properly, and the masses of particles do not vary, then I discover that two things happen:

1. The field equations for the metric tensor are not those of general relativity. They are modified equations.

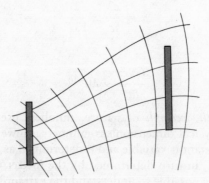

Figure 8-1 The unevenly spaced lines represent the curved geometry given by Einstein's equations relative to which the length of a meter stick varies from place to place as a function of the scalar field.

2. With these modified equations, the gravitational constant is no longer a constant, but varies from one place to another. All the other physical constants are properly constant.

This type of formalism, for which the equations of general relativity are replaced by some modified equations, was first introduced by Jordan.[2] The particular modification I shall use is closely related to one of the forms of Jordan's equations.

Modified Einstein Equations Incorporating a Scalar Field

The most compact way of presenting the theory is in terms of the variational principle from which the equations are obtained. In general relativity, one gets the Einstein field equations and equations for the motion of matter from a variational principle of this kind:

$$\delta \int (R + GL)\sqrt{-g}\, d^4x = 0 \qquad (8)$$

R is the contracted curvature tensor, G is the gravitational constant, and L is the Lagrangian density of matter. If we carry out the indicated variation for the metric tensor components, we obtain Einstein's field equations. If we carry out a variation on the particle coordinates that appear in the Lagrangian density for matter, we obtain the equations of motion of matter. All equations of gravitational physics are contained in the variational principle.

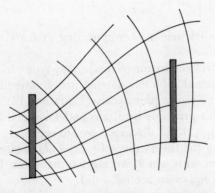

Figure 8-2 Relative to an appropriately redefined geometry not satisfying Einstein's equations, the length of a meter stick is constant.

In order to introduce a scalar field explicitly, I must add to the Lagrangian density of matter a Lagrangian density for the scalar field. The variational principle then has the form

$$\delta \int [R + G(L + L_\lambda)]\sqrt{-g}\, d^4x = 0 \qquad (9)$$

where for convenience we choose L_λ to have the form

$$L_\lambda = -G^{-1}(\omega + 3/2)\frac{\lambda_{,i}\lambda^{,i}}{\lambda^2} \qquad (10)$$

λ is the scalar field. ω is a constant that can be thought of as a coupling constant for the field. In addition to the scalar appearing explicitly in the scalar Langrangian density, it also appears implicitly in the matter Lagrangian, owing to the dependence of the particle masses on the scalar field. This is assumed to be of the form

$$m = m_0\lambda^{-1/2} \qquad (11)$$

I shall indicate later why this form is particularly interesting.

From Eq. (9) we obtain the Einstein field equations for the components of the metric tensor and new equations of motion for particles. In the units given by this geometry, meter sticks behave strangely. They contract and expand as they are moved from one place to another. Clocks run fast one place and slow another. But we can redefine the units of measure in such a way that meter sticks do not have this strange behavior. We discover that the corresponding transformation of the equations leads to the following variational principle, where ϕ is a new scalar with dimensions of G^{-1} and and $\phi \sim \lambda$:

$$\delta \int \left[\phi R - \frac{\omega\phi_{,i}\phi^{,i}}{\phi} + L\right]\sqrt{-g}\, d^4x = 0 \qquad (12)$$

In this equation the particle masses appearing in L are no longer variable but are now constant.

This is closely related to one of the Jordan-type variational principles. It leads to gravitational interactions that are described not by a metric tensor but by a metric tensor plus a scalar. Equation (12) was first discussed in relation to Mach's principle by Brans and Dicke.[5] The transformation from Eq. (12) to Eq. (9) was discussed by Dicke.[6]

For the form of the theory given by Eq. (12), matter obeys the usual equations of motion with which we are familiar from Einstein's theory, but Einstein's field equations are not valid.

To summarize, in the form of the theory in which Einstein's equations are satisfied, meter sticks behave in a strange way. In the form in which meter sticks behave properly, the Einstein field equations are not valid. We have the choice of one or the other form. They are completely equivalent physical descriptions. They differ from each other only in the way that we have defined our units of measure and, hence, our geometry. This equivalence has been discussed.[6]

An Implication of Modified Theory: A Time-Varying Gravitational "Constant"

It is interesting that equations of this kind seem to be compatible with Mach's principle. Also they imply a position and time-varying gravitational constant. It appears difficult to obtain a theory incorporating Mach's principle with only a metric tensor and without a scalar field. I shall indicate what this type of theory implies about the variation of gravity with time and position. Then I would like to describe as nearly as I can what would be the effect on the solar system of the gravitational interaction changing with time.

From Eq. (12) the scalar field equation for a static-matter distribution is

$$\nabla^2 \phi \sim T \tag{13}$$

where T is the contracted energy-momentum tensor of matter. For a time-varying-matter configuration, we must replace the Laplacian operator by the d'Alembertian operator. In a Minkowskian coordinate system, neglecting curvature effects, this operator has the form shown in Eq. (14).

$$\Box^2 \phi \equiv \nabla^2 \phi - \frac{1}{c^2} \frac{\partial^2 \phi}{\partial t^2} \simeq T \tag{14}$$

This equation implies, that, as the universe, assumed uniform, expands with time and the amount of visible matter in the universe changes, the scalar connected with that matter distribution changes.

As a consequence, gravitation must get weaker with time. One can make a quite reasonable guess as to how fast it should get weaker with time. This turns out to be of the order of a few parts in 10^{11} per year, assuming the theory as presented here is valid.

This variation implies many interesting observable effects concerning the history and present state of the solar system and the galaxy. However, the data that one has to deal with always have so many possible explanations that there is little if any hope of demonstrating from the following considerations that a variation in G occurs. But, on the other hand, if you were to give me a good laboratory proof that the gravitational constant is changing with time, my remarks concerning expected effects which would occur in connection with this changing G would not be unreasonable.

Effects of Varying G on Evolutionary Ages of Stars

One of the primary effects of a gravitational constant getting smaller with time is connected with stellar evolution. The reason for this is that the luminosity of a star is a rather sensitive function of the gravitational constant. If the gravitational constant were getting weaker with time, the luminosity of a star would be decreasing. This would affect our observations in two different ways:

1. The lifetime of a star is now determined from its present state of evolution, assuming a constant gravitation constant in the past. This determination would be wrong if the star had evolved more rapidly in the past because of a stronger gravitational constant.

2. The sun would have had a greater luminosity in the past than it has now. This would lead to higher surface temperatures of the earth and other planets in the past.

I shall examine the effect of a changing G on stellar evolution first. One can describe the situation rather simply. As a consequence of the virial theorem, the gravitational potential energy of a star is equal to twice the internal kinetic energy, or heat energy. This, in turn, is proportional to the central temperature of the star. Therefore, we may write

$$\frac{GM}{R} \propto T \tag{15}$$

where M, R, and T are the mass, radius, and central temperature of the star, respectively. If we hold the radius constant, while allowing the gravitational constant to change, we can see that the change in central temperature is proportional to the change in G. On the other hand, the rate at which a black-body radiates is proportional to the fourth power of the temperature. Therefore, in the most naive way, we would expect the luminosity to vary as the fourth power of the gravitational constant.

The situation is not quite this simple. First, this argument would only be true if the opacity were temperature-independent. In the case of very massive stars (very bright stars) where Compton scattering plays a dominant role in determining the opacity, the Compton cross section of electron is fixed and is independent of the temperature. In that case we do expect the luminosity to vary as

$$L \propto G^4 \qquad \text{for a very massive star} \tag{16}$$

However, in the case of a star of the order of the sun's mass, the bremsstrahlung process, or, as the astronomers call it, the free-free transition, is the dominant mechanism determining the opacity of the star. In this particular case the free-free transition is rather strongly temperature-dependent and contributes an additional third or fourth power to the dependence of the luminosity. For a star of roughly the sun's mass, the luminosity goes as

$$L \propto G^{7-8} \qquad \text{for a star of solar mass} \qquad (17)$$

The simplification of holding the radius constant is in no sense justified. The central temperature of a star is determined by the temperature at which nuclear reactions occur. This temperature does not depend strongly on G. What really happens is that the radius, rather than the central temperature, changes. However, from more careful considerations it turns out that the luminosity dependence on the gravitational constant we have obtained is approximately correct whether the radius or the central temperature changes.

Thus for a star of the sun's mass the luminosity is a rather sensitive function of G. The change of luminosity is of the order of 8 times the change in the gravitational constant. If the G variation is of the order of 3 parts in 10^{11} per year, the luminosity variation will be given by

$$\frac{\delta L}{L} \simeq 8 \frac{\delta G}{G} \sim 2.5 \times 10^{-10}/\text{year} \qquad (18)$$

In a period of 4 billion years, this would make this change in luminosity the order of 100 per cent. A variation of G at this rate could play a rather important role in stellar evolution rates and lead to a serious discrepancy in the presently determined stellar evolutionary age of stars.

Now I shall consider the history of the galaxy as we see it and discuss how an accelerated stellar evolution in the past would affect our observations. We picture our galaxy as originally a large mass of hydrogen, which, in a very short time after its formation, produced an initial population of stars. These stars are called population II. They are found in globular clusters and as field stars of high velocity. The reason for believing that the formation of population II stars all happened in a rather short time is that these high, random velocities appear to reflect the initial motions probably turbulent, of the gas.

If this is the case, it might mean that population II was formed in a time that is of the order of the characteristic time for turbulence to damp out in the galaxy. This time was probably under 200 million years.

Another possibility is that the initial population was so bright and active with large numbers of massive stars that the turbulence was driven by the ultraviolet radiation from these stars. Then it might have been maintained for as long as 1 billion years. The turbulence could not have been maintained by bright stars of the initial population for longer than 1 billion years, for the stars that have the right ultraviolet spectrum to drive

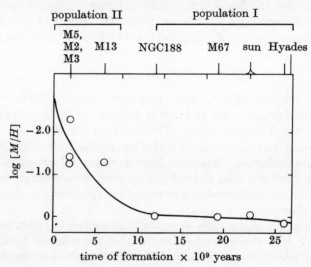

Figure 8-3 Stellar metal-to-hydrogen ratio, relative to that in the sun, as a function of the time at which the star clusters formed (Arp[7]).

turbulence have a short lifetime. Something under 1 billion years for the time of formation of the principal part of population II seems to be indicated.

This time scale seems to fit reasonably well with Salpeter's suggestion that the rate of formation of stars is proportional to the amount of gas present. This would lead to approximately two-tenths of the total life of the galaxy for the halo-formation period. This is somewhat longer than 1 billion years. It is of the order of 2 billion years.

Another characteristic of population II is the very small amount of heavy elements in these stars. They seem to have been formed out of hydrogen.

On the other hand the thing that characterizes population I stars is that they all have considerable heavy-element abundance. The measurements that Arp[7] and others have made indicate that the fractional abundance of heavy elements increases in time roughly as given in Figure 8-3. The logarithm of the ratio of metal abundance to hydrogen is plotted on some arbitrary time scale. The metal abundance rises very rapidly to solar abundance. The very old cluster NGC188 shown on the diagram after the formation of population II seems to have as much heavy-element content as the sun.

There is considerable uncertainty about the size of the numbers in

Figure 8-3 because it is quite difficult to measure small changes in heavy-element abundance. But the indication is that the principal heavy-element formation occurred in stars in the halo population. This is the reason that population II and halo stars are associated. After the halo population was completed, the lower-velocity stars started appearing. They seem to have had most of the heavy elements in them from the beginning. Very little more (20 to 40 per cent) had to be added later.

In the initial population, there were stars of a type no longer found in the galaxy, namely, massive population II stars. We no longer see them and do not know their properties on the basis of observations. They may have been supernova prone; they may have been the primary source of the heavy elements. With the assumption of a larger gravitational interaction in the past, this could have affected the stability of stars in such a way as to make supernova formation likely.

One has a way of dating stars that essentially depends on asking how long it takes them to burn their hydrogen. They start out with hydrogen and some heavy elements, and the nuclear reactions occur at the core. The burning in the core keeps moving out as the hydrogen at the center is used up. As it moves out, the luminosity increases slightly. Finally these stars reach a phase where they start changing their form completely. A great expansion takes place and they turn into red giants.

Figure 8-4 is the familiar Hertzsprung–Russell diagram for stars. The logarithm of the luminosity is plotted against the logarithm of the surface temperature. Luminosity is a measure of how rapidly a star is radiating. The sun's luminosity is 1 in these units. The sun's temperature is indicated in the diagram.

When a star is first formed it falls on the straight line referred to as the main sequence. The mass of the star determines its initial position on the main sequence. The more massive stars begin with higher luminosity and temperature. After the star has burned a certain fraction, some say 20 to 30 per cent of its hydrogen, it moves off the main sequence rather rapidly over into the red-giant region. After this, it is not completely clear what happens. Presumably the star ends up eventually as a white dwarf.

The procedure, then, for determining the age of a star in terms of its luminosity involves the time it takes for a star of a particular mass to burn some 20 to 30 per cent of its hydrogen. This percentage that the star must burn before moving off the main sequence is calculated from stellar evolution theory. A set of stars all made at the same time, the Pleiades cluster, for example, would initially have fallen along the main sequence. But the massive luminous stars burn up their hydrogen rapidly and move off the main sequence into the red-giant region. So we find that, at the present time, the Pleiades do not fall completely on the main sequence, but fall along the curve shown. The shape of this curve (the point at which it

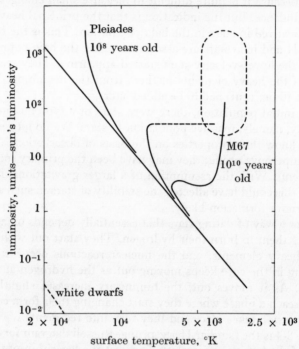

Figure 8-4   Hertzsprung–Russell diagram of stellar distributions.

leaves the main sequence) enables us to determine the age for this cluster of stars.

The Pleiades are quite young. In the case of an older cluster, the massive stars are already dead. They first turned into red giants. Then, presumably, they evolving quickly ended up as white dwarfs. The stars of a very old cluster, M67, are given in the lowest curve.

These curves do not represent a time sequence. A particular star does not move along the curve. The curves represent the distribution of stars at some particular time, now. This distribution enables one to obtain a measure of the age of the cluster. This is the basis for stellar evolutionary ages. If gravitation is changing with time, the ages determined this way will be faulty.

Table 8-1 gives the various ages in the galaxy determined from stellar evolution theory for constant G and for time-varying G. The globular clusters are among the oldest stars that we know. Their stellar evolutionary ages have been given as 25 billion years. However, there is considerable uncertainty in this age.

Table 8-1

Ages of Astronomical Objects[a]

Object	Type of age	General relativity, constant G	Positive curvature, Brans–Dicke, varying G, $\omega = 6$
Globular cluster	Stellar evolution	25	7.8
Old galactic cluster NGC188	Stellar evolution	16	7.0
Sun	Stellar evolution	4–15	2.5–6.9
Sun	Radioactivity	4.5	4.5
Galactic system	From depletion of hydrogen gas	5–12	5–12
Elliptical galaxies	Stellar evolution (mean age)	10–16	5.5–7.0
Uranium:			
25% prompt	Time of first formation	11.1	11.1
50% prompt	Time of first formation	7.5	7.5
Universe	Hubble (galactic expansion)	13.0	15.0
Universe, flat	Based on Hubble age	8.6	
Universe, closed	Based on Hubble age	<8.6	8.0
Universe, open	Based on Hubble age	<13 >8.6	

[a] In 10^9 years.

As mentioned above, there is considerable uncertainty about some of these values. The bolometric corrections to visual luminosities may be wrong. The absolute visual luminosities may also be incorrect. Also the calculated brightening of the star on the main sequence and fraction of hydrogen burned on the main sequence may be somewhat in error. Nonetheless, we would expect the globular clusters to be older than the oldest population I stars for which some of these uncertainties do not exist. Thus ages in excess of 16 billion years would be expected. For purposes of the following argument, we shall assume that 25 billion years is correct, nonetheless realizing its uncertainty.

Thus we shall take 25 billion years to be the evolutionary age of globular clusters assuming a constant G. Then, with the accelerated evolution that would result from increased gravitation in the past, this comes down to about 7.8 billion years. This is still a little uncomfortably close to the age of the universe that one obtains from the Hubble expansion. The

Hubble expansion age for the universe, assuming an evolving universe of the flat type, is about 8 billion years, and is less than 8 billion years for a closed universe.

Let me run through the effect of a varying G on some of the other ages as shown in Table 8-1. The age of the old galactic cluster NGC188 is reduced from 16 billion years to 7. Notice that for the globular cluster and the old galactic cluster NGC188, which differ very greatly in their composition, the 9-billion-year difference in ages computed for constant G is reduced to only 0.8 billion years for varying G.

There is not a good evolutionary age for the sun because we do not know its helium abundance. It is believed that the sun's evolutionary age could lie anywhere in the range shown. The radioactivity age for the sun, however, might be taken to be the age of the meteorites. This is of the order of 4.5 billion years.

The age for our galactic system is based on Salpeter's ideas about the way the galaxy evolves. His assumption is that stars are formed at a rate proportional to the amount of hydrogen present. From the present e-folding rate for the condensation of hydrogen into stars we obtain about 5 to 12 billion years for the age of the galaxy. In the case of elliptical galaxies, there is a determination of an age based on some work of Crampin and Hoyle.[8] From the color distribution of the elliptical galaxies, one determines an evolutionary age of the order of 16 billion years. This age becomes 5.5 to 7 billion years in the revised time scale for stronger gravity in the past.

Well, then, one effect of a stronger gravitational constant in the past is the shifting of these old stars down to younger ages. This gets them under the age of the galaxy based upon an expanding model of the universe. But, as I pointed out, there is considerable uncertainty about these ages. I remember it was only some 4 or 5 years ago that the globular clusters were said to be some 6.5 billion years old. So you see that this whole thing is considerably in flux, and one cannot be too much impressed by these numbers.

Uranium Ages

The age of the universe given by the decay of uranium is determined from the ratio of abundances of the two uranium isotopes U_{235} and U_{238}, assuming that their formation ratio is correctly given by the theory of nucleogenesis. The assumption is made that uranium production is such that its abundance is increasing linearly with time, which is the sort of thing that goes with Salpeter's model. In addition, there was some prompt production of uranium in connection with the halo population for reasons mentioned before. In one case, I assume 25 per cent prompt; in

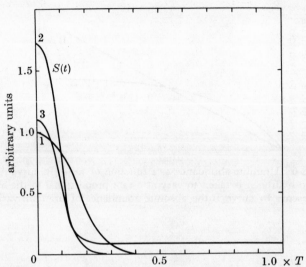

Figure 8-5 Uranium production rate in the galaxy (arbitrary units). T represents the present age of the galaxy.

the other 50 per cent prompt. More recently, I have calculated an age with the assumption that the uranium is produced by the halo population with distribution curves of the kind shown in Figure 8-5.[9] These three distribution curves give 9, 7.7, and 7.2 billion years for the first origin of uranium.

I have avoided using the ratio of uranium to thorium abundances since they have different chemistries and thorium has a long half-life. I do not believe anything can be concluded from thorium abundances. I have used only U-235 and U-238 abundances. Since U-235 has a relatively short lifetime, this age determination is very insensitive to what we assume about the initial abundances. The initial-formation ratio of U-235 to U-238 does not enter in a sensitive way.

It is possible that these time-distribution curves for the formation of uranium are incorrect. For example, if shortly before the solar system formed, a supernova occurred nearby, some of the uranium in the sun could have been produced at that particular time. This could have biased the U-235/U-238 ratio. Because of the short half-life of U-235, a significant portion of it, found in the solar system, might have been formed that way. On the other hand, U-238 has a longer lifetime and may have accumulated to a much greater extent from the past. Therefore its abundance is less sensitive to recent events in the solar neighborhood. In this way, the details

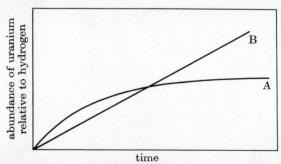

Figure 8-6   Uranium abundance as a function of time. In curve A the ratio of uranium to hydrogen is taken to vary at a rate proportional to the amount of hydrogen present. In curve B the absolute abundance of uranium varies at this rate.

of the formation curve can play an important role in determining the age that we get. It should be noted though that, at the time of formation of the solar system, the U-235/U-238 ratio was 0.34. Thus a very significant fraction of uranium must be assumed to have been formed just prior to this solar system if one is to conclude that this *is* the explanation for this short time scale.

The uranium ages I have given differ quite a bit from those of Hoyle and Fowler, who make a quite different assumption about the distribution in time of the formation of uranium. Hoyle and Fowler assume that uranium is produced in a kind of supernova that cannot occur until some 4 or 5 billion years after initial stellar condensation. So there is about a 4 or 5 billion year waiting time. They also assumed that the uranium abundance is an increasing function of time as shown in curve A of Figure 8-6. However, Salpeter's model would suggest that the abundance of uranium relative to hydrogen would increase linearly with time as shown in curve B of Figure 8-6. However, the reason for the discrepancy between the ages I have given and those of Hoyle and Fowler is the 4 to 5 billion year delay introduced initially.

My ages also differ from those of Cameron. In Cameron's model,[10] the primary (light) elements are assumed to be formed at the same rate as star formation, which is taken to be a decreasing exponential. The secondary elements are formed at a rate dependent on the build-up of the primary elements. For uranium, the production rate is complicated and rather different in terms of history from that of Fowler and Hoyle. But the conclusions about the age of the elements are essentially the same as theirs.

Affect of Varying G on Earth Temperature in the Past

Now what about the problem of the higher temperatures in the past? I find that, if we assume that the black-body radiation characteristics of the earth have not changed, a certain change in the solar temperature would lead to a corresponding change in the earth's temperature. If we go back some 4 to 5 billion years, the temperature would rise from about 300°K to about the boiling point of water.

This is not corrected for solar evolution and the motion of the sun along the main sequence. This would tend to pull the temperature down but not by a great deal. It might come down some 10°K, so that it would be 353°K or 363°K, still approaching the boiling point of water.

The total factor by which the luminosity changes, owing to changing G, is about 2.7 in 4.5 billion years. This is assuming a linear extrapolation. We take

$$\delta G/G = 3 \times 10^{-11}/\text{year} \tag{19}$$

An important influence on the effect of a change in the sun's luminosity on the temperature of the earth is the water vapor in the atmosphere. The effects of increased water vapor work in two directions at once. One is the increased greenhouse effect, leading to a rise in the temperature. The other is increased albedo and better heat transfer to high latitudes, leading to a decrease in the temperature. I think I would argue this way: With increased radiation, the first thing I would expect would be that the surface temperature would go up somewhat, leading to a higher vapor pressure and to an increased greenhouse effect, but, on the other hand, also to increased cloudiness.

However, there is an argument that there must be very large amounts of water vapor in the atmosphere before the cloud pattern changes very much. It is that, in the convection of the atmosphere, there are both up-going-air and downgoing-air currents. These occupy roughly equal areas, so that one would expect roughly 50 per cent cloud cover over a wide range of water-vapor content.

It is possible that, with an increase of radiation from the sun, the difference in the radiation absorbed at the equator and the pole would increase. This could result in more circulation and increased cloud cover where it is most effective. If the atmosphere approached something like 80 or 90 per cent water vapor, the circulation pattern would change in a rather interesting way. There would no longer be the convection cells of the kind that we are familiar with. The water vapor would rise in the equatorial regions and fall as rain, primarily in the polar regions. Then there could be nearly 100 per cent cloud cover.

These possible changes in the surface temperature of the earth might be significant for biological considerations. If the earth was too hot in the past, living organisms would have been uncomfortable. This is one of the only two sensitive tests of past temperatures that I can think of. The other is ancient glaciation.

But in the absence of further evidence, I think the moral is that the atmosphere is complicated. One cannot make any very firm predictions concerning the effect of an increased luminosity of the sun in the past on surface temperature. We cannot be sure how much the surface temperature would have changed.

In the case of the moon, things are certainly much more clear. We can predict unambiguously a higher peak-surface temperature for the moon in the past, approaching some 250°C 4.5 billion years ago.

The Expanding (?) Earth and Moon

Another interesting geophysical effect to be expected, associated with a decreasing gravitational "constant," is a steadily expanding earth. P. Jordan[2] first discussed the effect of decreasing gravitation on the earth. The earth is substantially compressed by the gravitational force. As this force gets weaker with time, the earth expands. With a rate of decrease of the gravitational constant of 3×10^{-11} per year, the earth would be expected to expand in circumference by approximately 150 km per billion years. This expansion rate is based on what one knows about the present amount of the compression of the earth. The corresponding number for the moon is of the order of 1 km change in the moon's circumference per billion years.

What is the evidence on the expansion of the earth? The traditional explanation for mountain formation, the classic one, is a contracting earth with the crust buckling and producing mountains. This classic explanation for mountain formation has fallen somewhat into disfavor in recent years. Many geophysicists no longer take this explanation seriously.

There are several striking indications of something like an expansion in the earth, but again the problem is one of the ambiguity of the evidence. Figure 8-7 shows an old classic problem faced by the geologists. This is a picture due to Carey,[11] who has been able to explain many geologic features as resulting from a large expansion of the earth. According to Carey, as the earth expanded, a great big crack opened along what is now the western coast of Africa and the continents of Africa and South America pulled apart. Figure 8-8 shows the rather good fit between the boundaries of these two continents. The outline shown is the continental margin, that is, the continental-shelf boundary.

Among other geologists who have suggested variations of this explanation are Egyed, Wilson, and Heezen. Wilson and Heezen have suggested

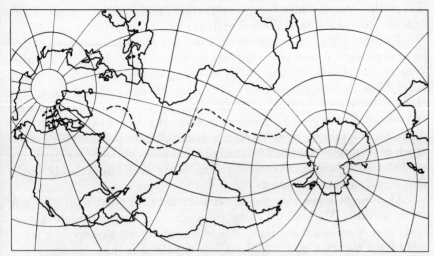

Figure 8-7 Map showing the coast lines of the Americas and Europe–Africa in relation to the mid-Atlantic ridge (from Carey[11]).

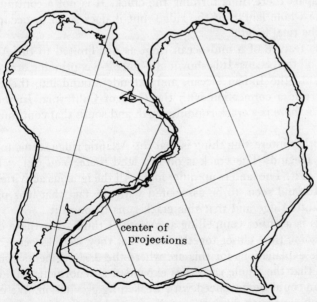

center of
projections

Figure 8-8 Map showing the fit between South America and Africa at the 2000-meter isobath along the slope below the edge of the continental shelf (from Carey[11]).

that earth expansion may be an explanation for the global system of rift valleys, such as the medial crack system along the mid-Atlantic ridge.

Unfortunately, an expanding earth is not the only possible explanation for the geologic features pointed out by Carey. The old explanation of Wegener (1915) and DuToit (1937) involving continental drift is a possibility. This idea was placed on a more reasonable basis when it was recognized that a convective mantle could result in motion of continental masses. In addition to the geologic features mentioned above, there is other evidence for the relative motions of continents. Recent paleomagnetic data, much of it taken and studied by Runcorn, has given evidence for continental drift (which would not require an expanding earth but probably would require a convective mantle).

One might argue that the coincidence between coast lines does not mean anything. With all the many complicated coasts, one might always find some coastlines that would fit together. However, a compelling argument for a common origin of these two coastlines is the existence of the mid-Atlantic ridge 1 to 2 km high shown in Figure 8-7. This mid-Atlantic ridge is quite accurately halfway between the continental coasts. It rather accurately represents a medial ridge down the Atlantic Ocean basin.

As mentioned above, this ridge has along much of its length a medial crack that is quite large, some kilometers wide. This is as if the earth were pulling apart there, thus forming the crack. It is not a continuous crack along the whole length of the ridge, but it does seem to occupy a large part of the total length.

This feature of a mid-ocean ridge is not limited to the Atlantic. It exists in all the oceans. It is shown in Figure 8-8 continuing around Africa. It goes into the Indian Ocean, and extends around into the Pacific. In fact, there is a connection with the Gulf of California. In the Gulf of California there is a crack running north and south that continues into the land.

Another interesting thing is that the Atlantic ridge seems to run right through Iceland. The crack is on dry land there. You can walk around and look at it. The land is up quite high. All the igneous activities that one sees in Iceland seem to be associated with the fact that it is part of the mid-Atlantic ridge and that this crack runs through it.

This is a rather compelling argument, I think, that these continents were at some time closer together and that they were associated in some way. The explanations for this are where the disagreements come. Carey suggests that the whole earth has expanded an enormous amount, much more than could be produced with weakening gravitation. We cannot get very much expansion from our small rate of decrease of gravity.

It is unlikely that changes in the structure of matter toward the center of the earth would lead to a disproportionately large radius change. The usual assumption is that the inner core is a solid form of iron and nickel, and the outer core is liquid. A change in G could change the phase boundary and cause the region of melting to shift. But I do not expect anything very discontinuous to happen. The effect of an expansion is one of absorbing heat and shoving of the reaction that provides the expansion back in the direction to turn it off. It is not something for which an instability develops. This enormous required expansion is one of the serious problems connected with Carey's ideas.

Another direct observational bit of evidence against Carey's ideas is the fact that, if the earth were expanding at the rate at which Carey says, it would lead to some very noticeable effects in the motion of the moon relative to the earth's rotation. The length of the day would be increasing at a rate decidedly greater than has been observed over historical times.

Convection in the Earth's Mantle

The explanation based on mantle convection for the apparent drift of continents is largely due to Vening–Meinesz. According to Vening–Meinesz, the early convective cooling of the earth was with a simple system of convective cells that became more numerous as the core of the earth developed. In this model, the mantle of the earth, although one would think that normally it is solid, is an almost viscous liquid in continual convection. As stated above, the convection has caused continents to pull apart, forming such oceans as the Atlantic. This is assumed to have happened in the recent past. Of the order of 100 to 200 million years ago they were joined together. They have separated since then.

As was mentioned briefly, the idea that the continents are moving around, because they are floating on the mantle, goes back to Wegener. He explained the ice ages by having continents drift up to the north pole where they undergo an Ice Age and then drift away again. He would have had the continents drifting around like bits of wood in a quiet pond of water.

There are a number of interesting things one can say about the effects of convection in the mantle, if it exists. If there is an uprising cell along the mid-ocean ridge, we would expect a higher heat flow. Well, one does see a higher heat flow. Also, if material is rising here, we might expect that this ocean bottom is rather recent. There would not be much in the way of sediment on it. Well, there is not much in the way of sediment. This is a rather surprising thing about all the oceans. There is very little in the way of sediments on the bottom. Using present sedimentation rates, one would expect that there would be considerably more than there actually is.

As mentioned above, the recent measurements on paleomagnetism rather strongly indicate continental drift is going on. But, if there is an existing continental drift associated with mantle convection, I think it would be very difficult to say anything about a general expansion. Effects of a general expansion are too small compared to these much larger effects, and they are easily masked.

The convection itself might be associated with a decreasing gravitational constant. This is because of the fact that, as you take the pressure off the earth in the interior, the melting point decreases. As the melting point gets closer and closer to the temperature that exists, there either is local melting or at least the viscosity falls to the point where convection starts. So there may actually be a connection between convection and a weakening gravitational constant.

A third explanation which has been given for continental drift is that in the early days of the formation of the earth there was a rather large amount of convection in the interior of the earth. This was either in the form of a solid mantle or else a molten earth associated with the heat of the initial radioactivity and the heat energy associated with the compaction, that is, the gravitational energy. The convection in the original earth produced the large convection cells that determined the land-mass distribution. Then these convection cells disappeared, so that the land-mass distribution that we have now is a fossil remnant of early convection cells. This explanation is favored in some quarters.

If it is true that this convection is not going on now, then there are quite reasonable explanations for the oceans' system of cracks. They might be due to a general expansion connected with weakening gravity. But, if the convection is going on now, I think the direct effects of general expansion in producing such features are minor.

In connection with the moon's expansion, there is a similar situation, except that there is no evidence for convection in the case of the moon. If there were convection, faulting of the surface would be expected. One would expect to find craters sliced in two, one half sliding with respect to the other half. These do not seem to appear. It is clear that the moon might actually be a better place for looking for expansion effects even though the expected expansion is much smaller. The effects of expansion would be expected to appear in the form of surface cracks or magma flows. Magma flows might be expected to result from an expansion of the interior, the only part requiring expansion. This could result in the internal, low-melting-point components forcing their way out through cracks in a rigid crust.

Figure 8-9 shows the moon's surface with its characteristic maria. We are all familiar with these large dark areas on the moon, which could be lava flows. It has been suggested by Gold that these are seas of dust. I

Figure 8-9   The moon's crust showing characteristic maria and craters (from U.S. Air Force Lunar Atlas, Plate D3-a).

Figure 8-10   Photograph of the moon's surface showing a gash (from U.S. Air Force Lunar Atlas, Plate C2-b).

doubt the validity of the "seas-of-dust" explanation. There are a number of craters flooded inside and out to the same level, as nearly as one can tell from the shadow measurements of height. It is very difficult for me to conceive how dust would establish hydrostatic equilibrium, filling up inside the crater to the correct height. This seems to suggest more directly a fluid, connected through surface fissures to a common subsurface magma pool. Also there are many old catch-basins in the upland regions that do not show the characteristic dark color of the maria, suggesting that the dark color is primarily due to a composition difference.

Figure 8-10 shows another feature, which was described at one time as a gash caused by a meteorite fragment. I think that one can soon convince oneself that a large, high-velocity projectile would not make a gash like this but would produce an intense shock wave that could result in a crater-like formation. I think a much more reasonable explanation for this parti-cular formation is a crack in the surface, a fissure filled by magma from the interior.

Anomalies in Moon Motion and Earth Rotation

Another effect of gravity getting weaker with time that would be expected is a gradual slowing of the moon in its orbit about the earth. This should lead to a discrepancy in the lunar position computed on the basis of constant *G*. Figure 8-11 shows the lunar-discrepancy curve as observed from telescope observations for the last 200 years.[12] The error in the moon's position, that is, the observed longitude minus computed longitude, is given as a function of time as determined by the earth's rotation rate. There are at least two effects contributing to this error. One is an irregular fluctuation effect, usually assumed to be due to an irregularity in the earth's rotation rate. (See Chapter 12 for an alternative explanation.) The other is a quadratic effect indicated by the parabolic shape of this curve. The quadratic effect is associated, in part at least, with the tidal interac-tions between the earth and the moon, which slow the earth's rotation and cause the moon to move out to a bigger radius with a longer period. One can eliminate the fluctuation effect resulting from the earth's erratic rota-tion and simply look at the tidal slowing down of the moon by combining the moon's observations with observations of the sun's and Mercury's positions.

Figure 8-12 shows how this combined data looks. The curve is a parabolic arc without fluctuations, the irregularities in the earth's rotation having been taken out. From this curve, one can determine the rate at which the moon has been slowing as a result of the effect of tidal interac-tions only. The tidal effects can be computed directly from the observa-tions.

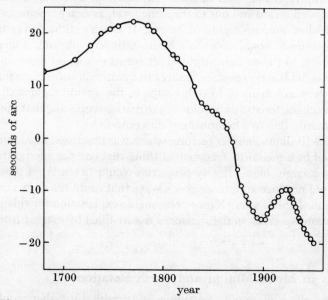

Figure 8-11 The discrepancy $f(T)$ of the moon's longitude based on occula-tions (after Munk and MacDonald[12]).

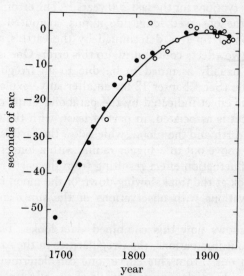

Figure 8-12 Weighted discrepancy differences: o for the sun, • for Mer-cury (prior to 1740 these depend on the extrapolated longitude of the sun) (from Munk and MacDonald[12]).

This slowing of the moon's motion, owing to a tidal interaction with the earth, implies also slowing of the earth's rotation. This is not the only tidal interaction with the earth's rotation that requires notice. There are other tidal effects one needs besides this. Two other tidal interactions affect the earth's rotation rate. In addition to the tidal coupling of the moon with the earth, the tides raised on the earth by the sun affect the earth's rotation. Also there is the atmospheric tidal couple. As mentioned above, from telescopic observations one can obtain the tidal slowing of the moon's motion and the resultant slowing of the earth's rotation rate. Assuming that the tidal slowing of the earth's rotation is proportional to the tidal driving force, the tidal slowing of the earth as a result of the sun can be computed. Also the measured atmospheric-pressure fluctuations allow the atmospheric tidal speeding of the earth's rotation rate to be computed. Combining all these effects, we can compute the expected slowing of the earth's rotation rate from all the tidal interactions.

There is another expected effect on the earth's rotation rate connected with the fluctuation of sea level. Figure 8-13, taken from Fairbridge,[13] shows the kind of data that one has on sea-level fluctuation that would have affected the moment of inertia of the earth. The sea level in the past is determined by radiocarbon dating of coastal shells. The old eclipse observations on the earth's rotation rate are primarily in the period when the sea

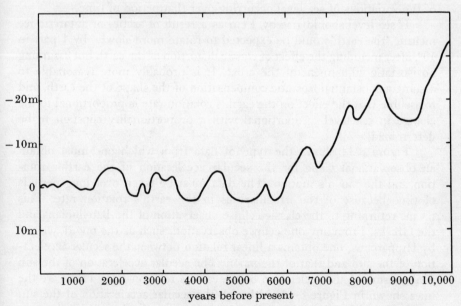

Figure 8-13 Historical variation in sea level in meters (from Fairbridge[13]).

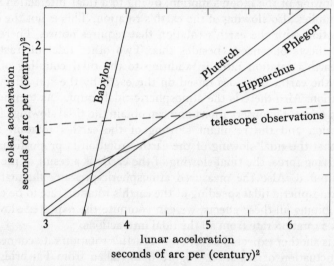

Figure 8-14 Fotheringham's[14] summary of consistent values of $f_{\mathbb{)}}/T^2$ and $f_{\odot}/T^2$ for the best of various ancient solar eclipses.

level was most rapidly changing. So we should take into account the effects of the variations of sea level occurring over that period of time.

If sea level should rise by 1 cm as a result of arctic- or antarctic-ice melting, the earth would be expected to rotate more slowly, by 1 part in 10^9, after including the effect of elastic distortion of the earth but assuming no isostatic adjustment of the crust. It is probably more reasonable to assume a substantial isostatic compensation of the shape of the earth, and to assume that the effect on the earth's rotation rate is proportional to the change in sea level, proportional with a proportionality constant to be determined.

Figure 8-14 shows the type of data from which one must obtain an observational value for the secular acceleration of the earth's rotation and the moon's motion. The data must be taken over long periods of time because of the irregularities in the earth's rotation rate. This means returning to the classic eclipse observation of the Babylonians and the Greeks. From any one eclipse observation, such as the one described by Hipparchus, one obtains a linear relation between the secular acceleration of the sun and that of the moon. The secular acceleration of the sun is a measure of the acceleration of the earth's rotation rate. These are the lines shown in Figure 8-14. Although the secular acceleration of the sun is a measure of the earth's rotational acceleration, the moon's acceleration is due to both effects, and acceleration of the moon and a slowing of the clock given by the earth's rotation.

In the framework of this analysis, a gradual slowing of the moon's motion and planetary motion, owing to a gradual weakening of the gravitational interaction, would appear as an unexplained residual speeding of the earth's rotation rate, after one makes allowances for all known effects on the earth's rotation. By combining modern telescope observations and the information obtained from these eclipse observations, one can get a secular acceleration for the sun and hence an effective average acceleration of the earth's rotation. The subtraction from this of the three tidal accelerations determined from the telescope observation and barometric-pressure fluctuation yields a residual discrepancy that is just about the right size to be a consequence of gravity getting weaker. It is found that the four best eclipse observations considered by Fotheringham, the only ones really worth discussing, are made more consistent if an allowance for sea-level fluctuations is included. The resulting derived proportionality between sea-level variation and the earth's rotation rate allows correction for sea-level fluctuations to be included. After this correction is included, the earth's rotation rate exhibits an even larger residual acceleration.

Unfortunately, there is one thing that we cannot really be sure about, and that is what the earth's core has been doing. The earth's core could have coupled with the mantle over a very long period of time, transferring momentum from the core to the rest of the earth. However, the westward drift of the earth's magnetic field suggests that the core is rotating more slowly, not more rapidly. One would expect the magnetic interaction (through induced eddy currents in the mantle) to slow the earth's rotation, not to speed it.

A Mechanism for Sustaining the Magnetic Field of Jupiter

I would like to mention one more place where it seems to me there might be a quite interesting effect. This is an effect connected with Jupiter's interior.

There may be a real problem of accounting for the magnetic field of Jupiter. The relaxation time for an electric current in the interior of Jupiter to die out is sufficiently short that Jupiter should not have a primordial magnetic field left over. One must account for Jupiter's magnetic field in terms of a mechanism presently stirring up the interior in a magnetohydrodynamic way that generates this magnetic field. The energy required to do this appears quite large. This is because the deep interior of Jupiter is, as far as one can tell, hydrogen in a degenerate form. It has a very good thermal conductivity. Therefore, it is quite difficult to drive mass convective currents with heat flow. Although convection in the outer part may be possible, this part is probably not a good electric conductor.

It is possible that there might be a nondegenerate solid core of heavy elements a few times the earth's mass. This is the suggestion of DeMarcus. Even with all the radioactivity that might be in such a core, it is quite difficult to get a large enough heat flow to produce temperature gradients sufficient for convection in the outer part of the metallic hydrogen phase.

It is conceivable that the field is produced in an iron inner core. But this does not fit what we know about Jupiter's magnetic field. The radio measurements suggest that the field is nothing like a centered dipole magnetic field. It appears to be way off to one side, and rather localized. Hence it is not likely that the magnetic field is produced at the center.

A varying gravitational constant provides a possible mechanism for driving currents outside the core. This depends on the existence of a phase change going from degenerate to nondegenerate hydrogen at some distance from the center, 0.6 or 0.7 of the radius of Jupiter. If G changes, the radius at which the phase change occurs should change as well. The radius of the phase discontinuity and the resulting discontinuity in density should move steadily inward as gravitation weakens.

This density change leads to a difference in the rotation rate of the inner part of Jupiter, relative to the outer part. The moment of inertia of the material involved in the phase change does not scale properly to maintain rigid-body rotation. Conservation of momentum leads to the inner part rotating more rapidly than the outer part.

How much energy is available from this? J. Peebles has investigated this point and finds that it could be substantially more than the energy that is available from radioactivity. This energy would be made available by some mechanism of damping out the differential rotation through magnetic coupling between the two conducting shells. Furthermore, this mechanism provides a shearing motion for the production of a magnetic field.

Magnetic-field lines cutting through the radius of phase change would be stretched out, wound like yarn on a ball, until magnetic pressure and tension effects become important. The resulting magnetic forces and tangle of magnetic-field lines could induce turbulence in the boundary region.

It is quite conceivable that, if anything like this should occur, it could be an important mechanism for stirring up the interior of Jupiter by producing a differential rotation of the interior.

I cannot give a detailed mechanism for the production of a magnetic field in this manner. It is difficult to understand how a magnetic field is sustained in any celestial body. But I could conceive of a situation in which this shear motion could be coupled to a nonaxially symmetric magnetic field. This might involve convective eddies and turbulent eddies, in the shear region (Figure 8-15).

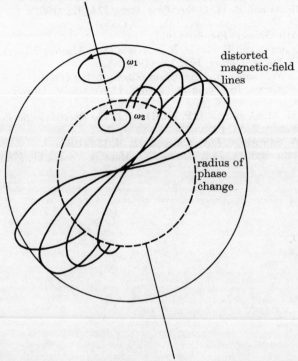

Figure 8-15 Schematic diagram of possible magnetic-field generation in Jupiter resulting from differential rotation.

It is interesting and may be significant that Jupiter does exhibit various rotation rates. The observable features seem to rotate at various rates depending upon latitudes. Also the magnetic field has its own characteristic, well-defined rotation rate, about the same as high-latitude visual features.

The effects I have discussed in this lecture do not demonstrate the existence of a time-varying gravitational constant, nor do any effects that I have been able to think of rule out such a variation. Rather, in many cases, a varying G provides a possible explanation for some little-understood features of astronomy and geophysics.

References
1. P. A. M. Dirac, *Proc. Roy. Soc.* (*London*), **A165**, 199 (1938).
2. P. Jordan, *Schwerkraft und Weltall*, Vieweg and Sohn, Brunswick, 1955.
3. J. Peebles and R. H. Dicke, *Phys. Rev.*, **127**, 629, (1962).

4. J. Peebles, *Ann. Phys.*, **20,** 240 (1962).

5. C. Brans and R. H. Dicke, *Phys. Rev.*, **124,** 925 (1961).

6. R. H. Dicke, *Phys. Rev.*, **125,** 2163 (1962).

7. H. Arp, *Science*, **134,** 810 (1961).

8. J. Crampin and F. Hoyle, *Roy. Astron. Soc. Monthly Notices*, **122,** 27 (1961).

9. R. H. Dicke, *Nature*, **194,** 329 (1962).

10. A. G. W. Cameron, *Phys. Chem. Earth*, **3,** 199 (1960).

11. W. S. Carey, In *Continental Drift: A Symposium*, University of Tasmania, 1958, p. 177.

12. W. H. Munk and G. J. F. MacDonald, *The Rotation of the Earth*, Cambridge University Press, 1960.

13. R. W. Fairbridge, *Phys. Chem. Earth*, **4,** 158 (1961).

14. J. Fotheringham, *Roy. Astron. Soc. Monthly Notices*, **80,** 578 (1920).

9

Relativity principles and the role of coordinates in physics

J. L. Anderson

The Idea of a Relativity Principle

It is generally agreed that two principles play a role in the formulation of the general theory of relativity. One of these, the principle of equivalence is usually accepted without question. The other, the principle of general relativity (or, as it is sometimes called, the principle of general covariance), on the other hand, has served as a topic of heated discussion ever since it was first put forward by Einstein in 1915. Kretchmann[1] was the first to raise objections to the principle and, more recently, the question has again been discussed quite forcibly by Fock in his recent book.[2]

The principle of general relativity is essentially the statement of certain invariance properties of a class of physical theories and is therefore of interest to the theoretical physicist for several reasons. Perhaps most important, an invariance principle associated with a group of transformations usually implies a limitation on the possible types of theories that one can formulate which satisfy it. Therefore, it will be of interest to examine the principle and to find limitations that it imposes on the possible forms for the equations of general relativity.

In 1918, Noether[3] showed that there is a very close relation between the invariance properties of a given theory whose equations of motion are derivable from a variational principle and the conservation laws of that theory. Consider first a theory that is invariant with respect to a group whose elements are specified by a finite number of parameters, that is, a Lie group. In this case, for every parameter there is an equation of continuity that is satisfied by real motions of the system. Furthermore, if the system is in some sense closed, one can convert this equation of continuity

175

into a conservation law, i.e., a statement that some dynamical variable is a constant of the motion.

If the invariance of the theory is with respect to a group whose elements are specified by one or more arbitrary space-time functions such as the gauge group of electrodynamics or the group of arbitrary coordinate transformations of general relativity, the relationship is not so clear. There is an equation of continuity corresponding to every arbitrary function. Now, however, these equations are identities; they are satisfied by the variables of the theory whether they describe a real motion of the system or not. Although it is possible to obtain from these identities a large number of continuity equations which are satisfied only for real motions of the system, they do not appear to lead to conserved quantities except in very special cases. A better understanding of the invariance properties of a theory may lead us to a better understanding of this type of conservation law.

Finally, as we shall see, the principle of general relativity is intimately related to the coordinatization of the underlying space-time manifold and hence may shed some light on the role which coordinates and the process of coordinatization of a manifold play in physics.

Two Formulations of the Principle of Special Relativity

Before we begin our discussion of the principle of general relativity it will prove helpful to discuss briefly a more familiar principle, that of special relativity. Even here things are not as straightforward as some books would make us believe. The basic intuitive idea is simple enough; we should not be able to distinguish between the totality of frames of reference moving uniformly and rectilinearly, with respect to each other, by any physical means. The difficulty with this definition lies in the apparently innocent phrase, "by any physical means." Almost any physical system, such as a box of gas or an electron, does in fact allow us to single out a particular reference frame among the totality of all those moving uniformly with respect to each other, namely, the frame in which it is at rest. Let us try to be more explicit about the term "physical means."

Imagine two identically constructed systems, such as two electrons or two identical boxes of gas, moving uniformly with respect to each other. Call them system A and B, respectively. We now imagine two observers or frames of reference, A and B, such that the system A is at rest in frame A and system B is at rest in frame B. Then the principle of special relativity requires that, if the initial state of system *as seen by observer A* is the same as the state of system B *as seen by observer B*, the final state of system A, as seen by observer A, will be the same as the final state of system B, as seen by observer B. Note that observer A never looks at system

B and vice versa; they merely compare results of what they see their own systems doing. If observer A were able to make measurements on system B he would, in general, obtain entirely different results from those obtained by observer B from system B. It is in the sense used above that we are to interpret the term physical means in our first formulation of the special-relativity principle. We can then rephrase our original statement so as to read: There exists no physical system or state of that system that will behave in different ways when placed in one or another of a collection of frames of reference moving uniformly with respect to each other.

There is another formulation of the principle that, at first sight, appears to be fundamentally different from the first. It asserts that the laws of physics can be put into a form that remains unchanged when the various quantities appearing therein are subjected to a Lorentz transformation. In order to be able to refer to it readily, we shall call this the principle of special convariance. In the first formulation there is no mention of how the various physical quantities transform under Lorentz transformations; we did not even mention Lorentz transformations. In fact, it is not always clear that it is meaningful to talk about the Lorentz transformation of a particular physical quantity.

To understand the distinction between the two formulations, let us consider two different physical systems and the laws associated with them. One system will be the electromagnetic field, the other a box of hydrogen gas. The laws associated with the electromagnetic field are of course Maxwell's equations. They apply to all conceivable electromagnetic fields: to the field of an electron at rest with respect to an observer as well as one moving uniformly, or even arbitrarily, with respect to the observer. Furthermore, the way in which the electromagnetic field is measured is independent of the particular field being measured. If we want to know the electric field at a point, we would hold a small test body there and measure the force on it. Another observer, moving uniformly with respect to the first, would measure the electric field he sees in exactly the same way. It is therefore meaningful to ask for the relation between the two measurements of the same field. It is a relation that, in principle, could be verified by observation. Let us now see how our two formulations of the principle of special relativity apply to the electromagnetic field and Maxwell's equations.

For our two systems in the first formulation, we could take an electron at rest with respect to A and another at rest with respect to B. All that is required is that the field measured by observer A, owing to electron a, be the same as the field measured by observer B, resulting from electron b. However, since both observers are able to measure any and all electromagnetic fields, we could interchange the roles of the electrons. A's system would then be an electron at rest with respect to observer B, whereas B's system would be an electron at rest with respect to observer A. And again, the field that A measures should be the same as that which B measures. A similar duality holds for any system of charges and fields. Since a physical law is a statement about the behavior of a collection of physical systems, all of which possess some common properties (in fact, the physical law is just a statement of these common properties) and since all of the electromagnetic systems that A observes are identical with the totality of electromagnetic systems that B observes, it follows that the physical laws governing these systems as formulated by B in terms of the fields he measures must be the same as those formulated by A in terms of the fields he measures in order that the principle of special relativity holds. Furthermore, since it is meaningful to talk about the relation between the values that A would measure for a particular field and those that B would measure for the same field, we can talk about the transformation of the laws that A has formulated into the laws that B has formulated. Since the two sets of laws have the same form, the transformation between the two fields must be such as to preserve this form. In this way, we are led to the statement of special covariance as we formulated it above. As we well know, it is just the Lorentz transformations that maintain the form of Maxwell's equations and not the Galilean transformations, although our first formulation of the principle of special relativity was equally applicable to both types of transformations.

Let me summarize what I have said concerning the electromagnetic field. Observer A looks at the totality of all electromagnetic fields and finds that they satisfy a set of laws that can be written in the form

$$F_{A,\nu}^{\mu\nu} = -j_A^\mu \tag{1}$$

and

$$F_{A\mu\nu,\rho} = 0 \tag{2}$$

where $F_A{}^{\mu\nu}$ is the usual antisymmetric matrix constructed from $\mathbf{E}_A$ and $\mathbf{B}_A$, the electric and magnetic fields, respectively, measured by A. j_A^μ is a column matrix constructed from the current and charge densities measured by A. I call these quantities matrices since, at this point, I wish to specify only their algebraic and not their transformation properties. Similarly, observer B looks at the totality of all electromagnetic fields and finds that they satisfy a set of laws that, if the principle of special relativity is to hold, must perforce have the same form as Eqs. (1) and (2) except that the subscript A is replaced by subscript B. Now, since the collection of fields that A measures to verify Eqs. (1) and (2) is the same as the collection of fields that B uses there must exist a relation between $F_A{}^{\mu\nu}$ and $F_B{}^{\mu\nu}$ as well as between the spatial and temporal measurements of A and B such that, when we substitute into Eqs. (1) and (2) for the quantities measured by A

in terms of the quantities measured by B, we obtain the correct equations satisfied by the B quantities. Poincaré[4] and Einstein[5] derived the correct transformation equations relating the A and B quantities. For spatial and temporal measurements they are

$$x_B^\mu = \alpha_\nu^\mu x_A^\nu + b^\mu \tag{3}$$

where the b^μ are a set of four numbers and α_ν^μ is a matrix satisfying the conditions

$$\alpha_\rho^\mu \alpha_\sigma^\nu \eta_{\mu\nu} = \eta_{\rho\sigma} \tag{4}$$

where $\eta_{\mu\nu}$ is the Minkowski metric in Cartesian coordinates and is given by

$$\eta_{\mu\nu} = \begin{pmatrix} -1 & 0 & 0 & 0 \\ 0 & -1 & 0 & 0 \\ 0 & 0 & -1 & 0 \\ 0 & 0 & 0 & 1 \end{pmatrix} \tag{5}$$

The fields are then related by

$$F_B^{\mu\nu} = \alpha_\rho^\mu \alpha_\sigma^\nu F_A^{\rho\sigma} \tag{6}$$

Let us emphasize again that the transformation equations, (3) and (6), although derived from the condition that the Maxwell equations (1) and (2) maintain their form when subjected to these transformations, are, in principle at least, subject to direct experimental verification. We see thus that electromagnetic fields satisfy both statements of the principle of special relativity.

Let us now consider the case in which the systems to be examined are boxes of gas. Observer A looks at all possible states of the gas for which he can measure thermodynamic quantities such as temperature, pressure, and entropy, and deduces from his measurements that the first and second laws of thermodynamics apply to these states of the gas. Similarly, B looks at his boxes of gas and, if the principle of special relativity holds, must find that the thermodynamic quantities he measures must also satisfy the two laws of thermodynamics in exactly the same form as found by A.

There is, however, an essential difference between the electrodynamic and thermodynamic cases. Thermodynamic quantities only have meaning in the rest frame of the system being observed. Thus, any measurement of the temperature of a gas streaming uniformly past the observer or, what is the same thing, for the observer to measure the temperature while holding a thermometer in his hand and running past the gas will, in general, depend on the kind of thermometer employed, how it is orientated with respect to the direction of motion, etc. This is not to say that an observer could not infer from measurements on a moving system what its rest temperature is. The point is that he must interpret these measurements in terms of the rest temperature of the system, since this quantity alone depends on thermodynamic state of the system. It is therefore not physically meaningful to talk about the transformation properties of thermodynamic quantities since such transformations could never, even in principle, be verified by observation. Thus the requirement of special covariance, as applied to thermodynamic systems, is without physical content. Although it is possible to *define* transformation laws for thermodynamic quantities so that the laws of thermodynamics retain their form when subjected to these transformations and so thereby formally conform to the requirement of special covariance, such a procedure is without physical content. Formulating thermodynamics in a special covariant form was actually carried out by Planck[6] and Einstein[7] and later elaborated upon by Tolman.[8]

Even though the formulation of thermodynamics in the sense outlined above is without physical content, I should point out that the relativistic treatment of an ideal gas is another matter altogether. Here we do not ask about the transformation properties of the various thermodynamic quantities; it is assumed that we always work in the rest frame of the gas. However, we ask for the modifications in the equations of state for the gas when the molecules or atoms comprising it are moving at relativistic velocities. Jüttner[9] was the first to work out the case for an ideal, relativistic gas. He proceded by calculating the partition function Z given by

$$Z = e^{-H/kT} \, dx_1 \cdots dx_{2N} \tag{7}$$

where H is the energy of the system and is a function of the $2N$ variables $x_1,..., x_{2N}$. This is the usual expression for the partition function as found in all books on statistical mechanics. Now however, instead of taking H to be $\sum_i (1/2)p^2$ for an ideal gas, Jüttner used the relativistic expression

$$H = \sum_i (m_0^2 c^4 + c^2 \mathbf{p}_i^2)^{1/2} \tag{8}$$

Thermodynamic quantities such as pressure and internal energy are derived in the usual manner by taking appropriate derivatives of $(\ln Z)/kT$. Notice that there is no attempt to modify the usual nonrelativistic formulation of statistical mechanics. It may conceivably require modification when we deal with systems whose components are moving with relativistic velocities, but the principle of special relativity offers us no clue as to the nature of the modification. The only thing it suggests is that we replace the nonrelativistic expression for H by the relativistic one given in Eq. (8).

What morals can we deduce concerning the principle of special relativity from our considerations above? Above all we must conclude that it is not so much a statement about the various physical systems that can exist in the space-time manifold. It says very little about physical systems and the form of the laws that are to describe them. This is especially true for the case of systems that uniquely define a rest frame, such as our box of gas did. There our first formulation told us nothing and our second formulation was satisfied in a trivial, nonphysical way by merely requiring that the various thermodynamic quantities transform in a manner so as to preserve the form of the laws of thermodynamics. Even for systems exemplified by the electromagnetic field, where there are no restrictions on which fields can be measured by which observers, the principle tells us very little unless we add the additional requirement that the laws should be *local* laws (that is, they should be capable of verification solely by means of measurements made in the immediate neighborhood of a point) and that the transformation laws between the physical quantities appearing in these laws should also be local in the same sense. If we further restrict our systems by requiring that the transformation laws between the quantities appearing therein should be linear and homogeneous (i.e., the quantities should transform as tensors, or tensor densities, spinors, etc.), then we very seriously restrict the possible types of systems and physical laws that can occur in nature.

We shall conclude this discussion of special relativity with a reformulation in geometric terms. We note first that, as a consequence of the axiom that the velocity of light is independent of the motion of the source, we can conclude that at every point of the space-time manifold there is an invariant geometric object, the light cone. Such an object would exist in a metric geometry and would consist of the locus of all points in the neighborhood of a given point that are at light-like distances with respect to it. Thus, if x^μ are the coordinates of the point in question, all other points $(x^\mu + dx^\mu)$ on the light cone originating from x^μ satisfy

$$ds^2 = g_{\mu\nu}(x) \, dx^\mu \, dx^\nu = 0 \tag{9}$$

where $g_{\mu\nu}(x)$ is the metric at the point x^μ. The principle of special relativity then asserts that the space-time geometry is homogeneous and isotropic. Hence there exists a ten-parameter group of motions which leaves the value of the metric unchanged in the sense described in Chapter 2 on Riemannian geometry. As a consequence we can conclude that the geometry is a flat geometry so that the curvature tensor satisfies

$$R_{\mu\nu\rho\sigma} = 0 \tag{10}$$

everywhere. Hence we can always find a coordinate system in which the metric is everywhere equal to the matrix $\eta_{\mu\nu}$, whose components are given by Eq. (5). The motions admitted by the geometry have, in this coordinate system, the form given by Eq. (3). Physical objects are then represented by geometric objects in this Minkowskian geometry, and physical laws are then statements of relations that exist between the various geometric objects. Of particular interest for physics are the local geometric objects that have linear, homogeneous transformation laws and the local relations that one can construct between them. We should emphasize that all our statements are geometric in nature and hold independent of the particular coordinate system actually employed.

General Covariance: a Trivial Extension

Let me now go on to the general theory of relativity. As I mentioned in the beginning of this talk, there are still many disparate views on the subject. Fock[2] has gone so far as to proclaim that, "As for the 'general Principle of Relativity,' no such principle exists," and that there is less relativity in "general relativity" than in special relativity. He bases his contention on the fact that, whereas the flat space-time geometry of Minkowski admits a ten-parameter group of motions whose group is just the Lorentz group, a general Riemannian metric may have no motions at all associated with it. Although this is true, it is not at all pertinent since, in the general theory, the metric is no longer taken to be given *a priori* as in the case of special relativity but is to be considered a dynamic quantity along with the other fields of nature. In fact, as we shall see, it is just the requirement of general relativity that forces us to treat the metric in this manner. Fock's objection is then equivalent to asserting that electrodynamics does not satisfy the principle of special relativity because the field of an electron depends upon the state of motion of the observer with respect to the electron. In other words, a particular metric is no more a law of nature in general relativity than is a particular electromagnetic field in special relativity.

As in special relativity, there are really two different formulations of the principle of general relativity. One formulation is analogous to our requirement of special covariance. We shall call it the principle of general covariance. It states that the laws of physics can be put into a form that remains unchanged when the various quantities appearing therein are subjected to an arbitrary coordinate transformation. And, like the principle of special covariance, the principle of general covariance is, by itself, devoid of physical content. Thus it has been argued, as an objection to the principle, that any system of equations, which are invariant in the sense defined by special relativity, can be put into what appears to be a generally covariant form by performing a coordinate transformation from a Cartesian coordinate system where $g_{\mu\nu} = \eta_{\mu\nu}$ to an arbitrary coordinate system where the metric will now be some space-time function. Thus we can rewrite our laws by replacing $\eta_{\mu\nu}$ by $g_{\mu\nu}$, replacing ordinary derivatives by covariant derivatives, and appending the Eqs. (10) for determining the metric. However, we have introduced the general metric in a rather trivial way, which adds no physical content to the theory. Adding physical content to the theory would require generalizing the $g_{\mu\nu}$ to include nonflat metrics for which Eq. (10) is not satisfied (that is, those not obtainable from the $\eta_{\mu\nu}$ by coordinate transformation).

There is another example of this kind of trivial extension of a theory that has a bearing on a proposal of Sakurai[10] to explain the strong coupling of strange particles. We know that the Dirac theory of the electron is invariant with respect to the group of gauge transformations of the first kind:

$$\psi^{*\prime} = e^{-i\alpha}\psi^*$$
$$\psi' = e^{i\alpha}\psi \tag{11}$$

where α is a constant. As a consequence of Noether's theorem[3] mentioned above, there is a current j^μ associated with the theory given by

$$j^\mu = -i\eta^{\mu\nu}(\psi^*\psi_{,\nu} - \psi\psi^*_{,\nu}) \tag{12}$$

which satisfies the conservation law

$$j^\mu_{,\mu} = 0 \tag{13}$$

for those spinor fields ψ that satisfy the Dirac equation.

We can, in complete analogy with the passage from Cartesian to arbitrary coordinates, enlarge the group by letting α be a general space-time function. The spinor fields will still be assumed to transform according to Eq. (11). We find that the transformed Lagrangian does not retain its form under this transformation but rather adds a term of the form

$$\int d^4x \, \alpha_{,\mu} j^\mu$$

We can compensate for this additional term by introducing a new field A_μ which transforms according to

$$A'_\mu = A_\mu + \alpha_{,\mu} \tag{14}$$

and adding a term,

$$-\int d^4x \, A_\mu j^\mu$$

to the Lagrangian. Then, in analogy to Eq. (10), we can require that A_μ satisfies the equations

$$F_{\mu\nu} \equiv A_{\mu,\nu} - A_{\nu,\mu} = 0 \tag{15}$$

These equations imply that A_μ can always be written in the form

$$A_\mu = \phi_{,\mu} \tag{16}$$

where ϕ is some space-time function. Consequently, we can always perform a gauge transformation leading to a new set of potentials $A'_\mu = 0$ by taking for α in Eqs. (11) and (14) the function $-\phi$ just as, in the relativistic case, we could always find a coordinate system in which $g_{\mu\nu} = \eta_{\mu\nu}$ for $g_{\mu\nu}$ satisfying Eq. (10). Again we have formally enlarged the covariance group of the theory without adding any new content to the theory. Furthermore, one can show that there is no enlargement of the conservation laws associated with the theory. This possibility of formally enlarging the covariance group of a theory from a finite-parameter Lie group to one involving a number of arbitrary functions apparently always exists. Because of this possibility, we see that there is not a one-to-one correspondence between the relativity principle for a given class of theories and their corresponding covariance group.

Kretchmann's Criterion for Obtaining Relativity Principle from Covariance Group

The question of the relation between the covariance group and the relativity principle of a theory has been raised since the early days of relativity theory. Kretchmann[1] proposed an answer that I would like to discuss briefly since it is often quoted in connection with this question and also because it is related to the role of coordinates in physics. Kretchmann said, in effect: In order to find the relativity principle associated with a given covariance group, one must find out how far he can restrict the covariance group by the imposition of noncovariant restrictions on the objects appearing in the theory without, at the same time, restricting the physical possibilities admitted by the original formulation. When one has restricted the covariance group in this fashion as much as possible, he will be left with some subgroup of the original covariance group. This subgroup is then defined to be the transformation group of the relativity principle.

As examples of such restrictions let me mention the gauge conditions of electrodynamics and the coordinate conditions of general relativity. In electrodynamics, we can limit the gauge transformations to those of the first kind where α is a constant by imposing, for example, the Coulomb gauge condition $\nabla \cdot \mathbf{A} = 0$. Kretchmann investigated to what extent it is possible to limit the group of all coordinate transformations. He proposed first a set of coordinate conditions that have lately been rediscovered by Komar[11] and used extensively by him and Bergmann in their discussion of the quantization of general relativity. These coordinate conditions are obtained by first constructing the 14 possible scalars that can be formed using only the metric and its first and second derivatives. For a metric that satisfies the equation of general relativity in absence of matter, $R_{\mu\nu} = g^{\rho\sigma}R_{\rho\mu\sigma\nu} = 0$, all but four of these scalars are zero. The four nonzero scalars in general have different values at different space-time points except in cases where the metric has associated with it a group of symmetries or of motions. (This concept of motion has been discussed in detail in Chapter 2.) Except in these cases, one can then use the values of the scalars at a point to serve as the coordinates of the point. These are the coordinate conditions that Kretchmann used. For the general situation there are no coordinate transformations that maintain the Kretchmann coordinate conditions. Hence he concluded that there is no relativity principle in general relativity.

Actually, Kretchmann's criterion is not a very good one for determining when a theory admits a relativity principle. For instance, if this criterion is applied to special relativity, one can limit the group of Lorentz transformations to be the identity element by non-Lorentz covariant restrictions. Hence one would conclude that there is no relativity principle in special relativity either. For example, we can destroy the special covariance of a theory like that of Maxwell's by imposing restrictions on the electromagnetic field. We could locate the origin of the reference frame by imposing conditions on the first moments of the total energy. Additional conditions could be used to fix the orientation of the axis. One can always find a Lorentz frame in which these conditions are satisfied unless the particular field we are looking at possesses some symmetry itself. In a similar manner, we can fix the α in the gauge transformation (11) by requiring, for instance, that $\psi^*(0)/\psi(0) = 1$.

Another Approach to the Relativity Principle; Absolute and Dynamic Elements of a Theory

What criterion, then, can we use to find the relativity principle for a given class of theories? I shall try to answer this question by first comparing the situation in which we have enlarged the covariance group of a theory without changing the physical content to the situation in which we also change the physical content. In the case of the Dirac field, we were able to enlarge the gauge transformations from those in which α was a constant to those in which it is an arbitrary space-time function. This enlargement brought in the new field A_μ, which we then required to satisfy Eq. (15). This enlargement of the theory does not change the physical situation. On the other hand, we could have required that A_μ satisfy the equations

$$F^{\mu\nu}{}_{,\nu} \equiv (A_{\mu,\nu} - A_{\nu,\mu})_{,\nu} = -j^\mu \qquad (17)$$

where j^μ is given by Eq. (12). This enlargement does change the physical content of the theory.

Similarly, we enlarged the covariance group from Lorentz to arbitrary-coordinate transformations and thereby introduced the metric as an additional element to be determined. Our requirement that it satisfy Eq. (10) introduced no new physics, since any metric that satisfies these equations is necessarily a flat metric of special relativity. We introduce new physics by requiring the metric to satisfy the Einstein field equation.

$$R^{\mu\nu} - \tfrac{1}{2}g^{\mu\nu}R = -T^{\mu\nu} \tag{18}$$

where $T^{\mu\nu}$ is the energy-momentum tensor associated with the other fields and particles of the theory.

In both the electromagnetic and the gravitation cases, the difference in the two extensions of the theory is apparent. In the case where we use Eq. (10) for the metric or Eq. (15) for A_μ, these variables are not dynamic objects, whereas in the case of Eqs. (17) and (18) they are. In the first case their determination is entirely independent of the other physical objects of the theory; in the latter case this is no longer true.

In order to make more precise these differences, I would like to distinguish between two different types of elements that may appear in a physical theory: absolute elements and dynamic elements. This distinction will prove important, since we shall use the absolute elements of a theory to define the relativity principle associated with the theory. Let me first say how one can determine the absolute elements of a theory.

Suppose that the theory is given as a set of functional relations

$$\mathscr{L}_i(y_A) = 0 \tag{19}$$

between the independent variables y_A of the theory. Furthermore, suppose that Eq. (19) has associated with it a particular covariance group of transformations. We now look at all the invariant functions that we can form with various subsets of the y's. By an invariant function, I mean one whose value does not depend upon a particular choice of gauge or coordinate system. In electrodynamics, the $F^{\mu\nu}$ are invariant functions of the A^μ. For the group of all curvilinear coordinate transformations of general relativity, invariants are more difficult to construct. By itself, a scalar-field variable is not an invariant. It becomes an invariant only if we give an invariant prescription for locating the point at which the scalar is to be evaluated. If the values of the invariant functions formed from a given subset are uniquely determined as a consequence of Eq. (19) and nothing more (for example, the remaining y's, boundary conditions, initial conditions, etc.), then the y's that make up this subset constitute an absolute element of the theory. Of course, these y's themselves are not generally invariant under the covariance group.

The test for absolute elements is not as difficult as it first might seem. To know if a particular subset forms an absolute element, we need only to construct, at most, as many independent invariants as there are members of the subset in question. If they are all determined uniquely, any other invariants formed from the subset will also be uniquely determined since they will be functions of these original invariants. Furthermore, it will usually be quite obvious for a particular theory what subsets form invariant elements.

In the theory with $F_{\mu\nu} = 0$, the A_μ are uniquely determined up to a gauge transformation, and hence any invariant formed from them is uniquely determined. Thus they form an absolute element. They do not form an absolute element when the customary Maxwell's equations (17) are assumed to hold. This is because the A's can be determined from Maxwell's equations only with the knowledge of the source currents and boundary conditions in addition to a knowledge of the gauge. Similarly, when $R_{\mu\nu\rho\sigma} = 0$, the $g_{\mu\nu}$ form an absolute object since they are uniquely determined up to an arbitrary coordinate transformation. But this is not the case when the g's are assumed to satisfy the Einstein equation (18).

As another example of a theory with absolute elements, I shall give one that was proposed in the early days of relativity as an alternate possible gravity theory. It required that the metric satisfy the equations

$$C_{\mu\nu\rho\sigma} = 0 \tag{20}$$

and

$$R = 0 \tag{21}$$

where $C_{\mu\nu\rho\sigma}$ is the conformal or Weyl tensor formed from the metric and its first two derivatives and R is the curvature scalar. It can be shown that any metric that satisfies Eq. (20) is conformally flat; that is, it can, by means of a coordinate transformation, be made to take the form

$$g_{\mu\nu} = \gamma(x)\eta_{\mu\nu} \tag{22}$$

where $\gamma(x)$ is an arbitrary space-time function. Along with boundary and initial conditions, $\gamma(x)$ is determined by Eq. (21). This theory possesses a spherically symmetric static Schwarzschild-like solution, but it gives the wrong value for the advance of the perihelion of Mercury. If we introduce new variables $(\sqrt{-g})^{-1/2}g_{\mu\nu}$ and $\sqrt{-g}$, the $(\sqrt{-g})^{-1/2}g_{\mu\nu}$ form an absolute element. It is interesting to note that Eqs. (20) and (21), Einstein's equations (18), and the flat-space equations (10) are the only generally covariant, local, second order equations that one can require the metric to satisfy.

Having defined the absolute elements of a theory, we can now determine the relativity principle for the theory. We shall define the relativity group associated with the relativity principle as the subgroup of the covariance group of the theory which leaves the absolute elements of the theory invariant. If there are no absolute elements, the relativity group is identical with the covariance group.

If we apply this criterion to the two electromagnetic theories characterized by Eqs. (15) and Eqs. (17), we see that, in the former case, since A_μ

is an absolute element, the relativity group is just the totality of gauge transformations of the first kind with α a constant. In the latter case, A_μ is no longer an absolute element, and hence the relativity group is that of all gauge transformations with α an arbitrary space-time function. Similarly, when the metric satisfies $R_{\mu\nu\rho\sigma} = 0$ it is an absolute element, and the relativity group is the group of Lorentz transformations. When the metric satisfies Eq. (18), it is no longer an absolute element, and so the relativity group is then the group of all arbitrary coordinate transformations with nonvanishing determinant. We see that, with the above definition of a relativity group, we obtain the expected results in each of the cases discussed.

The Notion of Preferred Coordinates

I want to discuss the significance of relativity groups and absolute elements in physics. But first I would like to criticize the approach to "preferred" coordinate systems in general relativity* taken by Fock[2] and to comment on the relation of conservation laws to relativity groups. Fock has suggested that the harmonic coordinate conditions

$$\{\sqrt{-g}\, g^{\mu\nu}\}_{,\mu} = 0 \tag{23}$$

together with certain conditions at infinity, such as no incoming gravitational radiation, determine a preferred set of coordinate systems. To justify the term preferred for these systems, Fock asserts with the support of plausibility arguments that, in the case of an isolated system of masses, the harmonic conditions together with suitable supplementary conditions determine the coordinate system uniquely up to a Lorentz transformation. He also points out that the harmonic coordinates satisfy a linear, generally covariant equation. Fock further argues that:

> Only if the existence of such a coordinate system is recognized as reflecting certain intrinsic properties of space-time can one speak of the correctness of the heliocentric Copernican system in the same sense as this is possible in Newtonian mechanics. If this is not recognized, or if the existence of the preferred coordinates is denied, one is led to the inadmissible point of view that the heliocentric Copernican system and the geocentric Ptolemaic system are equivalent.

Although Fock implies that the existence of his preferred coordinates reflect some intrinsic properties of space-time, he has not said what these properties are or how they are related to the harmonic coordinate systems.

---

* I shall continue to use the term "general relativity" to describe Einstein's theory in spite of Fock's objections to the term. I believe that I have given a precise definition which makes the term meaningful.

As far as I can see, his arguments in favor of the harmonic coordinates are of the same nature as those that might induce us to call the Cartesian coordinate systems preferred in special relativity. Whereas it is certainly true that the use of Cartesian coordinates in special relativity simplifies many things, there is no *physical* reason why we cannot set up other coordinate systems. In fact we often do. For example, the hydrogen atom is best described in spherical coordinates. What is essential in all cases are the geometrical properties of the theory, e.g., the absolute elements, the relativity group, etc. As such, these properties can be expressed in any allowed reference frame. The particular frame chosen to express these properties has no physical significance but merely a matter of convenience. Similarly, in the case where A_μ satisfies $A_{\mu,\nu} - A_{\nu,\mu} = 0$, the gauge frame in which $A_\mu = 0$ might be preferred on the grounds of simplicity. But nothing is changed physically if we use some other gauge frame. In either case, the relativity group is the group of gauge transformations of the first kind. Only if there is some physical reason why we can only use one or another coordinate system is it meaningful to talk about a preferred system. Otherwise, one is forced to use the vague criterion of "most natural" or "simplest" in picking out a preferred system.

Invariance Properties and Conservation Laws

At the beginning of this discussion, I mentioned the relationship that exists between the invariance properties of a theory and the conservation laws associated with this theory. This relationship is revealed in the theorems of Noether.[3] Usually the results of the Noether theorems are given in two parts. One part applies to p-parameter Lie groups of transformations and the other to groups of transformations that depend upon q arbitrary functions of the space-time coordinates. Actually the two cases are not basically different, as Bergmann[12] showed, since any group of the second kind contains an infinity of one-parameter subgroups, generated by all possible sets of the q functions.

The statement of the Noether theorem follows: We are given a theory with a relativity group (in the sense in which we have used the term) that is a p-parameter Lie group G_p and whose equations of motion for the field variables y_A are derivable from a variational principle. If $\epsilon^i(i = 1,...,p)$ are the parameters of the G_p, there exists a number of quantities $t_i^\mu(\mu = 1, ..., 4)$ that satisfy p continuity equations of the form

$$t_{i,\mu}^{\mu} = 0 \tag{24}$$

whenever the equations of motion for the field variables are satisfied. This result only holds provided that the group G_p is a true relativity group associated with a relativity principle and does not arise as a consequence of the introduction of absolute elements into the theory. Thus, even though the group of general coordinate transformations contains an infinity of one-parameter Lie groups, they do not, in general, lead to continuity equations of the form (24) if the metric is an absolute element in the theory. Only the Lorentz group leads to continuity equations in special relativistic theories. In these cases, Eq. (24) expresses the conservation law for the stress-energy tensor.

The conservation equations (24) are, as I said, only satisfied by solutions of the equations of motion and as a consequence are sometimes called weak laws. If the theory has a relativity group whose transformations depend on a number of arbitrary space-time functions and if this group contains G_p as a subgroup, the conservation laws associated with G_p can be extended to strong laws that hold whether or not the equations of motion are satisfied. These laws are

$$\Theta^\mu_{i,\mu} \equiv 0 \tag{25}$$

As a consequence, one can infer the existence of a set of superpotentials $U^{\mu\nu}_i$ with the properties that

$$\Theta^\mu_i = U_i{}^{\mu\nu}{}_{,\nu} \tag{26}$$

and

$$U^{\mu\nu}_i = -U^{\nu\mu}_i \tag{27}$$

In electrodynamics, the superpotentials are just $F^{\rho\sigma}\xi$, where ξ is an arbitrary space-time function. Thus there exists an infinity of conservation laws

$$\Theta^\mu_{,\mu} \equiv 0 \tag{28}$$

where

$$\Theta^\mu = (F^{\mu\nu}\xi)_{,\nu} \tag{29}$$

To date, the only one of these conservation laws that can be given a simple interpretation is for the case when $\xi = 1$. Then, when the field equations are satisfied, $\Theta^\mu = j^\mu$, and we have the usual continuity equation for the current-density four-vector. It is possible to interpret some of the terms appearing in other Θ's in terms of higher electric and magnetic moments of the charge distribution, but it is not clear that they lead to anything useful.

In the case of general relativity, there again exists an infinity of super-potentials that, in turn, lead to a corresponding number of continuity equations. There are actually a number of alternate expressions for the superpotentials that differ from each other by quantities that are skew-symmetric in the upper two indices. One set of superpotentials is

$$U^{\mu\nu} = (16\pi\sqrt{-g})^{-1}g_{\kappa\lambda}\{g(g^{\mu\delta}g^{\nu\kappa} - g^{\nu\delta}g^{\mu\kappa})\}_{,\delta}\xi^\lambda \tag{30}$$

where the ξ^λ are four arbitrary space-time functions. These superpotentials can again be used to construct conserved currents $\Theta^\mu = U^{\mu\nu}{}_{,\nu}$. If, in a particular coordinate system, one lets each of the ξ^λ take on the value unity while the others are set equal to zero, he obtains four continuity equations

$$\Theta^\nu_{\mu,\nu} \equiv 0 \tag{31}$$

where

$$\Theta^\nu_\mu = t^\nu_\mu + T^\nu_\mu \tag{32}$$

Here T^ν_μ is the stress-energy tensor resulting from matter fields, etc., while t^ν_μ is the Einstein pseudotensor of stress-energy. The usual interpretation of t^ν_μ is that it represents the stress-energy of the gravitational field. However, it does not transform like a tensor density under arbitrary coordinate transformations and, in fact, is not even a geometric object. This fact has given rise to endless discussions of the role and meaning of energy in general relativity. It seems fairly clear by now that any attempt to single out, from the infinity of continuity equations that follow from the super-potentials $U^{\mu\nu}$ of Eq. (29), four special ones to describe energy and momentum conservation is doomed to failure. Only in very special cases where the metric admits a motion group is this possible.[13] The essential point is that in general relativity the relativity group of all coordinate transformations leads to an enlarged class of continuity equations as compared to the situation in special relativity. Whether all these continuity equations are meaningful and can be tested, in principle at least, by observation is still an open question. A definitive answer one way or the other would, of course, shed a great deal of additional light on the general relativity principle.

Implications of the Formulation of the Relativity Principle in Terms of Absolute and Dynamic Elements

I have indicated how the relativity principle associated with a particular theory is determined by the absolute elements of that theory. I would like to conclude this discussion with a few words about the inverse relation. It is clear that some such inverse relation must exist. Thus, if we insist that the group of all coordinate transformations is a relativity group rather than just a covariance group for the theory, we are forced to treat the metric as a dynamic, as opposed to absolute element, since no metric admits the group of all possible motions. The requirement that the group of all coordinate transformations be the relativity group of physics is thus by no means a trivial statement. If we add the requirement that the equations that determine the metric are local equations and are of second-differential order in the metric, then there is just one system of equations that satisfy these requirements, namely, Eqs. (18).

From what we have said, it appears that the relativity principle which one assumes determines the absolute elements of the theory and, at the same time, greatly restricts the class of possible theories one can construct consistent with this relativity principle. We are thus supplied with a very useful tool to guide us in formulating physical theories. In particular, the relativity principle helps us single out the absolute elements in a theory. Suppose that a given theory has an obvious relativity principle associated with it, such as in the case of special relativity, and that the associated relativity group is a subgroup of some larger group, for example the group of all coordinate transformations. Then, in general, it may be possible to reformulate the original theory so that its covariance group is the larger group. However, to do so we must introduce additional, absolute elements into the theory. Actually these elements were there in the first place, although their existence was masked by the fact that they had been assigned particular values. That is, the $g^{\mu\nu}$ are present in special relativity with the fixed preassigned values of the Minkowski metric. However, once we have called attention to their role as absolute elements in the theory, we can raise the general question of the validity of a theory that admits them in this role. To elaborate on this, I shall discuss a "general principle of reciprocity."

It is seen that the absolute elements effect the physical behavior of a system. That is, a different assignment of values to the absolute elements would change the physical behavior of the system. For instance, the assignment of different values to the metric might result in particle paths that are circles rather than straight lines. On the other hand, the physical behavior of a system does not affect the absolute elements. An absolute element in a theory indicates a lack of reciprocity; it can influence the physical behavior of the system but cannot, in turn, be influenced by this behavior. This lack of reciprocity seems to be fundamentally unreasonable and unsatisfactory. We may express the converse in what might be called a general principle of reciprocity: Each element of a physical theory is influenced by every other element. In accordance with this principle, a satisfactory theory should have no absolute elements. It was this dislike for absolute elements that in part led Einstein to treat the metric as a dynamic element and to deduce the equations of motion (18).

What then is the value of the notion of absolute elements for examining various physical theories? It can be used to judge a theory with regard to its satisfying the above principle of reciprocity. If it contains absolute elements, it is unsatisfactory in this respect. We must then extend the theory so that these elements become dynamic elements and the relativity group becomes the entire group of transformations. Then there should be no remaining absolute elements. We can use the fact that our new equations must be covariant with respect to the enlarged relativity group of transformations to help discover the form of these equations. If, further, we require that these equations be local in the sense that they can be verified by purely local means, we can restrict the possible equations to a very few.

I would like to illustrate the consequence of the above discussion in terms of the justification it provides for introducing the Yang and Mills[14] type of fields into physics. From our point of view, these fields are always present in a theory that is invariant with respect to rotations in isospace, but they are predetermined absolute elements. When we enlarge the covariance group to include the possibilities of different rotations in different directions at each space-time point, these fields appear explicitly but can be required to satisfy equations analogous to (15); this requirement does not change their status as absolute elements. If we demand that these fields be physical elements, we must extend the theory as Yang and Mills did. This example suggests that we should examine other transformation groups in physics to see if they can be embedded in some larger group. Then the theory that admits the original group as a relativity group can be made to admit the enlarged group as a covariance group with the addition of new elements into the theory. We could then ask if these new elements should remain as absolute elements or if, instead, the theory should be enlarged so that the covariance group becomes a relativity group and the absolute elements become dynamic elements.

Absolute Elements and Symmetries in Physics

I would like to conclude this discussion of relativity groups and absolute elements with a few comments on approximate symmetries and the strong interactions of strange particles. When we speak of a symmetry of a system we refer to a particular physical situation. It is something that, in principle at least, can be observed directly. Thus we speak of the spherical symmetry of the field of a point electron. As a consequence of Noether's theorem, there are a number of conserved quantities associated with this symmetry—for example, the angular momentum of a charged particle moving in a spherically symmetric field. It sometimes happens that some element always appears to possess a certain type of symmetry whenever we look at it. We tend then to say that this symmetry is a law of nature and to formulate other laws of nature so as to include it. When we do so, the element with the symmetry becomes an absolute element in the theory. If we accept the hypothesis that there are, in fact, no absolute elements in physics, we see that the observed symmetry can be explained in the framework of the theory, wherein the absolute element is taken as a dynamic element, by saying that it interacts only very weakly with the rest of the physical system. The symmetry it would possess in the absence of interaction is thus approximately maintained in practice. Perhaps we can look upon the conservation laws and associated symmetries of strong interactions as being due to the presence of additional elements that interact only very weakly with the strange particles in much the same way as we now think of the gravitational field, which, in the absence of matter, has the symmetries of the Lorentz group but, when allowed to interact with matter, loses this symmetry.

References

1. E. Kretchmann, *Ann. Physik*, **53**, 575 (1917).
2. V. Fock, *The Theory of Space-Time and Gravitation*, Pergamon, New York, 1959.
3. E. Noether, *Nachr. Akad. Wiss. Gottingen, Math.-Physik. Kl.*, **1918**, 235.
4. H. Poincaré, *R. C. Circ. Mat. Palermo*, **21**, 129 (1906).
5. A. Einstein, *Ann. Phys. Lpz.*, **17**, 891 (1905).
6. M. Planck, *Berl. Ber.*, 542 (1907); *Ann. Physik.*, **26**, 1 (1908).
7. A. Einstein, *Jahrb. Radio ktivität und Elektronik*, **4**, 411 (1907).
8. R. C. Tolman, *Relativistic Thermodynamics and Cosmology*, Oxford, New York, 1934, Chap. V.
9. F. Jüttner, *Ann. Phys. Lpz.*, 34, 856 (1911); also G. E. Tauber and T. W. Weinberg, *Phys. Rev.*, **122**, 1842 (1961).
10. J. J. Sakurai, *Ann. Phys.*, **11**, 11 (1960).
11. A. Komar, *Phys. Rev.*, **111**, 1182 (1958).
12. P. G. Bergmann, *Phys. Rev.*, **2**, 287 (1958).
13. A. Trautman, Conservation Laws in General Relativity, a preprint.
14. C. N. Yang and R. L. Mills, *Phys. Rev.*, **96**, 191 (1954).

IO
The superdense star and the critical nucleon number

John A. Wheeler

Superdense Stars

The average density of the sun is about that of water. The density of a white dwarf is of the order of 10^6 g/cm^3. What happens to a star that is cold and massive and so dense that its central density rises many orders of magnitude above these figures—to nuclear densities and beyond[1]?

Too Faint to Be Seen?

There is no observational evidence for any star with the mass of the sun and with the density of nuclear matter, i.e., $\sim 10^{14}$ g/cm^3. Such an object will have a diameter of the order of 30 km. By reason of its high conductivity, it will cool rapidly. Even if its surface temperature is as high as that of the sun, it will put out only as much total power as falls on the earth from sunlight! There is about as little hope of seeing such a faint object as there is of seeing a planet belonging to another star.[2]

Not Known whether Astrophysical Evolution Leads to Superdense Stars

Moreover, one is very far today from being able to state any precise figure for the number of stars that, in the course of their evolution, ought to arrive in a condition of such high density. There are still problems to be solved about the burning of hydrogen and helium and about the transformation of lighter elements into heavier elements. One has to know how much matter is ejected by explosions. One has to analyze the effect of rotation upon all these processes and also the rate at which rotational angular momentum is carried away by interaction with large-scale magnetic fields.

Consider a star of mass equal to $70M_\odot$ ($M_\odot$ = mass of the sun = 2×10^{33} g) or less. As the material deep in the interior approaches the end point of thermonuclear combustion, the core becomes unstable against gravitational contraction. The energy set free in the sudden contraction of this core drives off the rest of the star as an exploding shell. Most stars will be rotating at the time such a process comes about. It might be thought that the contracting core will rotate faster and faster and undergo rotational disruption. However, magnetic fields will couple the core to the outer shell. This coupling will favor a common angular velocity for core and shell. Moreover, the moment of inertia will be associated primarily with the expanding shell. Therefore, the angular velocity of the core, as well as the shell, may well decrease during its contraction. For this reason, it is not at all impossible that stars of great density may be formed in the final stage of thermonuclear evolution.

A full treatment of all the successive stages of nuclear burning will take many years—and many more when allowance is made for rotation!

Whether or Not They Are Formed in Nature, Superdense Stars Pose an Issue of Principle

What will concern us here, however, will not be the frequency with which superdense stars occur, but their properties. We can even inquire about the physics of a star of nuclear and supernuclear density as a question of principle, without regard for how this state is reached. We can consider for comparison the burning of hydrogen in oxygen to form water! More than a dozen reactions are required to describe the combustion. The investigation of these processes forms one of the great topics in reaction-rate theory. Yet thermodynamics has taught that the *final equilibrium state* of the hydrogen-oxygen reaction can be analyzed without any knowledge at all of these mechanisms and their rates. In the same spirit, it is appropriate to consider superdense stars without being concerned about how they were formed. Instead, we may simply ask this question: *What is the final equilibrium state of an A-nucleon system under gravitational forces when A is very large?*

Final Equilibrium State of an A-Nucleon System— How Large Can A Be?

We may state the question in another way. Take a system consisting of A nucleons. It may be all hydrogen, or all iron, or an equimolal mixture of all 92 elements! Let the mass be drawn together by gravitational attraction. Let it be catalyzed so that all nuclear reactions proceed freely to the end point of thermonuclear evolution. Let the system be supplied with a cooling mechanism so effective that all heat of reaction is removed. If explosions occur and mechanical energy is set free, let the ejected pieces be caught and brought to rest. Let each piece be cooled and lowered gently back onto the central mass, so that it arrives in position with the minimum possible energy. Then the original number of nucleons A has been restored; but the mass-energy of the system has gone down. Ultimately, the star gets tired. It cannot eject matter. It cannot radiate photons. It cannot emit neutrinos. It comes into the absolutely lowest state possible for an A-nucleon system under the dual actions of nuclear and gravitational forces. It is this state itself, rather than the mode of reaching it or the time taken, in which we are interested.

If the star has angular momentum to begin with, even more energy can be extracted from it. Nevertheless, the final state is no different from that of an A-nucleon system that had no initial angular momentum.

Moderate A: A Piece of Iron

The question we have asked is so simple for small values of A that one hardly even bothers to ask it. Let $A = 560$. When this system is catalyzed to the very lowest possible energy state, it forms a solid lattice consisting of 10 atoms of Fe^{56}. In this case the hierarchy of forces is clear. Nuclear forces dominate. They say that Fe^{56} has the lowest energy. Next in order of importance come the chemical forces associated with electronic binding. They fix the lattice arrangement and lattice spacing. Gravitational forces, ultimately to be more important than any other forces, here are negligible.

Things are little different when A is a number as large as 2×10^{49}. One is now talking not about a speck of dust but about an object only a little smaller than the moon. The gravitational pressure at the center is still not enough to dominate over lattice forces. Both are negligible compared to nuclear forces. Consequently, the equilibrium composition is still controlled by standard considerations of nuclear stability and is 100 per cent Fe^{56}. The average density is inappreciably more than that of uncompressed iron, 7.8 g/cm^3. Thus, the equilibrium radius of the A-nucleon system, with $A = 2 \times 10^{49}$, is easily calculated to be 1000 km. We have a "moon" built of pure iron!

First Crushing Point:
Gravitational Forces Overwhelm Solid-State Forces

Increase the number of nucleons by three more orders of magnitude! Then gravitational forces at the center are so great that the density there goes up by one order of magnitude. Gravitational forces have at last over-whelmed valence forces. From this point on, interesting and important things begin to happen.

Further increases in the central pressure ultimately cause the atomic electrons to combine with nuclear protons in inverse β reactions. With the disappearance of most of the atoms, the material finds itself crushed to nuclear densities. We shall call the critical conditions where this transfor-mation occurs the Chandrasekhar crushing point.

Second Crushing Point:
Gravitational Forces Overwhelm Nuclear Forces

With still further increase in the central pressure, one comes to the point where even nuclear matter is crushed—the Landau–Oppenheimer–Volkoff crushing point.

At the first crushing point, gravitational forces have won out over the pressure supplied by electrons. At the second crushing point, gravitational forces have overwhelmed even the pressure of nuclear matter.

Puzzle of Supercritical Number of Nucleons

What happens for a number of nucleons in excess of the critical A value A_{crit} associated with the second crushing point? No equilibrium configuration exists when even a single extra kilo of nucleons is added to the critical system. What then happens? No one knows! No problem poses more strikingly than this the issues that stand at the frontier between elementary particle physics and general relativity.

Now it is in order to analyze a little more carefully the problem of the critical nucleon number before asking what conclusions are to be drawn from it.

Equation of State

The analysis itself is most conveniently divided into two distinct parts, one microscopic, the other macroscopic. The first has to do with the pres-sure-density relation, or equation of state, of highly compressed matter. The second has to do with the equation of hydrostatic equilibrium, which relates the pressure gradient at one point in the star to the gravitational pull from points closer to the center of the object.

Order-of-magnitude considerations will be enough to bring out the principal features of the equation of state (Figure 10-1). The information in sector ab of the graph comes from high-pressure measurements and experiments where iron is shocked by high explosives to a density of the

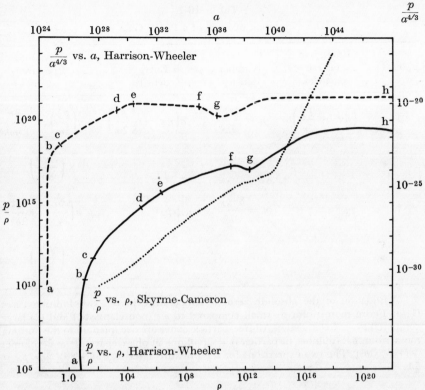

Figure 10-1 The pressure-density relation for matter at absolute zero and catalyzed to the endpoint of thermonuclear evolution. The smooth curve gives $p/\rho(\mathrm{cm^2/sec^2})$ as a function of the density $(\mathrm{g/cm^3})$. The dashed curve gives $p/a^{4/3}(\mathrm{g\text{-}cm^3/sec^2})$ as a function of the number density of nucleons a $(1/\mathrm{cm^3})$. At "low" pressures, the density is that of iron, 7.8 $\mathrm{g/cm^3}$. At the highest densities, the pressure is uncertain. It is taken here to be that of a relativistic gas of free particles: (8/9) neutrons, (1/9) protons, (1/9) electrons.[4] Calculations are by Harrison,[1] SÉU, and GMD. The asymptotic value of p/ρ is limited (1) to c^2 by the requirement of a speed of sound less than the speed of light and (2) to $c^2/3$ by the requirements for a positive trace for the stress-energy tensor.[7] The latter criterion is not satisfied by the dotted curve for p/ρ taken from Figure 2 of Reference 8.

order of twice normal. Section *bc* is interpolated. Section *cd* comes from correcting the Fermi–Thomas atom model for pressure effects according to the theory of Feynman, Metropolis, and Teller. In section *de* the nuclei are so closely packed that electrons run about practically freely as in an ideal, nonrelativistic electron gas. Thus, the pressure is given here to a good approximation by the formula for a free electron gas (Table 10-1).

Table 10-1

Equation of State of a Fermi Gas[a]

p_F/mc	Energy of fastest particles	Number density	Energy density	Pressure
$\ll 1$	$\left(mc^2 + \dfrac{p_F^2}{2m}\right)$	$n = \dfrac{8\pi p_F^3}{3h^3}$	$n\left(mc^2 + \dfrac{3}{5}\dfrac{p_F^2}{2m}\right)$	$n\left(\dfrac{p_F^2}{5m}\right) = \dfrac{8\pi}{15mh^3}$ $\times \left(\dfrac{3h^3 n}{8\pi}\right)^{5/3}$
$\gg 1$	cp_F	$n = \dfrac{8\pi p_F^3}{3h^3}$	$n(\tfrac{3}{4}cp_F)$	$n\left(\dfrac{cp_F}{4}\right) = \dfrac{2\pi c}{3h^3}$ $\times \left(\dfrac{3h^3 n}{8\pi}\right)^{4/3}$

[a] Equation at the absolute zero of temperature in the two limiting cases (1) of Fermi momentum p_F small compared to mc (nonrelativistic) and (2) large compared to mc (relativistic). All free-particle states are occupied up to the limiting momentum p_F: (number of particles) = 2(volume in phase space)/h^3 = 2(volume) $\times (4\pi p_F^3/3h^3)$. The two expressions for the pressure agree for $(3h^3 n/8\pi)^{1/3} = p_F = 5mc/4$.

Chandrasekhar has calculated in detail the transition in section *de* from the nonrelativistic regime to the regime where electrons are squeezed so tightly in coordinate space that, in momentum space, the typical momentum exceeds *mc*.

Pressure-Induced Transmutations

A still further increase in the pressure carries the energy to the point where the electrons transmute bound protons to neutrons. In consequence, cold matter catalyzed to the endpoint of thermonuclear evolution under these pressures no longer consists of Fe^{56}. The ratio of neutrons to protons in the nucleus has been increased. Therefore, the coulomb energy of the nucleus has a less important part in determining its stability. The binding is improved by rearranging the nucleons into nuclei of greater mass (section *ef* of curve; detailed calculation by B. K. Harrison based on the Weizsäcker–Green semiempirical mass formula).

With additional pressure, the ratio of neutrons to protons is so increased that the nucleus becomes unstable with respect to loss of neutrons. Matter now consists of a mixture of neutrons and heavy nuclei (neighborhood of *g* on the curve; also based on the semiempirical formula).

A little more pressure brings matter to a density $\sim 10^{14}$ g/cm³, of the order of that encountered in nuclei themselves. What goes on at still greater densities is more difficult to estimate. It is simplest to assume that the tighter the nucleons are compacted, the higher are their momenta and the less important are nuclear forces for the motion of these nucleons. Then one is led to the model of a Fermi gas for the nucleons—as one is led at lower pressures to the model of a Fermi gas to describe the electrons. Then one reapplies at once the formulas of Table 10-1—the first row in the table when the Fermi momentum of the nucleons is nonrelativistic, the second row when it is relativistic. In this high-velocity case, the formula for the pressure of a *nucleon* gas is the same as the formula for the pressure of an *electron* gas! The *rest mass* of the particles that supply the pressure is irrelevant when they are moving at nearly the speed of light! Of course, the *number density* of nucleons when nucleons become relativistic is much greater than the number density of electrons when electrons become relativistic, and the pressure is correspondingly higher—but the pressure still goes as the 4/3 power of the number density.[5]

Electric Field of Negligible Strength

One can have several concerns about the equation of state. First, consider the case where the electrons have not been crushed onto the Fe^{56} nuclei. The electrons carry the bulk of the pressure. On the other hand, the pull of gravity is concentrated almost exclusively on the nuclei. Will not the electrons and the nuclei be entirely separated from each other? No! Rudkjøbing[6] has pointed out that the star will be endowed with an electric field that points radially outward. It transmits to the protons the sustaining influence of the electron pressure. The strength of this field will be given to a good approximation by neglecting any pressure supplied by the protons themselves. Then the acceleration *g* of gravity must be balanced entirely by the electric force:

$$m_{Fe}g = Z_{eff}eE \qquad (1)$$

For an order-of-magnitude estimate of the largest fields that one will normally encounter, consider a star of 0.7 the mass of the sun, with a central density roughly 10^{16} g/cm³ or 100 times nuclear density and a radius of roughly 10 km. Calculate *g* at the *surface* of this object. This will give, within an order of magnitude or so, an estimate of the *highest* gravitational pull encountered anywhere in this star. If the density were uniform and if the curvature of space were small, then—one will recall—the gravitational acceleration would take on its greatest value at the surface itself (harmonic oscillator potential!) For g at the surface, we find

$$g \sim GM/r^2 \sim (7 \times 10^{-8} \text{ cm}^3/\text{g sec}^2)(1.4 \times 10^{33} \text{ g})/(10^6 \text{ cm})^2 \qquad (2)$$
$$\sim 10^{14} \text{ cm/sec}^2$$

The largest estimate for the electric field that sustains the nuclei will be found by attributing to the effective electric charge the smallest value $Z_{\text{eff}} \sim 1$; thus

$$E \sim m_{\text{Fe}} g/e \sim (56 \times 1.6 \times 10^{-24} \text{ g})(10^{14} \text{ cm/sec}^2)/(4.8 \times 10^{-10})$$
$$\times (\text{g cm}^3/\text{sec}^2)^{1/2}$$
$$\sim 20(\text{g cm}^3/\text{sec}^2)^{1/2}/\text{cm}^2 \qquad (3)$$
$$\sim 6000 \text{ volts/cm}$$

The energy density associated with this field is completely negligible in comparison to the energies of compression and of nuclear transformation. Therefore, it is reasonable to leave this electric field out of account.

The "Hard" Core

A second source of concern has to do with the assumption adopted in many accounts of nuclear matter that nucleons act upon each other with a so-called hard-core effective nuclear potential when they are separated by $\sim 0.5 \times 10^{-13}$ cm. If this potential were taken literally, it would imply that normal nuclear matter has only to be increased in density by a few factors of 2 to become incompressible. Thus, pressures would go up enormously in excess of those predicted by the simple Fermi gas model. However, incompressibility is an impossibility. An incompressible fluid would transmit sound at a speed

$$v_{\text{sound}} = (dp/d\rho)^{1/2} \qquad (4)$$

which is infinite! In contrast, the condition that signals cannot propagate faster than light sets the condition

$$dp/d\rho \leqslant c^2 \qquad (5)$$

Even *this* limit cannot be achieved, however. Consider a region of space filled with an isotropic distribution of electromagnetic radiation. Then the ratio of pressure to density has the well-known value

$$p/\rho = c^2/3 \qquad (6)$$

from which

$$dp/d\rho = c^2/3 \qquad (7)$$

More generally, consider any medium that is isotropic and unable to sustain a shear,[7] so that it admits of description in terms of the concept of *pressure*. If one then demands that the trace of the stress-energy tensor be positive definite, he arrives at the upper limit

$$p/\rho = c^2/3 \tag{8}$$

for the pressure-density ratio (see Figure 10-1). *This assumption, plus the principle of relativity, sets an upper limit of one third on the ratio of pressure to energy density.* This limit is approached more and more closely by an ideal Fermi gas as the Fermi energy of the particles in question comes to be a higher and higher multiple of their rest energy.

A Pressure Lowering?

Cameron has pointed out[8] that one could fear the opposite of incompressibility; namely, a pressure (at high densities) much *less* than that of a simple Fermi gas composed mostly of neutrons. When the Fermi kinetic energy of the nucleons reaches several hundred Mev, he notes, nucleons can and will transform into hyperons, in reactions in which strangeness may or may not be conserved. Of these one of the simplest is

$$n + n \rightleftharpoons \Lambda^0 + \Lambda^0 \tag{9}$$

If these hyperons are quite distinct in character from neutrons and protons, it is no longer necessary to have so high a Fermi energy to accommodate a large number a of baryons per unit volume. The pressure will be diminished.

Table 10-2 illustrates the type of changes that hyperons would make in the equation of state *if* the various types of elementary particles could be treated as ideal, noninteracting Fermi gases and *if* no fermion of one type (a Λ^0, for example) ever deprived a fermion of another type (a neutron, for example) of free access to all phase space—both presumably unrealistic assumptions. *On* these assumptions the four important physical quantities —the number density of baryons a, the density of electric charge ρ_e, the density of mass ρ (including mass equivalent of kinetic energy), and the pressure p—are given by summing contributions of the various particles multiplied by the weight factors in the table. The contributions depend upon two Fermi energies: E_e for electrons and muons, E_n for neutrons, Λ^0 particles, and Σ^0 particles. These two Fermi energies have to be adjusted (adjustment *not* carried out *here*!) to give the specified a value and the required electric neutrality. *Note:* All energies employed in Table 10-2 include rest energy, so that the Fermi momentum p_F is given by combining the data in columns 2 and 3 according to the formula $c^2 p_F^2 = $ (energy)$^2 - $ (rest mass)$^2 c^4$. When the quantity E_e reaches the π-meson mass energy,

Table 10-2

Idealized Analysis of Effect of Hyperons on Equation of State

Particle symbol	Fermi energy	Rest mass, Mev	Weight factor to multiply $8\pi p_F^3/3h^3$ to get contribution to baryon number	Weight factor to multiply $8\pi p_F^3/3h^3$ to get contribution to charge density	Weight factor to multiply $(8\pi/3h^3)\int_0^{p_F} vp^3\,dp$ to get contribution to the pressure	Weight factor to multiply $(8\pi/h^3c^2)\int_0^{p_F} Ep^2\,dp$ to get contribution to mass density
_e_	E_e	0.51	0	-1	1	1
μ	E_e	106	0	-1	1	1
_p_	$E_n - E_e$	938	1	$+1$	1	1
Σ^+	$E_n - E_e$	1190	1	$+1$	1	1
_n_	E_n	940	1	0	1	1
Λ^0	E_n	1115	1	0	1	1
Σ^0	E_n	1192	1	0	1	1
Σ^-	$E_n + E_e$	1196	1	-1	1	1
Ξ^-	$E_n + E_e$	1319	1	-1	1	1

From data below evaluate Fermi momentum p_F used in last 4 columns

Adjust E_e and E_n to make totals in first two columns have values assigned below

a	0

Totals of remaining columns give pressure and mass density for given number of baryons per cm³

$p(a)$	$\rho(a)$

π^- mesons are created. Thereafter charge equality is maintained by changes in the number density of π^- mesons, and not by change in E_e.[9]

Hence, from the above arguments, the higher the density becomes, the more baryon states are energetically accessible and the greater corresponding lowering of the pressure can be expected. If this argument held, one would only have to measure carefully appropriate features of the equation of state to deduce the entire mass spectrum of elementary particles. However, the argument cannot be upheld, not least because it neglects, as Cameron points out, all interactions between the baryons. Moreover, it is not clear that a baryon can escape the stringency of the Pauli principle for neutrons by transforming into a hyperon. Certainly it does not save neutrons and protons from the working of the Pauli–Dirac statistics in ordinary nuclei to group themselves into alpha particles, despite the Einstein–Bose character of these groupings! *Note:* Ambartsumyan and Saakyan[9] have pointed out that π^- mesons enter in an important way into the equilibrium when the number density of neutrons rises above a critical value of about $8.5 \times 10^{38}/cm^3$.

In summary, the pressure of cold matter catalyzed to the endpoint of thermonuclear evolution is uncertain at densities many times in excess of nuclear densities. It cannot exceed one-third the energy density.[10] However, the pressure comes closer and closer to this limit when calculated for an ideal Fermi gas at higher and higher densities. This is the limit approached by Harrison's equation of state of Figure 10-1—the equation of state employed in the quantitative analysis of Harrison, Wakano, and the author.[1] If hyperons *should* affect the equation of state strongly, it would only be by *lowering* the pressure available to sustain the mass of the star and thus *decreasing* the critical mass at which collapse sets in.

The Critical Mass

Why is there a critical mass? This question is most easily approached by asking how the star adjusts its radius so as to secure the lowest total energy. We shall first consider this question in the context of the following simplifying assumptions:

1. Assume special relativity, not general relativity; that is, neglect the curvature of space—a reasonable assumption at the first crushing point, and not badly in error even at the second crushing point. Also neglect in this approximation the effective mass associated with the *pressure* in the interior.

2. Assume only a single type of fermion sustaining the weight of the star by its Fermi pressure. In other words, idealize the stars in question, before the first crushing point, as supported by the pressure of electrons, against the pull of gravity on iron nuclei. Before the second crushing point,

Table 10-3

Idealizations for the Mass m_1 of the Fermion That Supplies the Pressure and the Gravitational Mass m_2 That Is Associated with One Such Fermion

Near which crushing point	Fermion and its rest mass m_1	Gravitational mass taken to be associated with this fermion	Mass of star in terms of number N of fermions
First	Electron m_e	$m_2 = m_{Fe}/26 = (56/26)m_n$	$M = Nm_2$
Second	Neutron m_n	$m_2 = m_n + \left(\begin{array}{c}\text{kinetic}\\\text{energy}\end{array}\right)_n\Big/c^2$	$M = Nm_2$

idealize the pressure *and* the weight as arising entirely from neutrons (Table 10-3).

3. Assume uniform density. Instead of adjusting the *distribution* of density all through the star so as to minimize its energy, reduce the problem to the simpler one of adjusting a *single parameter*, the radius R of a star of uniform density. Even easier to consider than the radius of the star is the radius of the region of space associated with *one fermion*— expressed for later convenience in terms of a simple multiple of the Compton wavelength of that fermion:

$$r = (4/3\pi)(\pi/3)^{1/3}\frac{(4\pi R^3/3N)^{1/3}}{(\hbar/m_1 c)} \tag{10}$$

The quantity r may be called the reduced-cell radius. A value $r \gg 1$ implies a long de Broglie wavelength and a nonrelativistic Fermi momentum. In contrast, a value of the reduced radius $r \ll 1$ indicates compression to extreme relativistic momenta. Specifically, the Fermi momentum is

$$p_F = (4/3r)m_1 c \tag{11}$$

4. The rest plus kinetic energy per fermion is taken to be equal to

$$m_1 c^2 (1 + r^{-2})^{1/2} \tag{12}$$

This expression checks to 7 per cent (Table 10-4) with the exact but complicated mathematical expression[11] for the energy of a Fermi gas.

Table 10-4

Comparison of Eq. (12) with the Correct Values for the Energy per Particle (Rest plus Kinetic) in a Fermi Gas in the Limiting Cases of Low Density (High Reduced-Cell Radius r) and High Density (Low r)

r	Exact value for average energy per nucleon in this limit	Volume given by the approximation of Eq. (12)
$\gg 1$	$m_1c^2 + \dfrac{3}{5}\dfrac{p_F^2}{2m_1} = (m_1c^2)\left(1 + \dfrac{8}{15r^2}\right)$	$(m_1c^2)\left(1 + \dfrac{8}{16r^2}\right)$
$\ll 1$	$\tfrac{3}{4}cp_F = (m_1c^2)/r$	$(m_1c^2)/r$

These simplifying assumptions make it easy to analyze the energy of a cold star, catalyzed to the endpoint of thermonuclear evolution, as it depends upon the radius of the star—or upon the reduced cell radius r:

$$\begin{pmatrix} \text{gravitational energy} \\ \text{of a sphere of radius} \\ R \text{ and mass } M, \text{ of} \\ \text{uniform density} \end{pmatrix} = -\frac{3}{5}\frac{GM^2}{R} \tag{13}$$

Denote by A the total number of nucleons in the star ("mass number"!). When the star is idealized to consist of a mixture of Fe^{56} nuclei and a free-electron gas, the total number of electrons is $(26/56)A$, and the gravitational energy is

$$-\left(\frac{256}{1125\pi}\right)^{1/3} \frac{G(Am_n)^2}{(\hbar/m_ec)(26A/56)^{1/3}r} \tag{13e}$$

When the star is idealized to consist entirely of free neutrons, the gravitational energy is

$$-\left(\frac{256}{1125\pi}\right)^{1/3} \frac{G[Am_n(1 + r^{-2})^{1/2}]^2}{(\hbar/m_nc)A^{1/3}r} \tag{13n}$$

Here the factor $(1 + r^{-2})^{1/2}$ in the numerator allows for the weight of the kinetic energy of the neutrons.

The rest-plus-kinetic energy of the particles in the electron-plus-Fe^{56} star (we neglect the binding energy of the nucleons in the iron) is

$$AM_nc^2 + (26A/56)m_ec^2(1 + r^{-2})^{1/2} \tag{14e}$$

In the case of the idealized neutron star, the rest-plus-kinetic energy is

$$AM_n c^2 (1 + r^{-2})^{1/2} \tag{14n}$$

Add the gravitational energy and the rest-plus-kinetic energy to get the total energy of the star. Consider only the compression-dependent part of this total energy in order to determine the optimum reduced cell radius r. Divide this energy through by the rest energy of all the fermions so as to be able to consider a simple dimensionless function:

$$\frac{\begin{pmatrix} \text{compression-} \\ \text{dependent} \\ \text{part of energy} \\ \text{of a star} \end{pmatrix}}{\begin{pmatrix} \text{rest energy of} \\ \text{the fermions} \\ \text{that supply} \\ \text{the pressure} \end{pmatrix}} = \begin{cases} \left(1 + \dfrac{1}{r^2}\right) - \dfrac{\lambda_e}{r} & \text{for } e\text{–Fe}^{56} \text{ star} \quad (15e) \\[2ex] \left(1 + \dfrac{1}{r^2}\right) - \lambda_n\left(\dfrac{1}{r} + \dfrac{1}{r^3}\right) & \text{for } n \text{ star} \quad (15n) \end{cases}$$

Here, λ is a *mass parameter* that measures the importance of gravitational energy relative to rest energy. It is directly connected with the two-thirds power of the number of nucleons A in the star:

$$A^{2/3} = (26/56)^{4/3} A_0^{2/3} \lambda_e \qquad \text{for } e\text{–Fe}^{56} \text{ star} \tag{16e}$$

$$A^{2/3} = A_0^{2/3} \lambda_n \qquad \text{for } n \text{ star} \tag{16n}$$

Here the *characteristic mass number* A_0 is defined by the equation

$$A_0^{2/3} = (1125\pi/256)^{1/3}(\hbar c/G m_n^2) \tag{17}$$

The dimensionless number

$$\hbar c/G m_n = 1.691 \times 10^{38}$$

has the same place in gravitational interactions that

$$\hbar c/e^2 = 137.037 \tag{18}$$

has in electromagnetic interactions. The enormity of the number is testimony to the many nucleons that have to be present before gravitational interactions overwhelm all other forces. Specifically, the characteristic mass number has the value

$$A_0 = 8.17 \times 10^{57} \tag{19}$$

Multiplying by the mass of a neutron, one finds a characteristic mass

$$A_0 m_n = 13.68 \times 10^{33} \text{ g} = 6.89 M_\odot \tag{20}$$

where $M_\odot = 1.987 \times 10^{33}$ g denotes the mass of the sun.

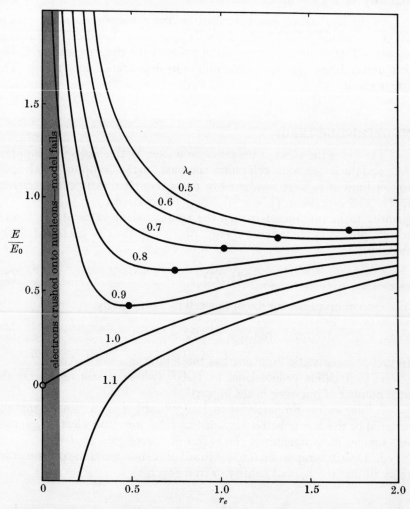

Figure 10-2 Energy as a function of size of the cell occupied by one electron in the approximation of special relativity for idealized stellar configurations artificially constrained to have uniform density throughout. The two forms of energy taken into account are (1) rest plus kinetic energy of the nucleons and (2) gravitational energy (assuming that the mass arises from one Fe^{56} nucleus for each 26 electrons). There is one configuration of stable equilibrium for every value of the mass of the system up to a critical value given by the mass parameter $\lambda_e = 1$. At the critical value itself the calculated density is infinite—a signal that the approximations fail by reason of electrons being crushed onto nuclei by inverse beta decay processes.

Stability of e-Fe^{56} Model for $\lambda_e < 1$

In the idealization just described the compression-dependent part of the energy of the e-Fe^{56} model depends upon the reduced cell radius r_e as shown in Figure 10-2. For any given value of the mass parameter λ_e less than unity, the energy has a minimum in its dependence upon radius. The star is stable.

Nonrelativistic Limit

The lower the value of the mass parameter λ_e, the less is the compression, and the larger is the cell radius compared to the Compton wavelength. In this limit of r_e large compared to unity, nonrelativistic considerations apply. The expression $(1 + r^{-2})^{1/2}$ may be replaced by $1 + (1/2r^2)$. The quantity to be minimized is then the nonrelativistic value of the kinetic energy, plus the gravitational energy, divided by the rest energy of all the electrons, or

$$(1/2r^2) - \lambda_e/r \tag{21}$$

The extremum comes for a reduced-cell radius given by

$$r_{\text{optimum}} = 1/\lambda_e \sim A^{-2/3} \tag{22}$$

In this nonrelativistic limit one has the following:

1. Cell radius proportional to $1/A^{2/3}$ (where A still represents the total number of nucleons in the object).

2. Star radius proportional to $1/A^{1/3}$ (until A is so "small" that the material of the star is better regarded as solid iron than electron gas; for still smaller mass number A the radius of course goes as $A^{1/3}$).

3. Density proportional to A^2 (until A is so low and the pressures are so small that the normal density of iron governs).

Critical Equilibrium for $\lambda_e = 1$

These proportionalities fail in the relativistic domain. The calculated reduced-cell radius of the idealized e-Fe^{56} model is

$$r_{\text{optimum}} = (1 - \lambda_e^2)^{1/2}/\lambda_e \tag{23}$$

For this radius to vanish, it is not required that the mass parameter λ_e go to infinity, as in Eq. (22), but only that it reach the critical value

$$\lambda_{e\text{critical}} = 1 \tag{24}$$

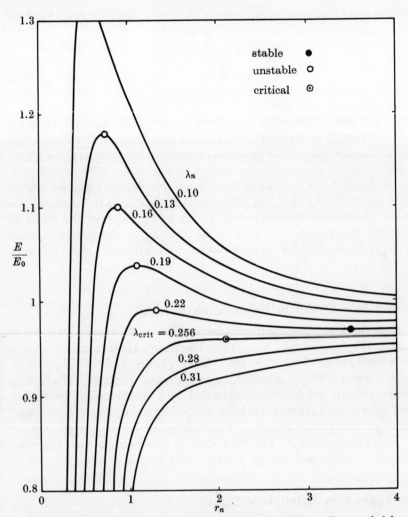

Figure 10-3 Energy as a function of the size of the cell occupied by one neutron for idealized stellar configurations artificially constrained to have uniform density, and for a simplified model which assumes (1) 100 per cent neutrons, (2) Fermi energy of an ideal neutron gas, (3) gravitational action by the *kinetic* energy of the neutrons as well as by the *rest* mass-energy, and (4) no general relativity corrections. There are *two* configurations of equilibrium—one stable, and one unstable—for values of the mass parameter λ_n less than the critical value $\lambda_n = 0.256$. For larger values there is no equilibrium; the system continues to fall inward.

Inserting this value into the equation of definition (16e) one finds a critical mass

$$M_{\text{crit}_1} = (26/56)^2 A_0 m_n$$
$$= 2.95 \times 10^{33} \text{ g} \tag{25}$$
$$= 1.48 M_\odot$$

As the mass approaches closer and closer to this critical value, the calculated density increases without limit. The cell radius goes to zero, and the Fermi momentum of the electrons becomes indefinitely large compared to $m_e c$.

In actuality, the physics changes when the electrons acquire several million electron volts of energy. They transmute protons to neutrons. The number of electrons per baryon drops far below the assumed figure of 26/56. For this reason, turn now to the idealized model for the neutron star and to Figure 10-3 for curves for *its* energy as a function of the reduced-cell radius r_n.

Neutron Star Model in Nonrelativistic Limit

Consider a fixed and not very large value of the mass parameter in Figure 10-3—for example, $\lambda_n = 0.19$. The energy shows a minimum at a reduced-cell radius about $r_n = 4.07$, not very different from $1/\lambda_n = 5.26$. One is dealing with an essentially nonrelativistic problem. The energy equation (15n) is not badly approximated by a nonrelativistic expression of the same form (21) that has been applied to electrons. In both cases, there exists a minimum because the nonrelativistic kinetic energy, positive and proportional to $1/r^2$, can always be put in balance with the nonrelativistic gravitational energy, negative and proportional to $1/r$.

New Feature in Relativistic Limit

Now let the same number of fermions be much more tightly compacted, so that they become relativistic. The kinetic energy goes up now only as the momentum, not as the square of the momentum—as $1/r$, not as $1/r^2$. In this respect, the neutron model does not differ from the e-Fe^{56} model. However, with respect to the gravitational energy there is a great difference. In the e-Fe^{56} model, the gravitational mass derived from *static* objects, Fe^{56} nuclei, and only negligibly from the electrons, whether they were relativistic or nonrelativistic. Not so in the neutron model! When the neutrons become relativistic, their kinetic energy contributes to the mass of the system in an *essential* way. The mass per particle goes up by the factor $(1 + 1/r^2)^{1/2}$. Moreover, this factor appears twice, multiplying the normal factor of $(1/r)$, which shows in the dependence of gravitational energy upon distance. The resulting gravitational term

$$-(\lambda_n/r)(1 + 1/r^2)$$

which appears in the energy formula (15n) and in Figure 10-3 therefore *dominates* over the kinetic energy at great compressions. In other words, if the object is compressed to more than a certain critical density (see maximum of curve in Figure 10-3), it will go on *compressing itself*. The maximum is a point of instability.

Critical Conditions for Neutron Model

As the mass parameter is increased, the configurations of unstable equilibrium and of stable equilibrium approach each other. Beyond the critical value

$$\lambda_{n_{\text{crit}}} = 2[(33)^{1/2} - 5]^{1/2}/[(33)^{1/2} + 1] = 0.256$$

$$A = \lambda_n^{3/2} A_0 = 1.058 \times 10^{57}$$

$$M_{\text{crit}_2} = A m_n = 1.77 \times 10^{33} \, \text{g} = 0.89 M_\odot \tag{26}$$

there is no longer *any* configuration of equilibrium, stable *or* unstable.

Exact Theory of Equilibrium

All the features disclosed by this approximate treatment show up when one analyzes by exact methods the equilibrium configurations of a mass of matter that satisfies the equation of state depicted in Figure 10-1. We assume (1) spherical symmetry, (2) no rotation, and (3) static equilibrium.

Instead of minimizing the energy with respect to a single parameter—the radius of a sphere of uniform density—one has to minimize it with respect to an infinity of parameters; that is, with respect to an entire distribution curve, a function $\rho(r)$, which gives the density in its dependence upon distance from the center. This minimization procedure, when applied to the *general relativity* expression for the energy of the system, leads, via the familiar Euler–Lagrange type of reasoning, to a differential equation for the pressure p as a function of the radial coordinate r. If one were dealing with an equilibrium in the context of nonrelativistic hydrostatics, the derivation of this equation would be simple. Consider a prism of matter of thickness dr and cross section 1 cm^2 at the distance r from the center. Equate to zero the net force on this volume element

$$p(r) - p(r + dr) - g(r)\rho(r) \, dr = 0 \tag{27}$$

Here the acceleration $g(r)$ of gravity arises entirely from the mass

$$M(r) \equiv \int_0^r \rho(r) 4\pi r^2 \, dr \tag{28}$$

which lies *within* a sphere of radial coordinate r; thus,

$$g(r) = GM(r)/r^2 \tag{29}$$

In this way, find

$$\frac{dp}{dr} = -\rho \frac{GM(r)}{r^2} \tag{30}$$

The correct equation (*correct* not only in the framework of special relativity, but also *in general relativity*[12]) differs from (30) by terms in $1/c^2$:

$$\frac{dp(r)}{dr} = -\frac{[\rho(p) + c^{-2}p]G[M(r) + 4\pi c^{-2}p(r)r^3]}{r[r - 2GM(r)/c^2]} \tag{31}$$

Cataloging All Equilibrium Configurations by Central Density

Wakano[1] integrated Eq. (31) employing the equation of state which was derived by Harrison and Wheeler and which is depicted in Figure 10-1. In doing the integration one cannot conveniently first specify the total number of nucleons and then find out how these nucleons distribute themselves. One might very well pick a number of nucleons that is too large (see Figure 10-3) to allow any equilibrium at all! But the differential Eq. (31) of hydrostatic equilibrium can give no help at all in dealing with such situations. Therefore it is necessary to limit attention to cases that admit equilibrium—whether stable or unstable. Now an equilibrium configuration will be characterized by a definite central density. Consequently we can obtain *all equilibrium configurations* if we consider all values of the central density.

The value of the central density even provides a way to *catalog* all equilibrium solutions. Thus, a definite value of this quantity determines all the other properties of the model star, by the following procedure for integration:

1. Pick the "catalog number" $\rho(0)$.
2. Conclude that the mass $M(r)$ out to r varies for *small* r as

$$M(r) \approx (4\pi\rho(0)/3)r^3 \tag{32}$$

3. Read off the central pressure $p(0)$ from the equation of state (Figure 10-1) for the value $\rho(0)$ of the density.

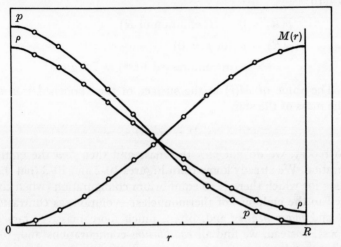

Figure 10-4 Schematic illustration of numerical integration of equation of hydrostatic equilibrium.

4. Pick an integration interval Δr that is small in comparison with the expected radius of the equilibrium configuration. One knows that Δr is small enough when a re-run of the integration with half the interval produces a negligible change in the calculated distribution of density and pressure.

5. The central conditions $p(0)$ and $\rho(0)$ determine from (31) the pressure gradient near the center

$$(dp/dr)_0 = -4\pi G(\rho_0 + c^{-2}p_0)([\rho_0/3] + c^{-2}p_0)r \qquad (33)$$

From this information one finds the pressure p at the point $r_1 = 1\Delta r$:

$$p_1 = -2\pi G(\rho_0 + c^{-2}p_0)([\rho_0/3] + c^{-2}p_0)(\Delta r)^2 \qquad (34)$$

6. Inserting this pressure into the equation of state one determines the density ρ_1 at the first point, and a corrected value for the mass M_1 out to this point.

7. By a similar procedure one finds ρ_2, p_2, and M_2 at the second point, $r = 2\Delta r$. Normally, one iterates the calculation (taking into account the *average* of p_1 and p_2, and the *average* of ρ_1 and ρ_2, and of M_1 and M_2) in evaluating "first improved values" for p_2, ρ_2, and M_2.

8. The integration proceeds in this way from interval to interval (Figure 10-4) outward to that value of r—call it R—at which the pressure

falls to zero:

$$p(R) = 0 \qquad \text{(definition of } R\text{)}$$
$$\rho(R) = \rho \text{ (for } p = 0\text{)}$$
$$= \rho \text{ (uncompressed } Fe^{56}\text{)} = 7.8 \text{ g/cm}^3 \qquad (35)$$

9. The value of $M(r)$ at the surface of the "polished iron sphere" gives the mass of the star,

$$M = M(R) \qquad (36)$$

To repeat, we do not *pick* the mass and then *find* the equilibrium configuration. We already know from Figures 10-2 and 10-3 that there will be masses for which there is *no* equilibrium configuration (when cold, and catalyzed to the endpoint of thermonuclear evolution, as contrasted with the *hot* and *lower density* and, often, much more massive stars seen in telescopes)! Instead, we find all *equilibrium* configurations and, for each, evaluate its total mass.

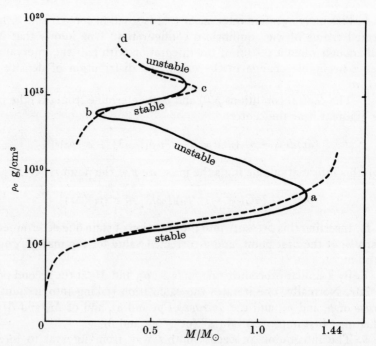

Figure 10-5   Mass as a function of central density for cold-catalyzed stars.

Our catalog of all equilibrium configurations is illustrated in Figure 10-5. In Figure 10-5, the mass is given in units of the mass of the sun, $M_\odot = 1.987 \times 10^{33} g$. The full line curve obtained by Harrison, Wakano, and Wheeler (HWW) was constructed from the results of 45 integrations performed on the MANIAC computer of the Institute for Advanced Study with the kind collaboration of Dr. H. J. Maehly and Mrs. Barbara Weymann using the equation of state of Figure 10-1. The lower dashed curve was deduced by Chandrasekhar without the use of general relativity and without allowing for the crushing of electrons onto the nuclei. In both respects, it is to be compared with the much-more idealized (uniform density) e-Fe^{56} model of Figure 10-2. In that model and on Chandrasekhar's dashed curve, the central density goes to infinity as the mass approaches the critical value. In contrast, the full-line curve shows a crushing point a at a *finite* density, where electrons have enough energy to combine with protons in large numbers. From a to b there is a sequence of configurations of equilibrium—but an equilibrium that is unstable and therefore nonphysical. From b to c the configurations are again stable. In the idealized, uniform-density neutron model of Figure 10-3, such a configuration corresponds to a black dot that lies at an energy *minimum*. The energy *maximum* (open circle) on the same curve (same A value, or same λ value) in Figure 10-3 is to be compared with a configuration of *unstable* equilibrium, on the sector cd in the present diagram. The point c, the second crushing point, corresponds qualitatively to the critical point, or point of inflection, in Figure 10-3.

Comparison of Detailed Calculations with Simple Models

The properties of these equilibrium configurations can be summarized briefly. The "catalog index," the central density ρ_0, rises only slowly with mass for a range of masses from that of a cannonball to a little less than the mass of the moon, then increases to about $4._5 \times 10^8$ g/cm³ at the first crushing point. Transformation of protons into neutrons by electron impact begins at a density of about 10^7 g/cm³ and becomes important when $\rho > 10^8$ g/cm³. Short of these densities, our curve agrees closely with that of Chandrasekhar. Any point on this curve represents a stable configuration in this sense: Apply a not-too-large pressure pulse to the star. It will oscillate with finite amplitude, the oscillation will ultimately damp out, and the star will return to its original equilibrium configuration.

At higher compressions our curve for mass as a function of density departs more and more from that of Chandrasekhar. His analysis (and the simple electron, Fe^{56} model of Figure 10-2) require *infinite* density to make the star have enough internal gravitational stress to collapse. In contrast to these models, the actual physics will give collapse at a finite density, owing to the electron-induced transformation of the nuclei. This mechanism causes all configurations from *a* to *b* to be unstable. If the star could, by magic, be created in such an equilibrium configuration, the slightest disturbance would set it off, either into implosion or explosion. For example, if the star is caused to shrink a slight amount, some more electrons are squeezed onto nuclei. In consequence, the pressure rise brought about by the contraction is not as great as it would otherwise have been. On the other hand, the gravitational forces will have increased substantially. The pressure will not keep up with this rise in the gravitational forces. The contraction will proceed more and more rapidly. One sees no escape from saying that part of the star collapses to nuclear densities and part is driven off.

Both Crushing Points Given by the One Equation of State

Oppenheimer and Volkoff computed the structure of neutron stars on the assumption of an ideal Fermi gas composed entirely of neutrons. Their results are described by the broken curve *bcd* in Figure 10-5. Not very different results are obtained from the equation of state of Figure 10-1

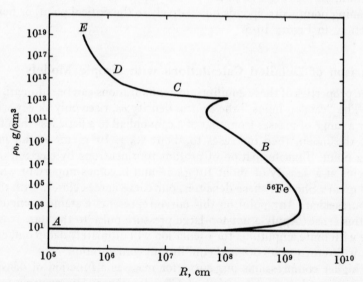

Figure 10-6 Radius and central density for the equilibrium configurations of HWW (equation of state of Harrison, Figure 10-1; general relativistic hydrostatic analysis of Wakano). The straight line at $\rho_0 = 7.8$ g/cm³ shows how the diagram would look if iron were incompressible.

Table 10-5

Conditions for Collapse of Cold and Catalyzed Stars Sustained by Electron Pressure and Neutron Pressure, Respectively[a]

Star model	e-Fe^{56}	n
Analysis of minimum energy	Fig. 2	Fig. 3
Critical mass parameter	$\lambda_e = 1.000$	$\lambda_n = 0.256$
Critical number of nucleons	$(26/56)^2 A_0 \lambda_e^{3/2}$ $= 1.762 \times 10^{57}$	$A_0 \lambda_n^{3/2}$ $= 1.058 \times 10^{57}$
This times m_n (mass before assembly)	$2.95 \times 10^{33}\,g$ $= 1.48 M_\odot$	$1.77 \times 10^{33}\,g$ $= 0.89 M_\odot$
"Reduced-cell radius"	$r_e \ll 1$	$r_n = 2.09$
Cell radius of one fermion	$(\hbar/m_e c)(r_e/0.431)$ $= r_e \times 8.95 \times 10^{-11}$ cm	$(\hbar/m_n c)(r_n/0.431)$ $= 1.017 \times 10^{-13}$ cm
Star radius	$r_e \times 1.082 \times 10^9$ cm	1.036×10^6 cm
Density (uniform in model)	$r_e^{-3} \times 5.6 \times 10^5$ g/cm³	3.8×10^{14} g/cm³

Results of HWW for the two crushing points derived from *one* equation of state

Density (central)	$4._5 \times 10^8$ g/cm³	$4._6 \times 10^{15}$ g/cm³
Radius	$0.3_4 \times 10^9$ cm	0.9×10^6 cm
Mass	$1.2 M_\odot$	$0.6_8 M_\odot$

[a] The first part of the table summarizes the results of the text for the simplified case of configurations of *uniform density*. The second part is obtained by numerical calculations from the exact equation (31) of hydrostatic equilibrium.

(smooth curve in Figure 10-5) *except* that this one equation of state *automatically*, without any special consideration of special models, gives *both* crushing points.

It is of interest to compare the characteristics of the two crushing points predicted by these detailed machine calculations (smooth curve of Figure 10-5) with the properties predicted by the two idealized uniform-density models (e-Fe^{56} and n) of Figures 10-2 and 10-3. The comparison, in Table 10-5, shows that these simple models do not do at all badly for predicting the critical *mass*. As for density, the central density of the critical-neutron configuration as predicted by the detailed calculations is—not unreasonably—about one order of magnitude higher than predicted by the model with uniform density. In contrast, the central density required for critical conditions at the *first* crushing point in the detailed calculations is

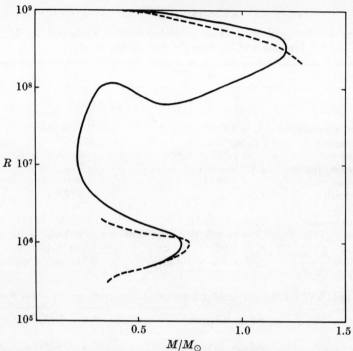

Figure 10-7   Relation between outer radius R (cm) and mass (in units of the mass of the sun) for the cold matter catalyzed to the endpoint of thermonuclear evolution, as calculated from the general-relativity equation of hydrostatic equilibrium and the equation of state of Figure 10-1 (HWW).

lower than the infinite density predicted by the simple e-Fe^{56} model, and for a simple reason: because that model does not allow for electrons being squeezed out of existence.

Figure 10-6 shows *radius* vs. central *density* according to HWW. Figure 10-7 shows the relation between radius and *mass*.

Discussion of Range of Error and of Uncertainties

Now we have to ask how great are the uncertainties in our analysis of the only configurations in which we are really interested: the configurations of *stable* equilibrium.

Up to the first crushing point only the most elementary ideas about a degenerate electron gas and about the equilibrium

$$n \rightleftharpoons p + e^- \tag{37}$$

for bound nucleons make an appearance. It is almost impossible to believe that the critical mass of the first crushing point can be in error by anything like 10 or 15 per cent. Furthermore, the theoretical value of the critical mass is consistent with the observed upper limit of the masses of white dwarfs.[13]

The second group of calculated equilibrium configurations, from b to c in Figure 10-5, covers the range from roughly half the density of nuclear matter to roughly 30 times the density of nuclear matter, and from $0.2M_\odot$ to $0.7M_\odot$. At the upper end of this domain, one is approaching the region on the equation of state of Figure 10-1 where the pressure p is not far below the limit $\rho c^2/3 = 3 \times 10^{20}\rho$. Such a pressure, it is already clear from the simplified neutron model of Figure 10-3, can never sustain a sphere of fermions against collapse. As the radius diminishes, the kinetic energy and weight of these nucleons goes up without limit, and gravitational forces win completely over the pressure.

If hyperons are produced in greater and greater numbers at high compressions, it is conceivable that more and more states can be made available in phase space without going to indefinitely high momenta. Then the pressure will not rise so close to $\rho c^2/3$ as would be expected from the equation of state in Figure 10-1. In this case crushing or collapse of the neutron star will occur at a *smaller* mass than that indicated in Figure 10-5. This effect does not manifest itself at ordinary nuclear densities—otherwise nuclear matter would not have its well-known high elasticity.[14]

Incompressibility: Unreasonable—But Discussable

What about the opposite assumption of an arbitrarily *high* pressure, such as would be given by an incompressible fluid? We ask this because of the prevalence of the concept of a so-called hard-core nucleon-nucleon interaction. The difficulties of this idea at relativistic velocities are evident, as are the more familiar problems with the conception of an electron of finite radius. In either case, in whose frame of reference is the radius to be measured? When the two colliding particles suffer a great change in relative momentum, is one expected to define the radius in an accelerated frame of reference; and if so, how? Is one to think of retarded interactions or time-symmetric interactions? No satisfactory answer has ever been given to such questions, nor to a still more pertinent inquiry: What justification is there in the known principles of physics, or what decisive indication is there in experiment, to think any such interaction makes any sense or is needed at relativistic velocities? Despite all these objections to the concept of an incompressible fluid, and despite the fact that a velocity of sound greater than c would violate causality in the most impossible way, it is of interest to look at the properties of a model star built from an incompressible fluid:

(1) because the state of affairs in such an idealized object is very easily analyzed; and (2) because *even for an incompressible fluid one finds that he cannot escape from the concept of a critical mass!*

The Nonrelativistic Case

For a first survey of the properties of a spherical mass of incompressible fluid, consider the case where the mass is so small that general relativity effects can be neglected. In other words, the curvature of space is slight. The gravitational red shift is negligible. The gravitational potential energy $\phi(r)$ of a unit test mass is small compared to the rest energy c^2 of that test mass.

Let ρ represent the density and R the radius of the sphere of fluid. Its mass is

$$M = (4\pi\rho/3)R^3 \tag{38}$$

The gravitational pull on a unit mass outside is

$$g(r) = d\phi/dr = G(4\pi\rho/3)(R^3/r^2) \tag{39}$$

and, on a unit test mass in a hole bored through the interior,

$$g(r) = d\phi/dr = G(4\pi\rho/3)(r^3/r^2) \tag{40}$$

The gravitational potential itself outside looks like that of a point mass. Inside it follows the dependence upon distance of a simple harmonic oscillator potential. More significant than the potential itself is the dimensionless quotient of the potential divided by c^2: the ratio between gravitational energy and rest energy; or still better, the ratio between total energy (gravitational *plus* rest energy) and rest energy alone. Thus,

$$\left\{\frac{\text{energy of a particle at rest}}{\text{energy at rest at infinity}}\right\}_{\substack{\text{Newtonian} \\ \text{value}}} = 1 + \phi(r)/c^2$$

$$= \begin{cases} 1 - (8\pi G\rho/3c^2)(R^3/2r) & \text{outside} \\ 1 - (8\pi G\rho/3c^2)[(3R^2/4) - (r^2/4)] & \text{inside} \end{cases} \tag{41}$$

General Relativity Solution

K. Schwarzschild studied the same problem in the context of general relativity. He chose for convenience a radial coordinate r such that proper distance on a circle about the origin is given by r multiplied by the change in the angular coordinate:

$$ds^2 = -e^{\nu(r)} dt^2 + e^{\lambda(r)} dr^2 + r^2(d\theta^2 + \sin^2\theta \, d\phi^2)$$

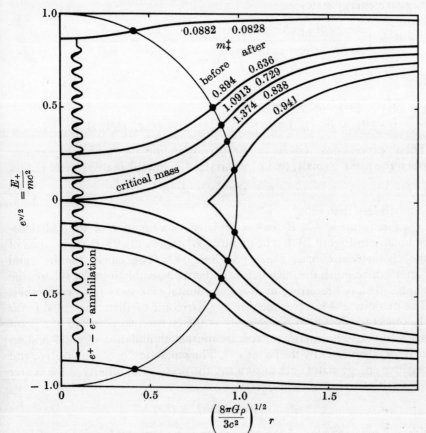

Figure 10-8 The general relativistic analog of the gravitational potential ($e^{\nu/2}$) plotted as a function of distance for selected values of the mass of a sphere of incompressible fluid.

The dilation factors $\nu(r)$ and $\lambda(r)$ are found from Einstein's field equations. The radial correction factor is

$$e^{-\lambda(r)} = \begin{cases} 1 - (8\pi G\rho/3c^2)(R^3/r) & \text{outside} \\ 1 - (8\pi G\rho/3c^2)r^2 & \text{inside} \end{cases} \tag{42}$$

reducing to unity at the center, as is required for regularity of the geometry there. More interesting because of its connection with the Newtonian gravitational potential is the time-dilation factor $e^{\nu(r)}$, the square root of which measures the separation between Dirac's seas of positive and negative energy states:

$$e^{\nu/2} = \left\{\frac{\text{energy of a particle at rest}}{\text{energy at rest at infinity}}\right\}_{\substack{\text{Einstein}\\\text{value}}} = \frac{E_+}{mc^2} = \frac{-E_-}{mc^2} = \frac{E_+ - E_-}{2mc^2}$$

(43)

$$= \begin{cases} [1 - (8\pi G\rho/3c^2)(R^3/r)]^{1/2} & \text{outside} \\ (3/2)[1 - (8\pi G\rho/3c^2)R^2]^{1/2} - (1/2)[1 - (8\pi G\rho/3c^2)r^2]^{1/2} & \text{inside} \end{cases}$$

These expressions reduce to the corresponding Newtonian expressions when the mass is small; that is, when the dimensionless measure of radius,

$$x = (8\pi G\rho/3c^2)^{1/2}R \tag{44}$$

is much less than unity.

The factor $e^{\nu/2} = E_+/mc^2$ is depicted as a function of the radial coordinate r in Figure 10-8. The quantity $m^\dagger$ represents the mass in units of the characteristic mass $(4\pi\rho/3)(3c^2/8\pi G\rho)^{3/2}$. The labels "before" and "after" distinguish the mass before and after assembly into the sphere, the phrase "before" referring to droplets infinitely far away from each other. The quantity $e^{\nu/2}$ behaves roughly as a harmonic oscillator potential *inside* the object (dashed line) and roughly as the Newtonian potential of a point mass *outside*. The energy set free by mutual annihilation of an e^+ and an e^- is less than $2mc^2$ by the factor $e^{\nu/2}$. The separation between positive and negative energy states goes to zero and the pressure to infinity at the center for a critical value of the mass[15]:

$$m^\dagger{}_{\text{critical}} = 0.8382 = (8/9)^{3/2}$$

For any greater value of the mass there is no acceptable solution of Einstein's field equations.

Decrease of Interval between Positive and Negative Energy States

The factor $e^{\nu/2} = E_+/mc^2$ has a simple significance. Consider the mutual annihilation of a positive and a negative electron. Under normal circumstances the energy release is $2mc^2$. One will find the same energy release when he proceeds as follows: Set the e^+ and the e^- free at great distances on opposite sides of the star. Let them be drawn toward the fluid sphere at ever-increasing speed by its gravitational attraction. Let them enter the opposite ends of a pipe thrust through the center of the object. Let them meet at the middle and annihilate. Let the two resulting high-energy photons ($E_\gamma > mc^2$) escape through the opposite ends of the pipe to infinite distance, undergoing gravitational red shift en route. Then each of the two gamma rays observed at infinity will have the energy mc^2. Now change the procedure to this extent. Lower the two particles *slowly* to the center by way of ideal long strings so that they annihilate with zero relative kinetic energy. The work done on the electrons by the gravitational force is now all given up to the experimenter through the strings that he manipulates. The annihilation gamma rays each have energy mc^2 in the Lorentz frame of reference appropriate to the center of the star. However, when the gamma rays get to infinity, each has the smaller energy, $mc^2 e^{\nu/2}$. The difference

$$2mc^2 - 2mc^2 e^{\nu/2}$$

represents the mechanical energy that the experimenter has been able to secure in the operation.

It is impossible, in principle, to secure from the electron pair (originally at rest at infinity) any more than the energy $2mc^2$. Therefore it is impossible for the factor $e^{\nu/2}$ ever to fall to a value less than zero. However, the calculated value of this factor—or the distance between Dirac's seas of positive and negative energy states—at the center of the fluid mass decreases monotonically to zero as the mass rises to the critical value (measured after assembly);

$$M_{\text{crit}} = 0.838(4\pi\rho/3)(3c^2/8\pi G\rho)^{3/2} \tag{45}$$

Any larger value for the mass of a *static* fluid sphere is not compatible with reasonable physics.

Pressure Diverges

Is there any way for the fluid itself to feel that the critical condition is being approached, apart from the fact that the difference between positive and negative energy states is going to zero? The *pressure* supplies such a physical effect. The pressure at the center becomes higher and higher and goes to infinity at the critical mass. Figure 10-9 shows the pressure as a function of the distance for various values of the mass, as calculated from the general relativity formula

$$p = \rho c^2 \frac{(1 - x^2)^{1/2} - (1 - x_R^2)^{1/2}}{3(1 - x_R^2)^{1/2} - (1 - x^2)^{1/2}} \tag{46}$$

Here x is the dimensionless radial coordinate of Eq. (43) and x_R is the value of this coordinate at the surface of the sphere.[16] One can say that the critical mass is inadmissible in a static situation because the pressure cannot become infinite.

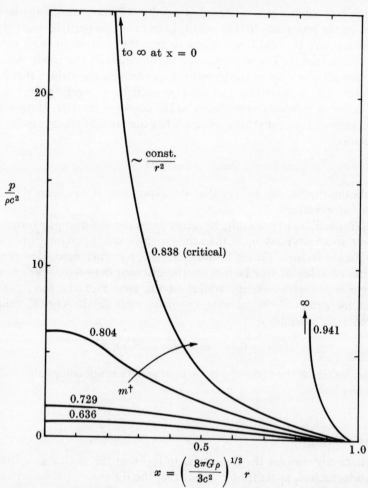

Figure 10-9 Pressure (in units ρc^2) as a function of distance from the center [in units $(3c^2/8\pi G\rho)^{1/2}$] as calculated from general relativity for a mass of incompressible fluid. The total mass of the fluid is given in units of $(4\pi/3)(3c^2/8\pi G\rho)^{3/2}$ by the mass parameter $m^\dagger$. The calculated pressure already goes to infinity at the center when $m^\dagger = 0.838$. Also the separation of positive and negative energy states goes to zero at that point (Figure 10-8). For a typical higher mass $m^\dagger = 0.941$ the separation of positive and negative energy states goes to zero farther out.

Existence of a Critical Mass Inescapable

Let us summarize this discussion of idealized models and the influence of one or the other equation of state upon the question of criticality. Evidently no equation of state—even the most extreme and nonphysical case

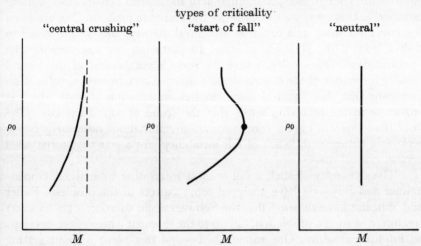

types of criticality

"central crushing" "start of fall" "neutral"

Figure 10-10 Curve for total mass as a function of central density as a means for distinguishing types of criticality: (1) "Central crushing," where the difficulty with a mass of the critical value or greater is the infinity in the pressure at the center. (2) "Start of fall" instability, where a system with more than the critical mass will fall inward at ever increasing speed. The type of instability is governed by the equation of state. Therefore one can define in principle a *neutral equation of state* for which one has the "neutral condition" of diagram (3). Here one is at the point of transition from "central crushing instability" to "start of fall instability."

of incompressibility—offers any escape from the conclusion that there is a *limit to the mass of any stable static collection of cold catalyzed matter.*

Two Kinds of Criticality

Any uncertainties about the equation of state of superdense matter affect, not the *existence* of a critical point, but its *character*. The analysis has disclosed two kinds of conceivable critical points, which for want of better names we may call the "central crushing" criticality and "start of fall" criticality.

The "central crushing" type of criticality is characterized by a pressure which grows without limit as the critical mass is approached. Examples are (1) the idealized e-Fe^{56} model of Figure 2; (2) Chandrasekhar's more detailed analysis of a gas consisting of electrons and nuclei.

So far the procedure has been to assume or to calculate an equation of state, and then to integrate the general relativity equations of hydrostatic equilibrium, and thus to find the mass and other properties of the equilibrium configuration as a function of the central density (the "catalog number"). However, we can consider the converse problem: We are *given* the curve for mass as a function of central density, and we are asked to *deduce* from it the equation of state. In particular, we can consider the "neutral case" (Figure 10), where the mass is *independent* of the central density for values of the central density above a certain critical value. Can one show that this "neutral case" implies an equation of state which is *impossible* in the following sense, that the speed of sound exceeds $c/3^{1/2}$ or c? If so, one will have a conclusive argument that one necessarily has to reckon in nature with "start of fall instability" for a star that surpasses a certain critical mass.

The dynamics of such a fall is most interesting to analyze. Oppenheimer and Snyder[17] have analyzed some aspects of the problem. Fuller and Wheeler have shown[18] that the Schwarzschild solution gives an exact treatment of such a problem of fall up to the moment where space develops an infinite curvature. One cannot go beyond this point without getting into deep issues of quantum physics and quantized general relativity.

No Way Evident to Uphold Law of Conservation of Baryons at Very High Pressures

Regardless of these unsolved problems, there appears no way to escape this over-all assessment of the situation: *The law of conservation of baryons must be abandoned* for a star that exceeds the critical baryon number. Thus, when one more kilo of baryons is added to such a star, either (1) the number of baryons remains at the *same* critical value as before the extra kilo was added, or (2) it is *increased* by the number of baryons contained in 1 kilo, or (3) it is an *undefined* quantity. If (1) applies, clearly baryons have been destroyed. If (2) applies, an indefinitely large number of baryons can be compressed into a finite amount of space—which is to say that the concept of the conservation of baryon number has no useful content; and so also in case (3).

It appears therefore that there is no escape from regarding a system of critical mass as a catalyzer which (by way of pressures enormously greater than those in nuclear matter) can convert nucleons into free radiation. The further analysis of the conservation laws associated with this transformation process—regarded as a *reversible* transformation— would seem to be one of the truly central problems of relativity physics.

References and Notes

1. The present survey draws on an earlier account by B. K. Harrison, M. Wakano, and J. A. Wheeler, "La Structure et l'évolution de l'univers," in *Inst. Intern. Phys.*, Stoops, Brussels, 1958 (cited hereafter as SÉU), and on additional

considerations in J. A. Wheeler, *Geometrodynamics*, Academic, New York, 1962 (cited hereafter as GMD), and on A. G. W. Cameron, *Astrophys. J.*, **130**, 884 (1959). See also E. E. Salpeter, *Ann. Phys.*, **11**, 393 (1960); *Astrophys. J.*, **134**, 669 (1961); and T. Hamada and E. E. Salpeter, *Astrophys. J.*, **134**, 683 (1961). For the first analysis of star collapse, and order-of-magnitude considerations showing that the critical mass for collapse of a *neutron* star is of the same order as the critical mass of a star sustained by *electron* pressure, see L. Landau, *Phys. Z. Sowjetunion*, **1**, 285 (1932). For more on the subject of neutron stars see J. R. Oppenheimer and R. Serber, *Phys. Rev.*, **54**, 540 (1938). See also References 8 and 12.

2. For a recent discussion of the possibilities of seeing such an object with the help of a telescope in space, see Lyman Spitzer, Jr., "The Beginnings and Future of Space Astronomy," *Am. Sci.*, **50**, 473 (1962).

3. For a review of work on this subject, see M. Schwarzschild, *Structure and Evolution of the Stars*, Princeton University Press, Princeton, N.J., 1958.

4. Hyperon and meson creation is neglected in this analysis of the high-pressure limit—a neglect which produces a *too high* pressure for a given density. On this conservative way of calculating one says (1) that the only particles present are neutrons, protons, and electrons, and (2) that the number densities of electrons and protons must be equal (charge neutrality). Then the Fermi momenta of electrons and protons are equal. This equality of momenta implies in the relativistic limit that the proton and electron Fermi energies are equal to each other and half as great as the Fermi energy of the neutron. Hence the number densities of protons and electrons are 1/8 that of neutrons.

5. An additional point should be mentioned. The number density of electrons n is (26/56) of the number density of nucleons a for the electron gas surrounding Fe^{56} nuclei. In contrast, the "nucleon" gas (under the assumed conditions of nucleonic interactions negligible compared to the relativistic energies of the nucleons) contains a number density of neutrons equal to $(8/9)a$ and a number density of protons—and electrons—equal to $(1/9)a$. Thus the pressure in the case of iron is

$$p = (26/56)^{4/3}(2\pi c/3h^3)(3h^3a/8\pi)^{4/3}$$

and in the case of neutrons is

$$p = [(8/9)^{4/3} + 2(1/9)^{4/3}](2\pi c/3h^3)(3h^3a/8\pi)^{4/3}$$

6. M. Rudkjøbing, *Pub. Københavns Obs.*, **No. 160**, 1952.

7. Ya. B. Zel'dovich [*Zh. Eksperim. i Teor. Fiz.*, **41**, 1609 (1961); translation in *JETP*, **14**, 1143 (1962)] has argued that a spin-one vector boson coupling between nucleons would work at high densities in such a way as to produce high rigidity and a speed of sound equal, not to $c/3^{1/2}$, but to c itself. Even such a rigidity cannot be compared with that of an incompressible fluid—for which there is still a finite critical mass. The author is indebted to Dr. H. Y. Chiu for reference to this paper and for discussion of this and other points.

8. A. G. W. Cameron, *Astrophys. J.*, **130**, 884 (1959).

9. V. A. Ambartsumyan and G. S. Saakyan, *Astron. Zh.*, **37**, 193 (1960), translated in *Soviet Astron.*, **4**, 187 (1960).

10. For densities up to 10^{15} g/cm^3 (roughly 7 times normal nuclear values), T. H. R. Skyrme [*Nuclear Phys.*, **9**, 615 (1959)] has calculated an equation of state, which, if extrapolated to 2×10^{15} g/cm^3 and higher densities would give (Fig. 2 of Cameron[8]) a pressure p in *excess* of $\rho c^2/3$. This circumstance would

seem sufficient reason for not employing this extrapolation in predicting the properties of the densest neutron stars.

11. The exact expression for the average energy (rest plus kinetic) per fermion is

$$E_{av}/m_1c^2 = (1 + x^2)^{1/2} - (8x^3)^{-1}[x(2x^2 - 3)(1 + x^2)^{1/2} + 3 \text{ arcsinh } x]$$

where

$$x = 4/3r = p_F/m_1c$$

This formula was used in calculating the middle column of Table 10-4. It was given by S. Chandrasekhar, *Monthly Notices Roy. Astronom. Soc.*, **95**, 207 (1935). See also M. Schwarzschild, *Structure and Evolution of the Stars*, Princeton University Press, Princeton, New Jersey, 1958, p. 57.

12. J. R. Oppenheimer and G. Volkoff, *Phys. Rev.*, **55**, 374 (1939).

13. See, for example, M. Schwarzschild, Reference 11.

14. See, for example, K. A. Brueckner and K. S. Masterson, Jr., *Phys. Rev.*, **128**, 2267 (1962).

15. *Note*: The mass before assembly, expressed in terms of the dimensionless parameter $x = (8\pi G\rho/3c^2)^{1/2}R$, and measured in the characteristic unit

$$(4\pi\rho/3)(3c^2/8\pi G\rho)^{3/2}$$

is

$$m_{before} = (3/2)[\arcsin x - x(1 - x^2)^{1/2}]$$

and after assembly is

$$m_{after} = x^3$$

The difference is represented for all allowable masses [m_{after} up to $(8/9)^{3/2}$] within better than 10 per cent by the Newtonian formula for the gravitational energy of a sphere,

$$(m_{before} - m_{after})_{Newtonian} = (3/10)(m_{after})^{5/3}$$

16. This general expression for the pressure reduces in the nonrelativistic limit to the standard Newtonian formula:

$$p = (\rho c^2/4)(x_R^2 - x^2) = (2\pi G\rho^2/3)(R^2 - r^2)$$

In the opposite limiting case of a mass close to the critical mass, or radius of the sphere close to the critical value $(3c^2/8\pi G\rho)^{1/2}(8/9)^{1/2}$, thus

$$x_R = (8/9)^{1/2}(1 - \epsilon)$$

one finds for the pressure near the center

$$p = \frac{(4\rho c^2/3)}{(4\epsilon^{1/2})^2 + x^2}$$

17. J. R. Oppenheimer and H. Snyder, *Phys. Rev.*, **56**, 455 (1939).

18. R. W. Fuller and J. A. Wheeler, *Phys. Rev.*, **128**, 919 (1962).

II
Gravitation and light

J. Weber

Gravitational Deflection of Light by a Nonrelativistic Method

The idea that light interacts with a gravitational field originated more than a century ago. In 1801 Soldner[1] considered the deflection of light by the sun's gravitational field from the point of view of the corpuscular theory and from Newton's laws of motion.

Consider the photon as a particle of mass m (it turns out that m is canceled out in the equation of motion, so that we do not need to worry about what value of m we must assign to a photon). It passes through the vicinity of a larger mass M as shown in Figure 11-1. Let the impact parameter be R. We use rectangular coordinates, such that, at infinity, the path of light is parallel to the x axis and the deflection of light occurs in the x-y plane. The equation of motion is

$$m \frac{d^2 y}{dt^2} = - \frac{GMm}{r^2} \frac{y}{r} \tag{1}$$

where

$$r^2 = x^2 + y^2 \tag{2}$$

If the deflection is small, then $y \approx R$. We write $x = ct$. With these substitutions, Eq. (1) may immediately be integrated to give

$$\frac{dy}{dx} = \frac{GMx}{c^2 R} \frac{1}{(x^2 + R^2)^{1/2}} \tag{3}$$

The angle of deflection of the path of light is

$$\theta \simeq \left(\frac{dy}{dx}\right)_{x=-\infty} - \left(\frac{dy}{dx}\right)_{x=+\infty} = - \frac{2GM}{Rc^2} \tag{4}$$

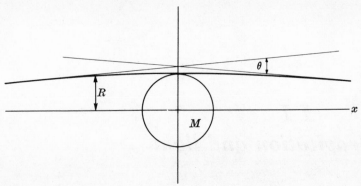

Figure 11-1   The path of a light beam bent by the gravitational field of the sun.

This is one-half the value predicted by Einstein and confirmed by astronomical observations during total solar eclipses. The disagreement in the two theories occurred because Soldner used the wrong equation of motion. His equation is valid for slow particles, but photons are not slow. We shall derive Einstein's result in the next section.

Relativistic Light Bending

The geodesic equation is

$$\frac{d^2y}{ds^2} + \Gamma^y_{\mu\nu}\frac{dx^\mu}{ds}\frac{dx^\nu}{ds} = 0 \qquad (5)$$

For light, all intervals are null. s is a parameter along the path. We may choose $s = x^0 = ct$. $\Gamma^\alpha_{\beta\gamma}$ is the Christoffel symbol of the second kind. If we use isotropic coordinates, ds^2 for the lowest order of departure from a Minkowskian line element is given as

$$-ds^2 \cong \left(1 + \frac{2GM}{rc^2}\right)(dx^2 + dy^2 + dz^2) - \left(1 - \frac{2GM}{rc^2}\right)c^2\,dt^2 \qquad (6)$$

With this metric, $\Gamma^y_{ox} = 0$. For the above choice of the parameter s, and for light traveling along the x axis, $dx^0/ds = 1$ and $dx/ds = 1$. To a good approximation, Eq. (5) becomes

$$\frac{d^2y}{dx^2} + \Gamma^y_{oo} + \Gamma^y_{xx} = 0 \qquad (7)$$

We have neglected terms involving the y component of velocity since it is very small. From the definition of $\Gamma^\alpha_{\beta\gamma}$ and Eq. (6), we have

$$\Gamma^y_{oo} = -\frac{1}{2}\frac{\partial g_{oo}}{\partial y} = \frac{GM}{r^2c^2}\frac{\partial r}{\partial y} = \frac{GMy}{c^2(x^2+y^2)^{3/2}} \tag{8}$$

$$\Gamma^y_{xx} = -\frac{1}{2}\frac{\partial g_{xx}}{\partial y} = \frac{GM}{r^2c^2}\frac{\partial r}{\partial y} = \frac{GMy}{c^2(x^2+y^2)^{3/2}} \tag{9}$$

where $\partial r/\partial y = y/r$. The deflection of light by a mass center can then be computed:

$$\theta = \left(\frac{dy}{dx}\right)_{-\infty} - \left(\frac{dy}{dx}\right)_{+\infty} = -4\frac{GM}{rc^2} \tag{10}$$

It is easy to see why we get an extra factor of 2. The deflection is given by the contribution of two identical terms Γ^x_{oo} and Γ^y_{xx}, each of which is equivalent to Eq. (1). In the classical theory, only one term is present (Γ^y_{oo}). At low velocity $dx/ds \sim v/c$ and $\Gamma^y_{xx}v^2 \ll \Gamma^y_{oo}c^2$; at $v = c$, both terms contribute equally. We can say the photon acts as if it has a gravitational mass twice its inertial mass.

Effect of the Photon Spin

Although in Eq. (2) we have taken into account the relativistic effect, we have not taken into account the spin of the photon. The equations of motion for spinning particles are somewhat different from the equations for spinless particles. I shall only state the results.[2] The angle of deflection is

$$\theta = -\frac{4GM}{Rc^2}\left(1 - \frac{\lambda}{R}\right) \tag{11}$$

if the spin of the photon is perpendicular to its direction of motion. λ is the wavelength of the photon. If the spin of the photon is parallel to its direction of motion, the extra term λ/R drops out. However, from quantum-field theory we know that, if the particle has zero rest mass, its spin must be parallel or antiparallel to its direction of motion. There are only two spin states for such a particle; full-spin ahead and full-spin backward. Therefore, by this coincidence, the effect of the spin disappears.

Gravitational Red Shift

The gravitational red shift of light has been discussed many times. However, for completeness let me include a few words about it. In the case

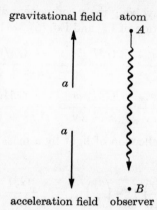

Figure 11-2 The equivalence of uniform gravitational and acceleration fields and the first-order doppler shift imply the gravitational red shift.

of the deflection of light by the sun, the naïve argument (Newtonian mechanics) does not lead to correct results, even in the first order. But for the red shift, the most naïve argument does lead to correct results in the first order, using only the principle of equivalence and the doppler-shift law.

The principle of equivalence states that, insofar as local observations are concerned, the effects of a uniform gravitational field are indistinguishable from those of an equivalent, uniform-acceleration field.

In Figure 11-2, the atom at A emits a photon of frequency ν. At some later time $t = l/c$ (where l is the distance between the observer and the atom) the observer at B in the equivalent accelerated frame detects the photon. Over this time interval t, the observer has undergone an acceleration of g, and at the end of this time interval has attained a velocity v.

$$v = gt = g(l/c) \tag{12}$$

In the gravitational field, we say this gives rise to the red shift; in the equivalent accelerated frame we call it a doppler shift. The change in frequency is, therefore,

$$\Delta \nu = -\nu \left(g \frac{l}{c} \right) \frac{1}{c} = -\nu \frac{\Delta \phi}{c^2} \tag{13}$$

Here $\Delta \phi$ is the change of gravitational potential, the potential at the location of the observer minus the potential at the location of the atom. Equation (13) is the first-order gravitational-red-shift formula.

Comparison of the Theories of Maxwell and Einstein

In the special theory of relativity, the Maxwell equations are

$$\Box A_\mu = -j_\mu \tag{14}$$

where A_μ is the four-potential and j_μ is the current density. There is a supplementary condition to Eq. (14):

$$A^\mu_{,\mu} = 0 \tag{15}$$

Equation (15) is the Lorentz gauge condition. On the other hand, the Einstein field equations are

$$R_{\mu\nu} - \tfrac{1}{2}g_{\mu\nu}R = \kappa T_{\mu\nu} \tag{16}$$

The two sets of field equations, (14) and (16), appear quite different. In classical electromagnetic theory, Eq. (14) describes the electromagnetic field in Minkowski coordinates. Charges and fields operate in a flat space in the Maxwell theory. In general relativity, the gravitational field is a property of space and is characterized by the geometry of the space. The presence of mass affects the geometry. Motions of spinless particles subjected to gravitational interactions are given by the geodesics. It was therefore believed that general relativity was fundamentally a different theory from electromagnetic theory. In recent years this view has changed somewhat.

In a more general treatment of field theories, there is a correspondence between the spin of the particle and the rank of the tensor that describes the field. In the case of the electromagnetic field, the photon has a spin 1, and a four-vector is employed. It was shown by Pauli and Fierz[3] that a second-rank symmetric-tensor field is required for relativistic wave equations for particles of spin 2. The reason for this is the following: A particle of spin 2 has five quantized spin orientations. Also there are two signs for the energy corresponding to particle states and antiparticle states. Hence we have a 10-component wave function for a spin-2 particle, which corresponds to the components of a second-rank symmetric tensor. This point is discussed in Chapter 5 in another connection.

Pauli and Fierz also showed that the relativistic wave equations for free, massless particles of spin 2 are

$$\Box U_{\mu\nu} = 0 \tag{17}$$

where $U_{\mu\nu}$ is the second-rank symmetric tensor. The supplementary condition was given by them to be:

$$U^{\mu\nu}_{,\nu} = 0 \tag{18}$$

(In this section we raise and lower indices with the Lorentz metric, $\delta^{\mu\nu}$.) Suppose now that we introduce interactions. These may be represented by some tensor $\theta_{\mu\nu}$. The field equations with interactions are then

$$\Box U_{\mu\nu} = k\theta_{\mu\nu} \tag{19}$$

Here k is a coupling constant. The supplementary condition, Eq. (18), now implies that

$$\theta^{\mu\nu}{}_{,\nu} = 0 \tag{20}$$

Since the matter stress tensor $T_{\alpha\beta}$ satisfies Eq. (20), we might associate $T_{\alpha\beta}$ with $\theta_{\mu\nu}$. The appearance of the stress tensor is to be expected in developing a theory of gravitation because stress and energy are the source of a gravitational field. The gravitational field itself is expected to contribute some stress and energy as well. We use $t_{\mu\nu}$ to denote such stress-energy. Hence the field equations are

$$\Box U_{\mu\nu} = k(T_{\mu\nu} + t_{\mu\nu}) \tag{21}$$

If $T_{\mu\nu} = 0$, the vacuum equations are obtained as

$$\Box U_{\mu\nu} = kt_{\mu\nu} \tag{21a}$$

Now we shall try to obtain Eq. (21a) from a variational principle. First we construct a Lagrangian density L for the field. The method of constructing L is described in standard textbooks on field theory[4]. The Lagrangian density for a free field is

$$L = -\tfrac{1}{2} U^{\mu\nu}{}_{,\alpha} U_{\mu\nu}{}^{,\alpha} \tag{22}$$

The action principle leads to the field equations

$$\frac{\partial}{\partial x^\alpha} \frac{\partial L}{\partial U^{\mu\nu}{}_{,\alpha}} - \frac{\partial L}{\partial U^{\mu\nu}} = 0 \tag{23}$$

An object constructed from L and satisfying the conservation law $t^\nu_{\mu,\nu} = 0$ is[5]

$$t^\nu_\mu = \delta^\nu_\mu L - U^{\alpha\beta}{}_{,\mu} \frac{\partial L}{\partial U^{\alpha\beta}{}_{,\nu}} = U^{\alpha\beta}{}_{,\mu} U_{\alpha\beta}{}^{,\nu} - \tfrac{1}{2}\delta^\nu_\mu U^{\alpha\beta}{}_{,\rho} U_{\alpha\beta}{}^{,\rho} \tag{24}$$

Equations (22) and (23) lead to the field equations

$$\Box U^{\mu\nu} = 0 \tag{25}$$

This does not include interaction of particles with themselves, according to Eq. (21a). We may obtain Eq. (21a) by adding a term f_1 to the Lagrangian density [Eq. (22)], obtaining

$$L' = -\tfrac{1}{2} U^{\mu\nu}{}_{,\alpha} U_{\mu\nu}{}^{,\alpha} + f_1 \tag{26}$$

The addition of f_1 to Eq. (26) leads to a new expression for $t_\mu{}^\nu$, which we denote by $t'_\mu{}^\nu$; so we require

$$\Box U^{\mu\nu} = t'^{\mu\nu} \tag{21b}$$

In order to obtain Eq. (21b), we must add a term f_2 to (26). But this leads to $t''_{\ \mu}{}^\nu$, which in turn leads to the requirement that new field equations

$$\Box U^{\mu\nu} = t''_{\ \mu}{}^\nu \tag{21c}$$

be obtained. By continuing this process, we obtain a Lagrangian density with an infinite number of terms. Gupta[6] carried these procedures through and found that this Lagrangian density with an infinite number of terms is indeed equal to the curvature scalar, the correct one required to deduce the equations of general relativity.

To summarize, the equations of general relativity can be deduced by using the same philosophical notions as in other field theories. We deal with particles with spin 2, and recognize that energy is the source of the gravitational field. The gravitational field itself contributes to part of the energy density, which in turn is a source of gravitational fields. This, then, leads to a nonlinear theory, to a Lagrangian density L with an infinite number of terms from which the curvature scalar can be obtained.

Electrodynamics in Arbitrary Coordinates and Its Geometrization

Equations (14) and (15) are the four-potential formulation of electrodynamics, in Lorentz frames. The field tensors $F_{\mu\nu}$ are given by

$$F_{\mu\nu} = A_{\nu,\mu} - A_{\mu,\nu} \tag{27}$$

and the Maxwell equations for $F_{\mu\nu}$ are

$$F^{\mu\nu}{}_{,\nu} = j^\mu \tag{28}$$

$$\frac{\partial F_{\alpha\beta}}{\partial x^\gamma} + \frac{\partial F_{\gamma\alpha}}{\partial x^\beta} + \frac{\partial F_{\beta\gamma}}{\partial x^\alpha} = 0 \tag{29}$$

(In this section the metric tensor $g_{\mu\nu}$ and its inverse $g^{\mu\nu}$ are used to raise and lower indices.) For any $F_{\mu\nu}$ defined in terms of a four-potential by— Eq. (27), Eq. (29) is satisfied as an identity in consequence of the vanishing of $\nabla \cdot \nabla \times A$. In arbitrary coordinates, Eq. (28) becomes

$$F^{\mu\nu}{}_{;\nu} = j^\mu \tag{30}$$

We use a semicolon to denote covariant differentiation.

Equation (29) becomes

$$[\epsilon^{\alpha\beta\gamma\delta}(-g)^{-1/2}F_{\alpha\beta}]_{;\delta} = 0 \tag{31}$$

In Eq. (31), $\epsilon^{\alpha\beta\gamma\delta}$ is the Levi Civita tensor density, $\epsilon^{0123} = 1$; it changes sign on interchange of any pair of indices and vanishes if two or more indices are the same. g is the determinant of $g_{\mu\nu}$. Using the standard formula for the covariant divergence of an antisymmetric tensor, we obtain again (29) as valid in arbitrary coordinates. The use of the standard formulas for covariant differentiation then leads to

$$A^{\nu,\mu} - A^{\mu,\nu} = A^{\nu;\mu} - A^{\mu;\nu} = F^{\mu\nu} \tag{32}$$

The generalized Lorentz gauge condition

$$A^{\mu}{}_{;\mu} = 0 \tag{33}$$

and the rules for changing the order of covariant differentiation then reduces (30) to

$$A_{\mu;\alpha}{}^{;\alpha} - R_{\mu\alpha}A^{\alpha} = -j_{\mu} \tag{34}$$

Here $R_{\mu\nu}$ is again the Ricci tensor. It seems from this that electrodynamics fits very naturally into the scheme of general relativity. But Einstein felt that this was not enough. Since the geometric interpretation of gravitation was successful, he thought perhaps one ought to try to geometrize electromagnetism.

Part of the motivation for the geometrization is the fact that, in general relativity, the gravitational forces are entirely taken into account by the geometry of the space. With electromagnetic forces, the spinless particles no longer move along geodesics, if they are charged.

For a long time it was believed that a partial geometrization of gravitation and charge-free electromagnetism could be achieved by elimination of the Maxwell field tensor[7,8] from the coupled Maxwell–Einstein equations. This can be accomplished in consequence of some quite special properties of the Maxwell tensor. These are

$$T^{\alpha}_{\alpha} = 0 \tag{35}$$

$$T^{\alpha}_{\mu}T^{\nu}_{\alpha} = \tfrac{1}{4}\delta^{\nu}_{\mu}T_{\alpha\beta}T^{\alpha\beta} \tag{36}$$

$$T_{oo} > 0 \tag{37}$$

These relations lead to the following equations:

$$R = 0 \tag{38}$$

$$R^{\beta}_{\alpha}R^{\gamma}_{\beta} = \tfrac{1}{4}\delta^{\gamma}_{\alpha}R_{\sigma\tau}R^{\sigma\tau} \tag{39}$$

$$\left[\frac{\epsilon_{\beta\lambda\mu\nu}R^{\lambda\gamma;\mu}R_{\gamma}{}^{\nu}\sqrt{-g}}{R^{\sigma\tau}R_{\sigma\tau}}\right]_{,\alpha} = \left[\frac{\epsilon_{\alpha\lambda\mu\nu}R^{\lambda\gamma;\mu}R_{\gamma}{}^{\nu}\sqrt{-g}}{R_{\sigma\tau}R^{\sigma\tau}}\right]_{,\beta} \tag{40}$$

The metric that satisfies these relations has as its source the stress energy of a field satisfying Maxwell's equation. It was shown by Witten[9] and, independently, by Penrose that the required Cauchy data to integrate these equations may correspond to more than one Maxwell field. This description is therefore not unique. The Maxwell tensor cannot be eliminated without elimination of at least part of the physics.

The attempts to achieve a complete geometrization[10] have extended over many years. When this program was begun, it was believed that gravitation and electromagnetism comprised all physics. Now geometrization would have to include quantum effects as well as the strong and weak interactions. The extraordinary difficulty inherent in such a program has resulted in its abandonment by all but a very few mathematicians and physicists.

Quantization of the Coupled Maxwell–Einstein Fields

Electrodynamics and gravitation may be written in Hamiltonian form and a quantization carried out in an approximation scheme.[11] For weak fields, we write

$$g_{\mu\nu} = \delta_{\mu\nu} + h_{\mu\nu} \tag{41}$$

We shall use roman letters for the space indices 1, 2, and 3. Coordinates may be chosen such that

$$g_{\mu 0} = \delta_{\mu 0} \tag{42}$$

With these assumptions, the Hamiltonian for the coupled Maxwell-Einstein fields may be written in the approximate form

$$H = H_{\mathrm{G}} + H_{\mathrm{M}} + \int \left(h_{rs}\eta_r\eta_s/8 - 2h_{lj}F_{ml}F_{dj}\delta^{md} \right) d^3x \tag{43}$$

In Eq. (43), H_{G} contains only the gravitational field variables and momenta; H_{M} contains only the Maxwell field variables A_k and the canonical momenta η_k. Let us consider the interaction terms in Eq. (43), when the theory is quantized. It is seen to be made up of sums of products, each containing one gravitational field operator and two Maxwell field operators. This interaction implies that a photon can decay into another photon and a graviton (Figure 11-3). A careful study of this process shows that the matrix elements for it do not vanish unless all three particles propagate in the same direction. However, all three particles have zero-rest mass. Energy

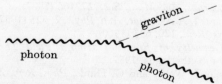

Figure 11-3 The decay of a photon into a photon and a graviton.

and momentum can be strictly conserved only if all particles propagate in the same direction. Therefore, this process cannot occur except, conceivably, at extreme energy where strict conservation of energy can be somewhat relaxed. By extreme energies we mean energies much greater than 10^{28} electron volts. This kind of process cannot, therefore, explain the red shift as a "tired-light" mechanism during the long propagation time from distant galaxies.

Further study of the interaction shows that we may expect graviton production if photons are incident on a coulomb field or a magnetostatic field. The cross section is very small. For a coulomb scatterer containing uniform electric or magnetic fields, with linear dimensions all large compared with the wavelength of the incident photon, the cross section for this process is

$$S = \frac{8\pi^2 GUl}{c^4} \tag{44}$$

Here U is the energy of the scatterer and l its linear dimension in the direction of propagation of the photon. For laboratory experiments, the cross section appears much too small. Thus, a cubic meter containing 10^{15} ergs of electric energy has $S \approx 10^{-30}$ cm^2. A galaxy with a magnetic field $\approx 10^{-6}$ gauss would have a cross section of $\approx 10^{28}$ cm^2 and convert roughly 1 part in 10^{16} of the incident photons to gravitons by this process. We note the absence of Planck's constant in (44). The interaction of two Boson fields has a classical limit. This is expressed by Eq. (44).

Acknowledgment. Research supported in part by the U.S. Air Force and in part by the National Science Foundation.

References

1. Soldner, *Berliner Astronomisches Jahrbuch* for 1804, p. 161, Späthen, Berlin, 1801.
2. E. Corinaldesi and A. Papapetrou, *Proc. Roy. Soc. (London)*, **A209**, 259 (1951).
3. M. Fierz and W. Pauli, *Proc. Roy. Soc. (London)*, **173**, 211 (1939).
4. See, for example: L. D. Landau and E. M. Lifshitz, *The Classical Theory of Fields*, Addison-Wesley, Reading, Mass, 1951.
5. J. Weber, *General Relativity and Gravitational Waves*, Interscience, New York, 1961, p. 73.
6. S. N. Gupta, *Phys. Rev.*, **46**, 1683 (1954).
7. G. Y. Rainich, *Trans. Am. Math. Soc.*, **27**, 106 (1927).
8. C. W. Misner and J. A. Wheeler, *Ann. Phys.*, **2**, 525 (1957).
9. L. Witten, *Phys. Rev.*, **120**, 635 (1960).
10. V. Hlavaty, *Geometry of Einstein's Unified Field Theory*, P. Noordhoff, Groningen, The Netherlands, 1957.
11. See, for example, J. Weber and G. Hinds, *Phys. Rev.*, **28**, 2414, (1962).

12
Possible effects on the solar system of φ waves if they exist

R. H. Dicke

Properties of a Long-Range Scalar Field

A ϕ wave is a wave in a long-range, i.e., zero-mass chargeless, scalar field. The question of the existence of these waves is probably the most important part of the title of this lecture—and the part about which we can say the least. On the other hand, we can describe with reasonable confidence the basic properties of these waves that follow from the requirement of relativistic invariance and the results of certain experimental observations. So we are in the unusual situation of knowing more about the properties of this field than about its existence.

I shall briefly review some of these properties, which are discussed in Chapters 7 and 8. In those two chapters, a long-range scalar field was introduced into gravitation theory in order to modify general relativity in such a way as to make it more compatible with requirements of Mach's principle. In such a modified theory, there are two alternative mathematical forms that the equations may take. In the first form, matter behaves in an ordinary fashion; that is, the rest mass and physical dimensions are constant from place to place. But in this form, the Einstein field equations are not valid. In the second form of the theory, the Einstein field equations are valid, but the scalar field, instead of appearing as part of the description of gravitation, appears as an ordinary matter field (such as electromagnetism). The scalar field has the interesting property that it affects the rest masses of elementary particles, hence that it gives rise to nonconstant atomic dimensions.

In the first form, the Jordan-type theory, the variational principle has the form

$$0 = \delta \int \left[\phi R + \frac{16\pi}{c^4}L - \frac{\omega \phi_{,i}\phi^{,i}}{\phi} \right] \sqrt{-g} \, d^4x \tag{1}$$

The first term, essential for the field equations for the components of the metric tensor, contains the scalar curvature R multiplied by the scalar field ϕ. The presence of ϕ in this term is responsible for the departure of these equations from the Einstein form. The second term, involving only the matter Lagrangian L, yields the usual geodesic equations for the motion of particles. The last term, along with a contribution from the first term, gives rise to a wave equation for the scalar field ϕ:

$$\Box \phi = \frac{8\pi}{(2\omega + 3)}T \tag{2}$$

$\Box \phi$ is the d'Alembertian of ϕ, T is the contracted energy momentum tensor for all particles and fields, and ω is a dimensionless coupling constant for the scalar field. ω is of the order of magnitude of unity. A comparison with observations suggests a value of at least 6. The gravitational constant G, which does not appear explicitly in the variation principle, is determined by the value of ϕ ($G \sim 1/\phi$).

The second form of the theory can be obtained by a transformation that corresponds to a redefinition of the units. Under this transformation, the units of length, time, and reciprocal mass are changed by a scale factor that is a function of ϕ, and the variational principle takes the form

$$0 = \delta \int \left[\bar{R} + \frac{16\pi G}{c^4}(\bar{L} + L_\phi) \right] \sqrt{-g} \, d^4x \tag{3}$$

The new curvature scalar $\bar{R}$ is obtained by a conformal transformation on the old one. The new Lagrangian density for matter $\bar{L}$ is modified as a result of the transformation of units. L_ϕ is the new Lagrangian density of the scalar "matter" field. In this form of the theory, the Einstein field equations for the components of the metric tensor are valid but the equations of motion of particles are modified. The scalar field enters as a long-range interaction of matter rather than as part of the description of the gravitation field (hence the geometry). Physically, both forms of the theory are equivalent. However, for the purpose of discussing ϕ waves, the second form given by Eq. (3) is more convenient. It is easier to visualize the effects of an ordinary long-range matter interaction than the effects of the complicated coupling between the ϕ field and the metric tensor as given by Eq. (1). The wave equation for ϕ from Eq. (3) is

$$\overline{\Box}(\ln \phi) = \frac{8\pi G \bar{T}}{c^4(3 + 2\omega)} \tag{4}$$

where $\overline{T}$ is the contracted energy momentum tensor derived from L only. In this form of the theory the mass of a particle is a function of the variable ϕ, such that

$$m = m_0\phi^{-1/2} \tag{5}$$

where m_0 is a constant. We may introduce this into Eq. (4) by writing the contracted energy-momentum tensor of matter:

$$\overline{T} = \overline{T}_0\phi^{-1/2} \tag{6}$$

where $\overline{T}_0$ does not contain ϕ explicitly. Then Eq. (4) becomes

$$\Box(\ln\phi) = \frac{8\pi G}{c^4(3 + 2\omega)}\overline{T}_0\phi^{-1/2} \tag{7}$$

Astronomical Sources of ϕ waves

Most astronomical bodies are of sufficiently low density that the generation of the gravitational field, as well as the scalar field (if it exists), can be treated adequately with the weak field approximation. The remainder of the lecture implicitly assumes the weak field approximation, with the zero-order approximation expressed in a coordinated system locally Minkowskian.

An interesting property of Eq. (4) is that, for matter in a localized bound system occupying a certain fixed volume over a long time average, the virial theorem implies that $\overline{T}$ is the integral over the volume of the total energy of this system. Consequently, for static systems the source strength of the scalar field is the same as that of gravitation, the total energy. However, $\overline{T}$ is not a strictly conserved quantity in this theory. For example, for a radially oscillating star the integral of this quantity over the star is an oscillating function of time. It oscillates about a mean value that represents the total energy of the star (Figure 12-1).

Such an oscillating star provides an oscillating monopole source for radiation of ϕ waves, which, in principle, might be detected elsewhere in space. This would be a new phenomenon that should not occur for the ordinary gravitational field. It is a well-known property of general relativity that a localized, radially oscillating star radiates no gravitational waves. This is because gravitational radiation is polarized quadrupole radiation. A radially oscillating star has spherical symmetry and cannot produce such polarized quadrupole radiation. We shall return to this in connection with the case of a collapsing star.

Another phenomenon associated with scalar monopole gravitational waves has been studied by Brill. He considered the radiation from planets moving in elliptical orbits. It is conceivable that monopole scalar-field

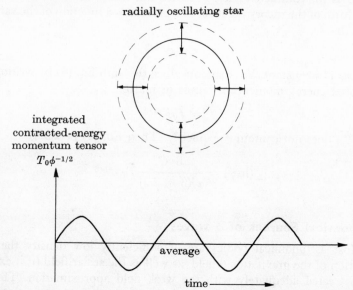

Figure 12-1 Radially oscillating star has an oscillating contracted energy-momentum tensor.

radiation would be so strong as to provide a damping mechanism for planetary motion that would be incompatible with observations. A planet moving in an eccentric elliptical orbit contributes to an oscillating contracted energy-momentum tensor integrated over the solar system (Figure 12-2). Hence monopole waves should be radiated. However, it turns out that this radiation is approximately as weak as conventional gravitational radiation resulting from the oscillating quadrupole moment of the solar system.

A collapsing star might provide a much stronger source of φ waves. The core of a massive star is believed to collapse under some circumstances

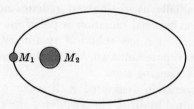

Figure 12-2 Monopole radiation for a two-particle gravitational system.

because of rapid thermodynamic change of state, which occurs at the end of thermonuclear evolution. At present, it is believed that supernova explosions are triggered by such a collapse. During the collapse phase, the quasistatic equilibrium state of the core is destroyed suddenly and the material of the star falls inward freely. The integrated contracted momentum-energy tensor $\overline{T}$ might change by nearly 100 per cent. The energy of the star, which could be radiated as a ϕ wave during such a collapse, is in order of magnitude

$$\frac{\text{energy in } \phi \text{ wave}}{\text{total energy of star}} \sim \frac{1}{(3 + 2\omega)}\left(\frac{GM}{Rc^2}\right) \tag{8}$$

where M is the mass of the star and R is the radius from which it starts to collapse. This radius can be very small since, as the core approaches the critical mass, it shrinks and becomes a degenerate body of a very small radius. (For a fuller discussion of degenerate stars, see Chapter 10.) Gm/Rc^2 may be of the order of 10^{-4}, or perhaps even larger. So we expect at least a millionth of the energy, perhaps much more, to be radiated in a wave of this kind.

It is very difficult to find mechanisms in the universe, as it exists now, by which very much larger amounts of this energy can be radiated. Another interesting possibility is the newly discovered bright compact galaxy, 3C 48.[1] If this is indeed a galaxy, and if gravitational collapse is the energy source for the unusually high optical radiation rate, such a body could be a strong source of ϕ waves. However, it would be difficult to believe that there are presently sources for this kind of a field that would lead to an energy density in space comparable to that of ordinary matter.

On the other hand, if the universe has evolved from a highly compressed state, it is possible that the early evolution of the universe could have generated a large density of ϕ waves that could have persisted until now. This could lead to a substantial part of the energy density of space being in the form of scalar-field waves.

Galactic Effects of ϕ Waves

The average energy density in scalar-field waves is related to the rate of change of the field in the following way:

$$\bar{u} \sim \frac{(3 + 2\omega)}{16\pi G}c^2\overline{\left(\frac{\dot{\phi}}{\phi}\right)^2} \tag{9}$$

where $\dot{\phi}$ is the time derivative of the field ϕ.

We can estimate the maximum possible value for $(\dot{\phi}/\phi)$ by assuming the energy density of these waves to be the average energy density required

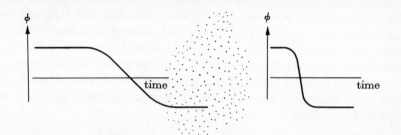

Figure 12-3   The sharpening of a wave front as a wave passes through matter.

by a cosmological model for the universe, expanding at a rate given by the Hubble constant. This energy density is about 10^{-29} g/cm³. Substituting this into Eq. (9), we get

$$\sqrt{\overline{\left(\frac{\dot{\phi}}{\phi}\right)^2}} \simeq \frac{1}{2 \times 10^{10} \text{ years}} \tag{10}$$

This is an average fractional change in the field of order of magnitude of 1 part in 10^{10} per year. Hence, if this energy density is relatively uniformly distributed, its effects would be very small and extremely difficult to observe. However, it is not clear that it is necessary to assume uniform distribution.

If there were a primordial scalar field, generated at the start of the expansion, it might be very non-uniform. Also, the character of the wave equation [Eq. (7)] provides some mechanisms that tend to sharpen the wave front. This can be seen qualitatively in the following way: Figure 12-3a shows φ at a point in space as a wave front. As this wave passes through matter, so that the local value of φ is increased, the energy associated with the matter is decreased as a consequence of the dependence of the mass of particles on φ [Eq. (5)]. Since the total energy is conserved, energy is transferred from the matter into the φ wave front (Figure 12-3b).

Another hypothetical but interesting effect of a φ wave passing through matter is provided by the "φ-wave maser." This might operate on the scale of a galaxy. In a galaxy of some 10^{11} stars, many are at the stage for which their burned-out core is approaching the critical Chandrasekhar limit beyond which they will undergo unstable collapse. A slight increase in the gravitational constant would lower the critical mass so that all those stars that were nearing the collapse point would suddenly exceed it and, as a consequence, begin an unstable collapse. This collapsing star then radiates a ϕ wave contributing to the strength of the wave front, as previously described. Thus we can visualize a ϕ wave passing through a galaxy initiating the collapse of many white-dwarf stars, which then contribute wavelets to maintaining and strengthening the wave front.

Conceivably, this model could be used to explain associated production of supernova that has been postulated as an explanation for very intense, extragalactic radio sources. These sources appear to be radiating energy at a rate too great to be due to a single supernova. It is necessary to assume a large number of supernova to produce radio sources this strong. Burbidge has argued that, in the center of the galaxy, there are many stars that have reached a critical state, about ready to become supernovae. By chance one goes off and produces a shock-wave that sets off others. Unfortunately, it has never been made quite clear how one supernova would set off another.

The ϕ-wave model provides a possible mechanism for associated production of supernova. A galaxy with 10^5 or 10^6 stars about ready to explode encounters a ϕ wave in the form of an extraordinarily large bump in the gravitational constant. All those stars that are ready to go, go all at once, each one radiating a ϕ wave capable of triggering other supernova explosions. All these supernova explosions acting in concert could stir up the ionized gas of the galaxy sufficiently to provide a very strong radio source.

There is another rather interesting effect that can occur to a degenerate star which has a mass very near the critical mass. Under these conditions, its equilibrium radius and energy are a very sensitive function of the gravitational constant. A change of perhaps 1 part in 10^6 in the gravitational constant could affect the total energy to the order of 1 per cent or so. If such a greatly contracted star were intercepted by a ϕ wave, corresponding to a weakening of gravity, the star would puff up to reach its new equilibrium size, and in doing so would absorb some energy from the ϕ field. On the other hand, if the ϕ wave corresponded to an increasing gravitational constant, it would cause a further contraction and decrease in energy of the star. In this way, the equilibrium energy of the star could be a rather sensitive function of the ϕ field. If the wave front were sufficiently sharp, so that the star could not follow the change in ϕ quasi-statically through a series of equilibrium states, the star might pulsate for a while about the new equilibrium state after the wave front has passed. This could lead to ϕ-wave radiation.

We have been speaking mainly of the effects of single ϕ-wave fronts without being concerned with what frequency range would characterize these waves. It is difficult to say what this range should be. The mechanisms for production of ϕ waves are not likely to be on the atomic scale.

The coupling strength of this field is of the order of 10^{-40} of other atomic-coupling strengths. Hence, competing radiation and energy exchange processes would rule out significant φ-wave radiation on an atomic scale.

It is more likely that mechanisms for φ-wave radiation would involve coupled phenomena where many particles move together. Systems of particles as large as the sun do not move together unless they move relatively slowly. Thus a reasonable lower limit for the period of φ waves is given by the free-fall time of a degenerate star. This time is in the range of seconds. However, if the main source of φ-wave radiation occurred at the time the expansion of the universe started, this radiation would have been red shifted ever since, and periods of seconds might have been shifted into hours or days. Other processes could have produced waves with periods now of the order of tens of years. We really do not know what period to expect for φ waves except that the range of hours to tens of years might be in a reasonable range. We can only say that, if such fields exist, they could have some interesting effects on galaxies and stars.

φ Waves in the Solar System

Another interesting question is whether a field of this kind would have effects on the solar system, for which we have precision observations. To be able to conclude that the field exists on the basis of what one sees in the solar system is, I think, extremely unlikely. The earth and the planets are sufficiently complicated so that there are usually alternative explanations for any small effects which might be observed. However, we can determine what the implications of φ waves impinging on the solar system would be, and then ask whether we can rule out a field of this type on the basis of what is observed.

As a starting point, I am going to assume the largest rate of G variation that might have escaped detection by present methods of observation. This rate corresponds to a fractional change in one year:

$$\frac{\Delta G}{G} \simeq 10^{-8} \tag{11}$$

This variation is considerably larger than that resulting from the secular rate of change of φ of the order of 3 parts in 10^{11}, associated with the cosmological solution of the scalar theory for an expanding closed universe (Chapter 8). In fact, if space were filled with a φ field whose time rate of change corresponds to this variation in G, the energy density of the field would be 10^4 times that permissible on astronomical grounds [Eq. (9)]. Hence, on the average, no more than 10^{-4} of space can be filled with φ waves of this strength. Thus the a priori probability of such a wave impinging on the solar system in any given year is 10^{-4}. This is a small probability.

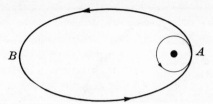

Figure 12-4   Effect on planet orbit of abrupt changes in G.

Its major significance is that we cannot rule out the existence of ϕ waves on the basis of a lack of observation of the effects of a ϕ wave of this strength. Furthermore, if we cannot rule out a G variation this large by observation, we certainly cannot rule out a more reasonable smaller variation.

What are the effects of strong ϕ waves on planetary orbits? For one thing, the eccentricity of a planetary orbit would be changed by the passage of a ϕ wave front (Figure 12-4). For example, if the ϕ wave causes a sudden decrease in G for some position A of the planet in a circular orbit, the planet will continue its motion in a new eccentric orbit B. The variation in eccentricity that would be expected from a change in G over a time short compared with the period of revolution of the planet is of the order of 10^{-8}, with the above assumptions. We expect about 10^{-4} such disturbances per year. In the 4.5×10^9 years that the solar system has been in existence, there would have been on the order of 4.5×10^5 such jumps in the eccentricity. These should occur as a random walk. Thus, the expected departure of the eccentricity of a planet, initially in a nearly circular orbit, over 10^9 years would be

$$\Delta\epsilon \simeq \sqrt{4.5 \times 10^5} \times 10^{-8} \simeq 7 \times 10^{-6} \tag{13}$$

This is much smaller than the planetary eccentricities that are observed, so that this effect does not rule out the existence of ϕ waves. Nor have I found any other effects to be observable that would have affected the forms of orbits in the solar system strongly in historical times.

On the other hand, there are uncertainties, variations, or systematic discrepancies in planetary orbits that are not understood and for which no one has an explanation. The fact that the orbits do not follow exactly what one predicts from conventional theory is a loophole for allowing disturbances of this kind to exist. For example, Clemence has pointed out that there seems to be a correlation in the residuals in Saturn's orbit and in Jupiter's orbit. It would be interesting to see whether these correlation effects could be tied to a common cause.

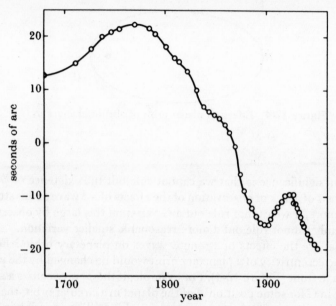

Figure 12-5   Discrepancy in the moon's longitude relative to the earth's period.

The Enigma of Irregularities in the Moon's Motion

We may also ask about the effects of φ waves for which the gravitational constant changes over a period that is long compared to the orbit period. With such a slow (adiabatic) change, the orbit merely breathes in and out without changing its eccentricity. The most interesting place to look for an effect of this sort is with the moon's motion. If the gravitational constant were to have changed slowly by 1 part in 10^8 over 200 years, the moon would move now at a new rate compared with an atomic clock. Unfortunately, we have not had atomic clocks over the last 200 years. However, we can compare the moon's motion with the earth's rotation over this period of time. Figure 12-5 shows the lunar discrepancy curve over the last 200 years. The difference between observed and calculated positions are plotted in seconds of arc. The origin is arbitrarily chosen for a zero discrepancy at 1870. In addition, there is an arbitrary constant that establishes the initial ratio of the moon and earth *clock* rates. It can be used to eliminate a linear term in the curve. The remaining wiggles and curvature are real and cannot be removed by an arbitrary choice of constants.

The points prior to 1900 fit quite well to a parabolic curve. This represents a uniform acceleration over this period with some wiggles super-imposed on top of it. The truly remarkable disturbance occurred rather recently in 1900, while fairly good observations of all kinds were being made. At this time there was a big bump in the discrepancy curve. One can interpret this particular bump in two different ways. One is to say that the rotation of the earth changed slightly. The other is to say that the period of the moon changed.

Could the earth have changed its rotation rate by a sufficient amount to account for this bump and how this could have happened? This question has been discussed rather completely by Munk and MacDonald.[2] It is an historically old problem with which many astronomers have been very much concerned, even before this very large discrepancy in 1900 was observed. To illustrate the extent of the problem, I record a statement made by the famous orbit astronomer, Newcomb, in 1902[3] and quoted by Munk and MacDonald:

> I regard these fluctuations as the most enigmatical phenomenon presented by stellar motions, being so difficult to account for by the action of any known cause that we cannot but suspect them to arise from some action in nature hitherto unknown.

Then Munk and MacDonald point out that

> Sea level variations, continental unrest, melting on Antarctica and other observable processes cannot possibly be the cause. The only known hope is the core; we have arrived at this conclusion by what Sir Edward Bullard has called the Sherlock Holmes procedure, of eliminating one possibility after another.

To account for such a large change in the earth's rotation rate requires unreasonably large disturbances on the earth. For example, the level of the sea would have to have changed by many tens of centimeters to account for this change in the earth's rotation rate.

A further difficulty in reconciling this variation with known causes is the fact that the earth's pole did not change its location appreciably in this period of time. For example, the explanation in terms of a change in the ocean level of one meter, owing to melting of ice in Antarctica, would have resulted in the north pole of the earth moving some 100 to 200 ft from where it was. This is because the Antarctic ice is not distributed sym-metrically about the earth's axis of rotation. The stability of the position of the earth's rotation axis over recent times requires that any mechanism postulated to cause a change in the moment of inertia of the earth by the necessary amount be so symmetrical as not to change the rotation axis.

Another possible cause for a change in the earth's rotation rate is a change in the angular momentum carried by the atmosphere. Unfortunately this is roughly two orders of magnitude too small to account for the observed change in rotation rate.

Could it be due to continental blocks moving up and down? We know roughly how much continents are moving vertically from observations of sea-level variations. These motions are also orders of magnitude too small to produce the necessary effect on the earth's rotation rate. Furthermore, an explanation in terms of continental blocks moving would again run into trouble with the motion of the earth's pole.

Of all the effects that could occur near the earth's surface, nothing really fits. The only remaining possibility seems to be a possible change in the angular momentum of the earth's core. This is quite difficult to get at.

But there is some evidence that the magnetic field of the earth, which is presumed to be connected with currents in the core, has been drifting from east to west. Also, there is some indication that there was a change in the rate of drift of the magnetic field at the time of the large bump in Figure 12-5. Thus, through some way not understood in detail, there could have been a transfer of angular momentum to the earth's core to change its rotation rate.

Now I would like to turn to the possibility that the discrepancy is, at least in part, due to a variation in the moon's period. It is interesting that the change in the period in 1900 of 4 parts in 10^8 is even greater than the rate of change considered in the above discussion of the effects of φ waves. It would be difficult to exclude a variation of G accounting for at least a part of this discrepancy. It is even possible that a φ wave could account for all the 1900 to 1920 disturbance.

Do φ Waves Trigger Earthquakes?

This raises the interesting question: If this were actually a change in the moon's motion, owing to a change in G rather than to a change in the earth's rotation, what other effects would be expected to be associated with this? We have concluded that one rather sensitive test for a variation of G is the frequency of earthquakes. The reason for this is the following:

Stresses across a fault plane in the earth build up slowly through normal tectonic processes. Lateral displacements of the order of 1 cm per year occur. The dimensions of a fault plane may be of the order of a thousand kilometers, with strains building up at the rate of 1 part in 10^8 per year. These strains continue to build up until the strength of the material is exceeded. Then the material flows or slips along the fault plane and earthquakes are produced.

It is clear from Figure 12-6 that the normal stresses across the fault

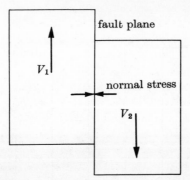

Figure 12-6 Illustration of the inhibition of earthquakes along a fault plane resulting from normal stresses.

plane will influence the ease with which motion along the fault plane can occur. Thus small changes in the normal stresses can provide a trigger mechanism for initiating or inhibiting earthquakes. If G were to become a little smaller, the earth would expand slightly, and these normal stresses would get smaller regardless of the orientation of the fault plane. If G were to vary by the order of 1 part in 10^8 in a year, the resulting expansion of the earth would be of the order of a one-tenth of that, about 1 part in 10^9. However, the stresses along the fault planes are accumulating on the order of 1 part in 10^8 in a year. So the variation of normal stress is quite appreciable in comparison with the rate at which the stress is building up, and the determination of whether an earthquake should go or not can be rather strongly affected by a variation of G of that order of magnitude.

What effect on earthquakes then would we expect to be associated with the bump on the moon–earth rotation discrepancy curve in 1900? If, at that time, the moon started to move more rapidly, this implies that G became larger. This would make the normal stresses larger, having the effect of turning off earthquakes. About 20 years later G becomes smaller again; normal stresses become smaller and the earthquakes should occur more frequently. So we expect a period of 20 years with a low earthquake rate, followed by an enhanced earthquake rate during the period following a decrease in G.

The upper curve in Figure 12-7 shows the variation of the frequency of earthquakes over this period of time. Indeed, this data shows a very low earthquake frequency, followed by an enhanced frequency coinciding roughly with the bump in the curve in Figure 12-5. This coincidence encourages us to examine the comparison between the earthquake rate and the moon's motion in greater detail.

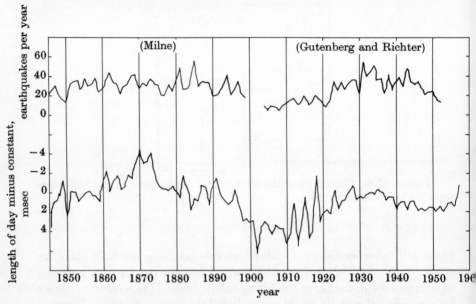

Figure 12-7 Comparison of number of earthquakes per year with the moon's motion. (The length of day was measured by comparing the rotation of the earth to the period of the moon, and so contains any information of a change in the moon's period.)

The lower curve in Figure 12-7 shows the year-by-year average of the moon's motion. The moon's motion is much more noisy in this curve than in Figure 12-5 because it has not been smoothed to the extent of the previous graph. The data for the period of time from 1904 to 1952 was obtained from seismometer observations[4] and, for the period prior to 1900, from newspaper reports. There is no immediately apparent correlation prior to 1900 between the newspaper reported earthquakes and the moon's motion. On the other hand, I do not expect newspaper reports to be a source of information with a good signal-to-noise ratio.

One of my students, Jason Morgan, has calculated the correlation between earthquake frequency and the discrepancy in the moon's motion during this period. The correlation coefficients all have the right sign and have a reasonable significance level. He found the calculated correlation coefficient prior to 1900 to be 0.26. The probability of obtaining a correlation that good by accident with random numbers is only of the order of 3 per cent. The correlation for the period after 1900, during which the earthquake data is from seismometer observations, is 0.71. The probability of getting this value accidentally with random numbers is very small, approximately 10^{-6}.

Morgan examined in detail the data since 1900 to see where the correlation arises. Is it in only the low-frequency fluctuations or are the high-frequency variations meaningful? There are several very large bumps in the moon's motion on the lower curve in Figure 12-7. We might ask whether these big bumps correlate with bumps on the upper curve. It turns out that they do.

The analysis was made by fitting a cubic curve to these two plots and then subtracting the cubic in order to leave only the "noise" fluctuations for which a correlation is computed. These two difference curves are shown in Figure 12-8. The cubic curves correlate nicely with each other with a correlation coefficient of 0.94. The remainder correlates to the extent of 0.20. The probability of getting that kind of correlation with random numbers is 8 per cent. Thus all the correlations have the same sign, and they are all reasonably above the level for which we would expect to get them through accident. These correlations fit very well with the hypothesis that (1) the disturbances on the earth–moon rotation rate discrepancy curve are associated with variations in the moon's period; (2) these

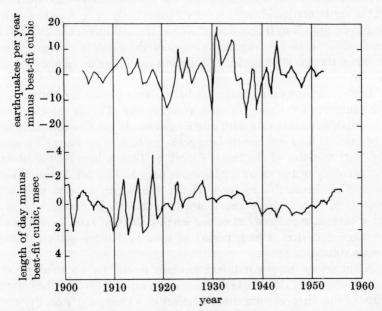

Figure 12-8 Length of day and earthquake frequency after subtracting cubic curves.

variations and the variations in earthquake rates have a common origin in fluctuations of the value of the gravitational constant; and (3) this could be caused by the passage of ϕ waves.

Earth Rotation Variation: Also a ϕ-Wave Effect?

We may also ask the question whether the correlations fit the hypothesis of undisturbed motion of the moon and variations in the earth's rotation rate of some unknown origin. I believe that they can be made to fit but not as convincingly as they fit the hypothesis of irregular moon motion. If the earth changes its rotation rate in such a way as to speed up, there is a centrifugal expansion of the earth and a release of strains. The normal stresses become smaller by 0.1 per cent of the fractional change in rotation rate (since centrifugal forces account for about 0.1 per cent of g at the surface of the earth). If we wish to say that this is the mechanism for the strong correlation, we must assume that earthquakes are extremely sensitive to small variations in normal stresses. However the fractional change in stresses produced in this way is only of the order of 10^{-10}, which is about 10^{-3} of the tidal variation in stresses. Hence the tidal effects would appear to dominate and mask any small effects of a varying earth rotation rate. However tidal periods do not show up strongly in earthquake rates.

Another possible mechanism for the correlation in earthquake rate with the earth rotation changes is the variation in sheer stresses between the core and mantle. But, if this were the case, the maximum earthquake rates should occur when the angular velocity of the earth is changing, rather than when the moon's angular velocity is a minimum as appears to be the case.

In the last few years, there has been a very promising source of data on the subject of variation in earth rotation rate. This is the comparison of the earth's rotation rate with atomic clocks. As yet this comparison has not been made for a sufficiently long period of time to have any correspondingly good measure of the moon's motion. This is because the observational accuracy of the moon's position is poor and its period much longer than that of the earth's rotation. Hence short-term data on the moon's motion is extremely noisy and is not of much use in comparison to the precise current measurement of the earth's rotation rate. It is necessary to average data over a long period of time to achieve sufficient moon-period accuracy.

A change in the gravitational constant should have a small effect on the earth's rotation rate. As G decreases, the earth expands. The compressibility of the earth is such that the effect of a changing G on the earth's rotation rate ought to be about one-tenth of the effect on the moon's motion. Morgan has looked at the correlation between earthquake rates and changes in the earth's rotation determined by comparison with atomic clocks over the past 6 years. He has found a correlation that has the same sign as previous correlations provided the effect is interpreted in terms of a changing G. But it has the opposite sign if the effect is interpreted solely in terms of the earth's rotation.

The fact that the recent comparison of atomic clocks with the earth's rotation has shown a variation in the rotation rate indicates either that part or all of the discrepancy in the lunar motion is due to rotational fluctuations of geophysical origin, or else that fairly large variations in G, inducing changes in the earth's rotation rate, have occurred in the past 6 years. It appears to be too early to exclude either of these alternatives, but it seems likely that the new techniques employing atomic clocks will force a decision in the next 5 years.

Although this and the previous effects discussed do not prove the existence of ϕ waves and the consequent G variations, they do provide a tantalizing invitation to explore further the hypothesis of scalar waves. They certainly do not give us grounds for rejecting the possibility of their existence.

References and Notes

1. J. L. Greenstein and T. A. Matthews, *Nature*, **197**, 1041 (1963).
2. W. H. Munk and G. J. F. MacDonald, *The Rotation of the Earth*, Cambridge University Press, Cambridge, 1960.
3. S. Newcomb, "Fluctuations in the Moon's Motion," *Monthly Notices, Roy. Astronom. Soc.*, **69**, 164 (1909).
4. All earthquakes of magnitude $M \geq 6.5$ are listed in B. Gutenberg and C. F. Richter, *Seismicity of the Earth*, Princeton University Press, Princeton, N.J., 1954.

13

The Lyttleton-Bondi universe and charge equality

V. W. Hughes

The Question of Electron–Proton Charge Equality

Whether the electron charge magnitude exactly equals the proton charge magnitude is an interesting and fundamental question in physics. In this lecture I should like to discuss the theoretical arguments on this question, some implications to physics, astronomy and cosmology of a slight departure from charge equality, and the most recent experimental determinations of the electron-proton charge ratio.

As you know, experimental findings of the late nineteenth and early twentieth centuries, culminating in Millikan's oil drop experiment, led to the conclusions that electric charges occur always as integral multiples of a smallest unit and that the smallest unit for positive charge (the proton) is equal to the smallest unit for negative charge (the electron). Thus an atom or molecule, which consists of equal numbers of electrons and protons, should be electrically neutral. In 1932 the neutron was discovered and it was found to have zero charge. By now there are some 30 so-called elementary particles known, and each appears to have a charge of $+1$, 0, or -1 electron charge unit.

Implications of a Charge Difference

Ideally, elementary particle theory should predict the observed spectrum of the elementary particles, including their charge and mass ratios. Modern quantized field theory can describe discrete particles but cannot predict the values of a particle's mass and charge. These must be obtained from experiment. The invariance of the theory under charge conjugation

259

(the interchange of particle and antiparticle) does provide a theoretical prediction that a particle and its antiparticle should have charges that are equal in magnitude but opposite in sign. For example, the electron and positron charges should have the same magnitude. Also the proton and antiproton charges should have the same magnitude. However, theory does not predict the ratio of the magnitudes of the charges on two different particles, for example, the ratio of the electron to proton charges.

Indeed, in view of modern charge renormalization theory, the question of the electron-proton charge ratio becomes rather deep and somewhat ambiguous. If the bare charges of the electron and proton were equal, conventional renormalization theory with gauge invariance would require that the renormalized electron and proton charges should also be equal. However, Gell-Mann and Nambu[1] have remarked that, if in addition to the photon there were another neutral vector particle that was coupled to the proton but not to the electron, then, even though the bare charges of the electron and the proton were equal, the renormalized charges would be expressed in terms of ambiguous, quadratically divergent integrals and might not be equal.

Feinberg and Goldhaber[2] have discussed the connection between the conservation laws and charge equalities of particles. At present the absolute conservation laws of charge, baryon number, and lepton number are all independent and are believed valid for any particle reaction. Because of the independent conservation laws for baryons and leptons, use of charge conservation in the known reactions involving elementary particles does not of itself determine the ratios of the charges of all the elementary particles. For example, the apparent absence of the reaction $p \to e^+ + \pi^0$ leaves the ratio of the electron to proton charges undetermined. Conversely, if the electron (lepton) and proton (baryon) charge magnitudes were different, the absence of such a reaction, or, more generally, the conservation of baryons would follow from the conservation of charge instead of being an independent principle.

In the twentieth century, there has been considerable speculation about the effect on large-scale matter of a slight difference δq in the magnitudes of the electron and proton charges. Questions have been raised concerning the effect of such an inequality on gravitation, on the magnetic fields of astronomical bodies, and on cosmology.

As to the relevance of charge inequality to gravitation it is suggestive to compare the electric force between two protons to their gravitational force. This ratio is

$$\frac{F_{\text{el}}}{F_{\text{grav}}} = \frac{e^2/r^2}{Gm_p^2/r^2} = 1.2 \times 10^{36} \tag{1}$$

which is, of course, a very large number. If the electron charge is $q_e = -e$

and the proton charge were a slightly different magnitude,

$$q_p = (1 + y)e \qquad (2)$$

then the charge on the hydrogen atom would be $+ye$, and the ratio of the electrostatic force between two hydrogen atoms to their gravitational force would be

$$\frac{F_{el}}{F_{grav}} = \frac{(ye)^2}{Gm_H^2} = 1.2 \times 10^{36} y^2 \qquad (3)$$

This ratio is 1 when $y = 0.9 \times 10^{-18}$. Therefore if there were 1 part in 10^{18} difference between the proton and electron charge magnitudes, the electrostatic force between two hydrogen atoms would be equal in magnitude to the gravitational force.

The very large ratio of electric to gravitational forces and their similar dependence on the inverse square of the distance between the particles suggest the possibility that gravitational forces might arise as a result of some small breakdown of the normal theory of electric forces. Lorentz proposed that the gravitational force might arise because of a slight difference between the force of repulsion between two particles with charges of the same sign, and the force of attraction between two particles with charges of the same magnitudes but of unlike sign. Swann[3] has also discussed this possibility and has considered it in connection with matter and antimatter.

The origin of the magnetic fields of astronomical bodies is another problem for which the possibility of a slight charge difference may be relevant. Einstein[4] remarked that a slight difference between the proton and electron charge magnitudes would, of course, lead to a net volume charge for matter composed of equal numbers of protons and electrons. Hence a rotating object such as the earth would have an associated magnetic field similar to that of a magnetic dipole. At the pole the field would be

$$H_{pole} = 2P/R^3 \qquad (4)$$

where R is the radius of the earth and P is its magnetic dipole moment:

$$P = \frac{0.2\omega M R^2}{c} \frac{\sigma}{\rho} \qquad (5)$$

where ω is the angular velocity of the earth, M is the mass, σ is the charge density, and ρ the mass density. For a proton charge given by Eq. (2)

$$\frac{\sigma}{\rho} = \frac{ye}{m_H} \qquad (6)$$

where m_H is the mass of the hydrogen atom. If we assume that the earth's magnetic field of 0.6 gauss at the pole is entirely due to this charge inequality, then $y = 2 \times 10^{-19}$.

Blackett[5] observed in 1947 that the ratios of the magnetic dipole moment as computed from Eq. (4) to the angular momentum for three astronomical bodies—the earth, the sun, and the star 78 Virginis—have nearly the same value of P/I.

$$\left(\frac{P}{I}\right)_{\text{earth, sun, star}} \simeq 1 \times 10^{-15} \tag{7}$$

Furthermore, the ratio of the orbital magnetic moment to the orbital angular momentum for an electron is

$$\left(\frac{P}{I}\right)_{\text{electron orbital motion}} = \frac{e}{2m_e c} \simeq 0.9 \times 10^7 \tag{8}$$

and the ratio of these two quantities is

$$\frac{(P/I)_{\text{astronomical bodies}}}{(P/I)_{\text{electron}}} \simeq 10^{-22} \tag{9}$$

This dimensionless ratio is nearly equal to the dimensionless constant

$$\frac{G^{1/2}m_e}{e} = 4.9 \times 10^{-22} \tag{10}$$

Blackett considered it unlikely that this approximate numerical equality should occur accidentally. Therefore he proposed that it should be true in general that

$$(P/I)_{\text{astronomical body}} = (P/I)_{\text{electron}} \frac{G^{1/2}m_e}{e} = \frac{G^{1/2}}{2c} \tag{11}$$

It was found subsequent to Blackett's paper that the magnetic field of the sun is nearer to 5 gauss than to 50 gauss, which was the value he used, so the ratio P/I for the sun actually does not have the value given in Eq. (7). There are many more stars whose magnetic fields have been determined by now, and it would be interesting to compare these new data with Eq. (11). The relation (11) is consistent with the model of a rotating charged earth that Einstein proposed. However, the simplest model of a rotating charged body gives much too high an electric field at the surface of the earth, so the theory must be modified to include surface charge as well as volume charge in order to give a reasonable value for the electric field as well as for the magnetic field.

A third general area in which an electron-proton charge inequality might have some interesting implications is cosmology. Lyttleton and Bondi[6] suggested that the observed expansion of the universe might be understood as an electric repulsion due to a slight charge difference. They discussed this suggestion first in the context of simple Newtonian

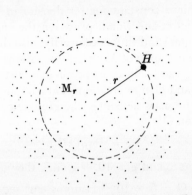

Figure 13-1 Model of a uniformly charged universe.

theory using the model of a smoothed-out, spherical universe composed of hydrogen atoms with a mass density ρ and a corresponding charge density σ, where

$$\sigma = \rho \frac{ye}{m_H} \tag{6}$$

and y is assumed to be positive. (See Figure 13-1.) The electrostatic force on a hydrogen atom at a distance r from the center of this charge distribution is

$$F_{\text{el}} = \frac{(ye^2)}{r^2 m_H} M_r \tag{12}$$

where M_r is the total mass within the radius r. The gravitational force is

$$F_{\text{grav}} = \frac{M_r m_H G}{r^2} \tag{13}$$

We define the ratio of the electrostatic repulsive force to the gravitational attractive force to be

$$\mu = \left(\frac{ye}{m_H \sqrt{G}} \right)^2 = (1.1 \times 10^{18} y)^2 \tag{14}$$

which is the same as Eq. (3). The net repulsive force is then

$$F = F_{\text{el}} - F_{\text{grav}} = (\mu - 1)F_{\text{grav}}$$
$$F = (\mu - 1)\tfrac{4}{3}\pi\rho m_H Gr = kr \tag{15}$$

If $\mu - 1 > 0$, there will be a repulsive force that is proportional to r and that will lead to an expansion of the universe.

In order to achieve constant matter density in the universe despite the expansion, Lyttleton and Bondi proposed the continuous creation of matter (hydrogen atoms) and thus, necessarily, also the creation of charge. They proposed a modification of Maxwell's equations to allow for the non-conservation of charge and solved the problem of a steady state expanding universe with mass and charge creation. They obtained the following relationship between the mass density ρ, the Hubble constant T^{-1}, and the rate of matter creation Q:

$$\rho = \tfrac{1}{3}m_H QT \tag{16}$$

Using $T = 3 \times 10^{17}$ sec and $\rho = 10^{-29}$ g/cm³, they obtained

$$Q = 6 \times 10^{-23} \text{ H atoms/cm}^3\text{-sec}$$

which corresponds to a creation rate of one hydrogen atom per sec in a cube of 250 km on an edge.

With constant matter density ρ, the repulsive force given in Eq. (15) is consistent with a velocity that increases linearly with distance

$$v = \sqrt{Kr} \tag{17}$$

where

$$K = (\mu - 1)\tfrac{4}{3}\pi\rho G$$

The observed expansion of the universe is

$$v = r/T \tag{18}$$

Equating (17) and (18) gives

$$T = \frac{1}{[(\mu - 1)\tfrac{4}{3}\pi\rho G]^{1/2}} \tag{19}$$

and hence

$$\mu = 5$$

and

$$y = 2 \times 10^{-18} \tag{20}$$

This is the charge inequality that Lyttleton and Bondi proposed to explain the observed expansion of the universe with a theory in which they allow for charge creation and a modification of Maxwell's equations. They also formulated their theory in the more general terms of de Sitter space-time to satisfy the cosmological principle that the universe appears the same as viewed from any position. The more general theory introduced no essential modifications of the basic conclusions of the Newtonian picture.

When ionization occurs, electrically neutral units will grow from the background of smoothed-out, un-ionized matter. These units are identified with galaxies or clusters of galaxies. Ions—primarily protons—that are expelled from these units by the electrostatic forces are identified with the hard component of the cosmic rays.

Hoyle[7] pointed out an error in the treatment of the modified Maxwell theory of Lyttleton and Bondi. The principal difference in conclusion reached by Hoyle is that the potential resulting from a charge will be of the form

$$\phi = e/r \cos\left[(-\lambda)^{1/2} r\right] \tag{21}$$

where r is the distance from the charge and λ is a cosmological quantity

$$(-\lambda)^{1/2} \simeq \frac{1}{\text{radius of the universe}}$$

From Eq. (21) it is clear that the potential will change sign at sufficiently large distances, and thus the force between two like charges will change from repulsive to attractive.

Hoyle's interpretation then is that the electrostatic force would not be repulsive on a cosmological scale and lead to an expansion of the universe in the manner Lyttleton and Bondi proposed, but would rather be primarily attractive. Hoyle noted however that, if matter and antimatter are both created at the same rate, if a hydrogen atom has a charge ye and an anti-hydrogen atom a charge $-ye$, and if matter and antimatter become sufficiently separated, then repulsion of matter and antimatter will occur according to Eq. (21) and expansion of the universe would take place. Hoyle's theory also requires that $y \simeq 2 \times 10^{-18}$.

Experimental Evidence on Charge Difference

Now I would like to discuss what terrestrial laboratory experiments have established about the electron-proton charge difference.

One of the earliest experiments was the Millikan oil drop experiment.[8] Millikan studied the motion of droplets of various liquids that had been charged by different means such as by friction, by use of x rays, or by capture of ions from the air. From the observation of the motion of these droplets under the forces of gravity, of viscous drag, and of an electric field, Millikan was able to show that, in all cases, every droplet had a charge which was an integral multiple of the smallest unit. He studied charges of both signs and he found that

$$\frac{\text{positive charge unit}}{\text{negative charge unit}} = 1 \pm 1/1500$$

A macroscopic interpretation of this result can be given in terms of the electron-proton charge difference.[11] A typical oil droplet is a sphere with a radius of about 10^{-4} cm and a density of 1 g/cm³. The number N of proton-electron pairs in one of these droplets is then $N \simeq 2.5 \times 10^{12}$. Millikan's observations require that

$$Nye < e/1500$$

and hence

$$y < 3 \times 10^{-16}$$

Another macroscopic experiment by a gas efflux method was first done by Piccard and Kessler[4] and will be discussed later.

I should like to discuss next an atomic beam experiment that has recently been done by Zorn, Chamberlain, and Hughes.[9,10,11] The method of the experiment is to study the deflection of a molecular beam in a homogeneous electric field. If an atom is neutral, it will not be deflected, but, if there were a difference between the electron and proton charge magnitudes, an atom would have a net charge and it would be deflected. We used a classical molecular beam technique[12] as illustrated in Figure 13-2. The beam is defined by a source slit and a collimating slit so that it has a ribbon-like cross section that is narrow in the transverse horizontal direction and long in the vertical direction. This beam passes through a

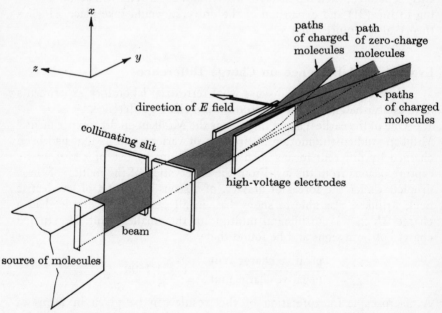

Figure 13-2 Molecular beam measurement of atomic or molecular charge.

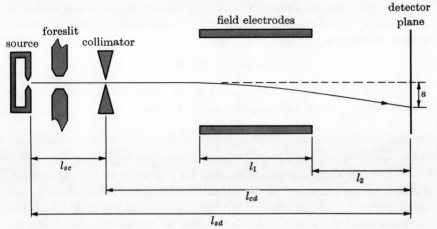

Figure 13-3   Geometry of apparatus, showing trajectory of an atom which is deflected by the electric field.

homogeneous electric field, which would deflect the beam if the atoms were charged.

Figure 13-3 shows a horizontal cross section of the apparatus in greater detail. In terms of the geometry of Figure 13-3, the deflection that a charged molecule of velocity v would experience as a result of the electric field is given by

$$s_v = \frac{qE}{2mv^2}l_1(l_1 + 2l_2) \tag{22}$$

where q, m, and v are the charge, mass, and velocity of the particle in the beam, and E is the electric field strength. In particular, a molecule with the most probable velocity α of molecules in the source ($\alpha = \sqrt{2kT/m}$) is deflected by the amount

$$s_\alpha = \frac{qE}{4kT}l_1(l_1 + 2l_2) \tag{23}$$

where T is the source temperature and k is Boltzmann's constant.

In our recent experiment

$$l_1 = 200 \text{ cm} \qquad l_2 = 30 \text{ cm}$$

and

$$E = 10^5 \text{ volts/cm}$$

The experiment was done for cesium and potassium atoms, and the oven temperature was about $500°K$. Our detector sensitivity was such that a deflection of 10^{-5} cm could be detected. Hence the minimum detectable atomic charge was

$$q \simeq 3 \times 10^{-17}e$$

For cesium the atomic number is 55; so the minimum detectable charge on an electron-proton pair δq is smaller by a factor of 55:

$$\delta q \sim 6 \times 10^{-19}e$$

This sensitivity is in the range of interest for the Lyttleton-Bondi theory.

There are some complications that are important to the experiment. Because of the smallness of the deflections being observed, electric field inhomogeneities can produce comparable deflections associated with the polarization of the atoms. The atoms have no permanent electric dipole moments, but in an electric field an electric dipole moment is induced. If the field is inhomogeneous, there will be a force on this induced electric dipole moment. In our experiment, such field inhomogeneities arise at the ends of the field region. If the energy of the atom in the field is $W(E)$, the force resulting from the induced dipole moment is

$$\mathbf{F} = -\nabla W(E) = -\frac{\partial W}{\partial E}\nabla|E| \tag{24}$$

It is apparent from the form of Eq. (24) that the direction of the force does not change with the direction of the field. Hence by reversing the polarity of the potential across the electrodes, we can distinguish between this dipole polarizability force and the force on a net atomic charge.

Another complication in interpreting the deflection measurements is the spread in velocities of the atoms. The velocity distribution is Maxwellian for particles effusing through an opening in the oven:

$$I_v \, dv = \frac{2I}{\alpha^4}v^3e^{-v^2/\alpha^2} \, dv \tag{25}$$

where I is the total beam intensity. The observed deflection is given by an average over this velocity distribution.

Figure 13-4 illustrates a third complicating factor that must be considered. The source and detector slits have finite widths, so that we obtain a beam intensity distribution in the detector plane that is trapezoidal. In addition, the detector has a finite width.

In order to relate the observed intensity pattern to s_α, it is necessary to integrate over the width of the beam path and over the velocity distribution. The relation between s_α and the change in intensity with the detector

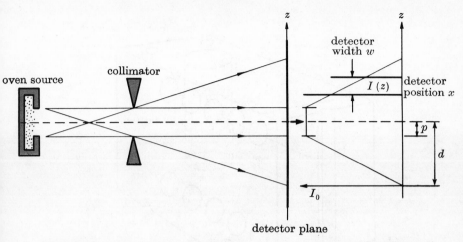

Figure 13-4   Effect of finite slit widths on beam intensity distribution.

positioned where the beam intensity has one-half its maximum value is

$$\frac{\Delta I}{I} = \frac{2s_\alpha}{d - p} \tag{26}$$

where d and p are defined in Figure 13-4 and $W = d-p$. The analysis has also been done in another way, which does not require an a priori knowledge of the slit geometry and alignment but uses only the observed beam intensity distribution.

Some technical features of the experiment and of the apparatus will now be discussed. The choice of the atom is dictated largely by atomic beam technology. The only property of the atom that appears in the deflection equation (23) is the temperature at which it must be produced. This should be as low as possible. For this experiment, we desire an atom containing many electron-proton pairs. Alkali atoms are used because they are produced conveniently in beams at relatively low temperatures, and they are detected efficiently with a hot-wire surface-ionization detector. Figure 13-5 shows the oven used to produce the beam of potassium or cesium atoms. It is used at a temperature of about 500°K.

Figure 13-6 shows the observed and calculated beam intensity distribution with oven and collimator slit widths of 0.004 cm. The detector width is also 0.004 cm. The agreement between the two curves is good; the small discrepancy is attributed to atomic beam scattering, slit misalignment, and imperfect knowledge of slit dimensions. The detector is placed

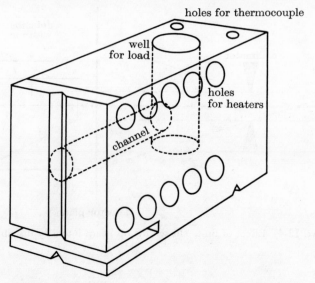

Figure 13-5   Conventional oven used for alkali atoms.

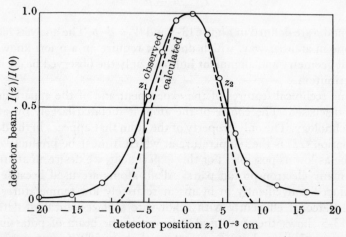

Figure 13-6   Theoretical beam shape for classical trajectories and ideal geometry compared to an observed intensity distribution for potassium atoms with zero electric field.

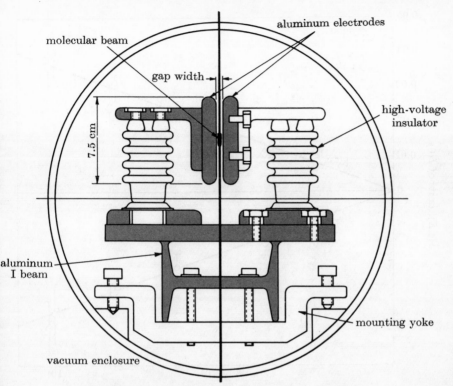

Figure 13-7 Cross section of electrode assembly.

at one of the two half-maximum intensity points in order to obtain the maximum change in intensity for a given s_α.

Figure 13-7 shows the electric-field assembly in vertical cross section. The parallel plates are made of aluminum and are about 2 m in length with a spacing of 1 or 2 mm. Electric fields of 100 kv/cm are obtained before breakdown occurs.

Figure 13-8 shows some of the observed data. The change in beam intensity Δ observed with the detector placed at the two half-maximum intensity points (z_1 and z_2) is plotted as a function of electric field for both polarities of the field.

The deflection of the beam, owing to a net atomic charge, is directly proportional to E, and, at the field strengths used in this experiment, the deflection from the induced dipole moment is proportional to E^2. The observed dependence of $\Delta(z_i, E)$ is shown in Figure 13-8. It is seen that $\Delta(z_i, E)$ is linearly proportional to E^2 up to a field E of about 10^5 v/cm, as

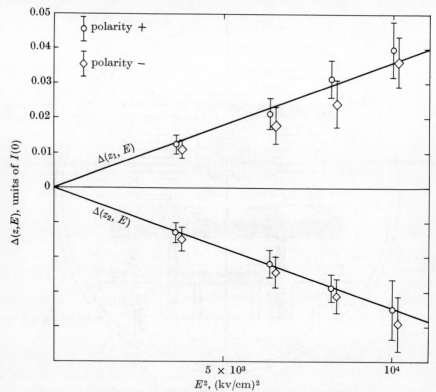

Figure 13-8 Change in intensity as a function of electric field at half-maximum intensity points (z_1 and z_2).

expected for deflections resulting from dipole polarizability alone. At still higher fields, Δ is no longer proportional to E^2; indeed both $\Delta(z_1, E)$ and $\Delta(z_2, E)$ decrease with an increase of E at sufficiently high values of E. This behavior is not consistent with deflection that results from a net atomic charge and a dipole polarizability but rather is explained by an attenuation of the atomic beam at the higher fields. The beam appears to be attenuated in proportion to the gap current, and this gives rise to a field-dependent signal change $D(z_i, E)$ not associated with an electric deflection of the beam atoms.

Table 13-1 shows the results deduced from such measurements on potassium and cesium atoms and on hydrogen and deuterium molecules. The upper limits for the charges are given. The upper limits on the charge are considerably higher for hydrogen and deuterium than for the alkalis.

Table 13-1
Summary of Atomic Beam Charge Measurements

Results[a]	Interpretation[b]
Gases	
$|q(H_2)| < 2 \times 10^{-15} q_e$	$|\delta q| < 1 \times 10^{-15} q_e$
$|q(D_2)| < 2.8 \times 10^{-15} q_e$	$|q_n| < 2.4 \times 10^{-15} q_e$
Alkalis	
$q(K) = (-3.8 \pm 11.8) \times 10^{-17} q_e$	$q(K) = 19\delta q + 20 q_n$
$q(Cs) = (+1.3 \pm 5.6) \times 10^{-17} q_e$	$q(Cs) = 55\delta q + 78 q_n$

[a] δq: electron-proton charge difference; q_n: neutron charge; q_e: absolute value of electron charge.

[b] If the value of δq is considered independent of q_n, these equations for the alkalis are a pair of equations in two unknowns; solution gives the limits
$$\delta q = (-.85 \pm 2.7) \times 10^{-17} q_e$$
$$q_n = (+.61 \pm 2.0) \times 10^{-17} q_e$$
But the neutron decay: $n \rightarrow p + e^- + \bar{\nu}$ indicates $\delta q = q_n$, so
$$\delta q = (1.0 \pm 4.2) \times 10^{-19} q_e$$

This is due to the fact that the Pirani detector for hydrogen is not as efficient as the hot-wire surface-ionization detector for the alkalis, so that the gas apparatus was shorter and less sensitive to small deflections than the alkali apparatus.

The charge of an atom or molecule is assumed to be completely given by the scalar sum $q = Z\delta q + N q_n$, where Z is the number of electron-proton pairs, $\delta q = q_p - q_e$ is the electron-proton charge difference, N is the number of neutrons, and q_n is the neutron charge. The most direct determination of a limit for δq is obtained from the measurement of the net charge of the hydrogen molecule:

$$|\delta q| = \frac{|q(H_2)|}{2} < 1 \times 10^{-15} q_e \tag{27}$$

In addition, the result from deuterium gives a limit for q_n:

$$|q_n| < 2.4 \times 10^{-15} q_e \tag{28}$$

Smaller limits than the above can be obtained from the experimental values for the charges of cesium and potassium.

$$q(\text{Cs}) = 55\delta q + 78q_n = (13 \pm 56) \times 10^{-18}q_e \qquad (29)$$

$$q(\text{K}) = 19\delta q + 20q_n = (-38 \pm 118) \times 10^{-18}q_e \qquad (30)$$

Treated as simultaneous equations in δq and q_n, Eqs. (29) and (30) give the solutions

$$\delta q = (-8.5 \pm 27) \times 10^{-18}q_e \qquad (31)$$

independently of the value of q_n, and

$$q_n = (6.1 \pm 20) \times 10^{-18}q_e \qquad (32)$$

independently of the value of δq.

A still smaller limit for the electron-proton charge difference can be given if one assumes $\delta q = q_n$. This relation follows from the usual assumption that charge is conserved in the beta decay of the neutron ($n \rightarrow p + e^- + \bar{\nu}$) and that the charge of the antineutrino is zero.[13] Then $\delta q = q(\text{atom})/(Z + N)$, and we obtain from $q(\text{Cs})$:

$$\delta q = (1.0 \pm 4.2) \times 10^{-19}q_e \qquad (33)$$

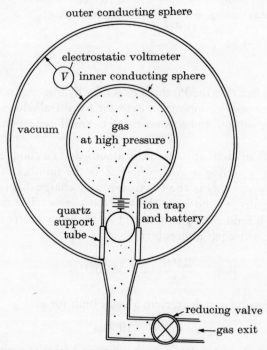

Figure 13-9 Schematic diagram of Piccard-Kessler apparatus for gas efflux experiment.

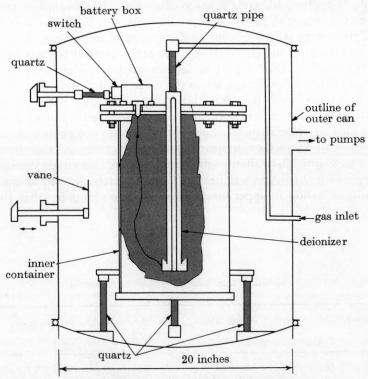

Figure 13-10 King apparatus for gas efflux experiment.

With improved vacuum, electric field conditions, and detector stability, we believe our atomic beam experiment on the alkalis could be improved in sensitivity by about a factor of 100. An atomic beam experiment on thermal neutrons was done by Shapiro and Estulin,[14] who obtained an upper limit for the neutron charge of $6 \times 10^{-12}q_e$.

I would like to discuss briefly the macroscopic gas efflux experiment done first by Piccard and Kessler,[4] which measures the total charge Q of N gas molecules by observing the change in potential of a metal container relative to its surroundings when gas effuses from the container. Figure 13-9 shows their apparatus consisting of two concentric conducting spheres that form a spherical capacitor. The inner sphere can be filled with a gas. The voltage between the two spheres depends on the capacity, on the surface charge on the inner sphere, and on the volume charge carried by the gas.

Piccard and Kessler filled the inner sphere with 20 to 30 atm of CO_2

or N_2. They then allowed the gas to effuse from the inner sphere and measured the change in potential across the capacitor. If the gas were neutral and there were no changes in the dimensions of the sphere, there should be no change in the potential. On the other hand, if the gas had a net charge resulting from a proton-electron charge difference, the potential would change when the gas leaves the inner sphere. The efflux of ions or electrons was prevented, or at least made difficult, by biasing a small obstacle in the throat of the exhaust tube relative to the inner sphere such that ions are trapped in the inner sphere and are not exhausted with the neutral gas. From their measurements they determined that $\delta q \le 5 \times 10^{-21} q_e$. Figure 13-10 shows a modern version of this same experiment by King[14] using hydrogen and helium. Conservatively, we can interpret his results as setting an upper limit for the charge on H_2 of less than $10^{-19} q_e$.

Table 13-2

Measured Limits for the Charge of Molecules[a]

Method	Molecule	q(molecule) in units of q_e	$\delta q = \dfrac{q\text{(molecule)}}{(Z+N)}$	Investigators
By gas efflux	CO$_2$	$<2.2 \times 10^{-19}$	$<5 \times 10^{-21}$	Piccard & Kessler[4]
	A	$(4 \pm 4) \times 10^{-20}$	$(1 \pm 1) \times 10^{-21}$	Hillas & Cranshaw[16]
	N$_2$	$(6 \pm 6) \times 10^{-20}$	$(2.1 \pm 2.1) \times 10^{-21}$	Hillas & Cranshaw[16]
	H$_2$	$(-2.5 \pm 1.5) \times 10^{-20}$	$(-1.3 \pm 0.8) \times 10^{-20}$	King[15]
	He	$(4 \pm 2) \times 10^{-20}$	$(1 \pm 0.5) \times 10^{-20}$	King[15]
	CsI	$<4 \times 10^{-13}$	$<1.5 \times 10^{-15}$	Hughes[11]
	Free neutron	$<6 \times 10^{-12}$		Shapiro & Estulin[14]
By beam deflection	CsF	$<2 \times 10^{-14}$	$<1.3 \times 10^{-16}$	Zorn, Chamberlain & Hughes[9,10]
	KF	$<1 \times 10^{-13}$	$<1.7 \times 10^{-15}$	,,
	H$_2$	$<2 \times 10^{-15}$	$<1 \times 10^{-15}$	,,
	D$_2$	$<2.8 \times 10^{-15}$	$<0.7 \times 10^{-15}$	,,
	K	$(-3.8 \pm 11.8) \times 10^{-17}$	$(-1 \pm 3) \times 10^{-18}$	,,
	Cs	$(1.3 \pm 5.6) \times 10^{-17}$	$(1 \pm 4.2) \times 10^{-19}$	,,

[a] By Mössbauer effect, a limit of $1 \times 10^{-15} q_e$ for the charge of the photon has been established by Grodzins, Engelberg, and Bertozzi, *Bull. Am. Phys. Soc.*, **6**, 63 (1961).

A modern extension of Millikan's oil drop experiment using a small, magnetically suspended metal sphere has been proposed to achieve a higher sensitivity in the determination of δq.

Table 13-2 presents a summary of experimental information on the electron-proton charge difference.

Interpretation of Results

The atomic beam deflection experiment on the alkali atoms provides a limit for δq of $5 \times 10^{-19} q_e$. This limit is about one-fourth the value of δq required by the theory of the expanding universe proposed by Lyttleton and Bondi. Furthermore, the macroscopic experiments by the gas efflux method provide the even smaller limit of $10^{-21} q_e$ to $10^{-20} q_e$. All these results provide strong evidence against the form of the Lyttleton-Bondi proposal which requires $\delta q = 2 \times 10^{-18} q_e$; they do not test the alternative, although less attractive, form of the Lyttleton-Bondi proposal, which requires a greater number of protons than electrons in the universe.

The equality of the electron and proton charge magnitudes has been established with unusually high precision in this and other recent experiments; hence they offer no support for the suggestion that baryon conservation might be simply a consequence of charge conservation. Furthermore, it would seem that any theory of elementary particles should require that the renormalized electron and proton charge magnitudes be equal.

It has been pointed out by Chiu and Hoffmann (see Introduction) that these experiments which establish the charge neutrality of atoms also establish that the electric charge of an electron is independent of the velocity of the electron. The independence of charge on velocity can be deduced, of course, because electrons move with different average speeds in different orbits and in different atoms. Thus whereas an outer electron in an atom with atomic number Z moves with an average speed of approximately αc (c = velocity of light and α = fine structure constant, $1/137$), an inner electron moves with an average speed of approximately $Z\alpha c$. Hence we note that the charge neutrality of a light atom or molecule such as He or H_2 (charge $< 10^{-19} q_e$) establishes the charge equality of the electron and the proton at nonrelativistic velocities or at rest. If we assume that the electron charge varies with velocity according to the equation

$$q_e(v) = q_e(0)[1 + a(v/c)^2] \tag{34}$$

and further if we assign any net charge of a high Z atom (such as A, $Z = 18$, with charge $< 10^{-19} q_e$) to the velocity dependence of the charge of the inner electrons, then we find $a < 3 \times 10^{-18}$. This limit provides the most sensitive test we have for the velocity independence of the electron charge. The independence of charge on velocity is a basic assumption in the Lorentz invariance of electrodynamics.

References and Notes

1. M. Gell-Mann, *Proceedings of the Tenth Annual International Conference on High-Energy Physics*, Interscience, New York, 1960, p. 792.
2. G. Feinberg and M. Goldhaber, *Proc. Natl. Acad. Sci. U.S.*, **45**, 1301 (1959).
3. W. F. G. Swann, *Phil. Mag.*, **3**, 1088 (1927); *Astrophys. J.*, **133**, 733 (1961).
4. Einstein's remarks are reported in A. Piccard and E. Kessler, *Arch. Sci. Phys. et Nat.* (*Geneva*), **7**, 340 (1925).
5. P. M. S. Blackett, *Nature*, **159**, 658 (1947).
6. R. A. Lyttleton and H. Bondi, *Proc. Roy. Soc.* (*London*), **A252**, 313 (1959).
7. F. Hoyle, *Proc. Roy. Soc.* (*London*), **A257**, 431 (1960).
8. R. A. Millikan, *The Electron*, 1st ed., University of Chicago Press, Chicago, Ill., 1917, pp. 80–83.
9. J. C. Zorn, G. E. Chamberlain, and V. W. Hughes, *Bull. Am. Phys. Soc.*, **6**, 63 (1961); *Proceedings of the Tenth Annual International Conference on High-Energy Physics*, Interscience, New York, 1960, p. 790; *Bull. Am. Phys. Soc.*, **5**, 36 (1960).
10. J. C. Zorn, G. E. Chamberlain, and V. W. Hughes, *Phys. Rev.*, **129**, 2566 (1963).
11. V. W. Hughes, *Phys. Rev.*, **76**, 474 (1949); *ibid.*, **105**, 170 (1957).
12. P. Kusch and V. W. Hughes, "Atomic and Molecular Beam Spectroscopy," in S. Flügge (ed.), *Handbuch der Physik*, 37/1, Springer-Verlag, Heidelberg, 1959.
13. An upper limit to the neutrino charge can be obtained by considering that the neutrino is a Dirac particle with a mass of 500 ev (upper limit to the allowed neutrino mass) and computing the upper limit to the charge that is consistent with neutrino cross-section data. (See J. S. Allen, *The Neutrino*, Princeton University Press, Princeton, N.J., 1958.) The limit found for the neutrino charge in this way is about $10^{-9} q_e$.
14. I. S. Shapiro and I. V. Estulin, *JETP* **3**, 626 (1956).
15. J. G. King, *Phys. Rev. Letters*, **5**, 562 (1960).
16. A. M. Hillas and T. E. Cranshaw, *Nature*, **184**, 892 (1959); *ibid.*, **186**, 459 (1960); H. Bondi and R. A. Lyttleton, *Nature*, **184**, 974 (1959).

14

Quantization of general relativity

J. L. Anderson

Historical Perspective

Since the early days of quantum mechanics, many people have felt that a complete quantized theory of matter must include the theory of gravitation. For this reason, there has been much effort to join together these two fundamental aspects of the physical world. One of the earliest attempts at this union is the program outlined by Bergmann[1] in 1947. Since then many other approaches have been taken.[2]

Studies on the quantization of general relativity to date have concerned themselves mainly with a better understanding of the classical formulation of general relativity as a prelude to applying one of the several techniques of quantization to it. Historically, and most commonly, the quantization of a given classical system proceeds from the Hamiltonian formulation of that theory. Given the canonical coordinates and momenta that describe a state of the system and the Hamiltonian as a function of these variables, there is a more or less unique algorithm for constructing the corresponding quantum description of the system. Thus, much of the effort in quantum relativity has been towards constructing a Hamiltonian formulation of general relativity.

However, because of difficulties inherent in a Hamiltonian formulation of general relativity, other procedures of quantization are being tried. One such procedure, under current investigation by Bergmann and Komar[3] and also DeWitt,[4] is to look at the coordinate invariant quantities one can construct in the theory and calculate their commutators in the classic theory. Once these commutators are known for a complete set of invariants, one can hope to find an operator representation for them that reproduces their classical commutator algebra. DeWitt has employed a generalization of the method of constructing commutators developed by Peierls,[5] whereas Bergmann and Komar have made extensive use of the theory of infinitesimal canonical transformations.

Another approach, currently being worked on by Wheeler and his group,[6] is that of the Feynman path integral formulation of quantum mechanics. The Schwinger variational principle has also been applied to general relativity by Arnowitt and Deser.[7]

These alternate approaches to the usual Hamiltonian quantization have all been initiated with the hope of overcoming the difficulties associated with Hamiltonian quantization. This goal has not been reached. The difficulties in Hamiltonian quantization reappear in one form or another. Since an exhaustive treatment of each of these methods of quantization as applied to general relativity would be impossible here, we shall concentrate our attention mainly on the Hamiltonian form of quantization. This form contains all the essential difficulties to be encountered in quantizing general relativity. Furthermore, this quantization scheme is the one we understand the best.

Motives for Quantizing the Gravitational Field

Before I discuss the details of the difficulties, I would like to point out some of the pros and cons of such an undertaking.

It has been argued by many people that, since the gravitational field is an extraordinarily weak field, around 10^{-40} of the strength of the electromagnetic field, one should not expect to see any effects of gravitation on a microscopic atomic or nuclear level. Consequently, gravitation will play no essential role in elementary particle processes or any of the other microscopic phenomena we know about. For this reason, many people do not believe in the necessity of quantizing the gravitation field. However, there are a number of arguments that suggest that this argument, based solely on the weakness of the gravitational field, may be misleading.

First, the general theory of relativity is a nonlinear theory and is intrinsically nonlinear, unlike electrodynamics, which only becomes nonlinear through its coupling with the Dirac field. The gravitational field is nonlinear even without coupling to some other source field. Thus there is no assurance that the concepts and procedures developed in electrodynamics are meaningful in the case of general relativity. We do not even know if the gravitational analogue of the photon exists.

Recently, however, Feynman has taken the position that it would be interesting to see how far one could get by applying the concepts and procedures usually used in quantum field theories to general relativity, and by treating it as a linear theory with the nonlinear part acting as an effective self-interaction. In this way, he has obtained the classical results of general relativity concerning the three experimental tests of the theory.[8]

On the other hand, one can argue that the full nonlinearity is an essential feature of the problem and cannot be treated as a small perturbation. It is possible that, when one gets very close to an elementary particle, the gravitational field becomes large enough that the nonlinearities begin to play an essential role and begin to change the character of the problem in a qualitative manner. This corresponds to a situation in the theory of differential equations: In a nonlinear system there exist solutions that cannot be reached by linear approximations.

There is an example of such a situation in classical field theory. This is the Born-Infeld theory of electrodynamics. Born and Infeld found an exact solution corresponding to a point charge. In the full nonlinear theory, the self-energy of the charge is infinite and there is an automatic cut-off to interactions of the charge with electric fields of arbitrarily high frequency. The linear approximation to this theory is Maxwell electrodynamics where those results do not hold, even if nonlinear terms are included as perturbations. This example shows that, in some aspects of the theory, one cannot expect qualitative similarities between a nonlinear theory and its linearized version. This is directly related to the problem discussed by Fuller and Wheeler.[9] There they introduced non-Euclidean topology into the theory. As long as the topology is Euclidean, we are justified in making a linear approximation of the gravitational field equations with the nonlinear term taken to be a small perturbation.

However, if one takes seriously the idea that, in the neighborhood of elementary particles, the topology may be different from Euclidean, it is not possible to treat the gravitational field as a weak field. There is no suitable first-order approximation to the field. It is necessary to quantize the whole theory right at the beginning.

There are also several other arguments in favor of quantizing the gravitational field. It is believed that all particles produce gravitational fields. If these gravitational fields are effectively classical, then, by measuring all components simultaneously, one can determine both the position and velocity of a particle simultaneously and thus violate the uncertainty principle. Hence the gravitational field must not be classical but must fluctuate in order to be compatible with quantum concepts.

Pauli argued that such fluctuations in the gravitational field may smear out the light cone. This in turn might conceivably furnish a natural cut-off in the theory. It is still too early to tell if these conjectures are actually true.

Quantization Procedure

The usual formulation for the equations of general relativity is in terms of the action principle (discussed in Chapter 4):

$$S = \int R\sqrt{-g}\, d^4x \tag{1}$$

However, as mentioned above, this formulation is not convenient for quantization. Rather we desire a Hamiltonian formulation. Therefore, one of the first problems in quantizing gravitational field is to formulate general relativity in a Hamiltonian form—that is, to construct a Hamiltonian for the theory, to find the canonical variables, and to apply the ordinary commutation relations to obtain eigen solutions. However, to obtain a Hamiltonian formulation of the theory is a difficult task in itself because of the general covariance of the theory.

The Hamiltonian Formulation of General Relativity

The Hamiltonian equations for any system described by the canonical variables q_i and p_i are of the following form:

$$\dot{q}_i = \frac{\partial H}{\partial p_i} \quad \text{and} \quad \dot{p}_i = -\frac{\partial H}{\partial q_i} \tag{2}$$

where H, the Hamiltonian, is a function of the q's and p's. Given q_i and p_i initially, we can then find their first derivatives from Eqs. (2) in terms of these initial values. By successive differentiations we can find all higher derivatives in terms of them. Thus we can expand the solution $q_i(t)$ in a power series about t_0 as

$$q_i(t) = q_{io} + \dot{q}_{io}t + \cdots = q_{io} + \left(\frac{\partial H}{\partial p_i}\right)_0 t + \cdots \tag{3}$$

and

$$p_i(t) = p_{io} + \dot{p}_{io}t + \cdots = p_{io} - \left(\frac{\partial H}{\partial q_i}\right)_0 t + \cdots \tag{4}$$

Thus, in a conventional Hamiltonian theory a knowledge of the initial q's and p's leads to a unique determination of their values at any future time. This situation, however, cannot hold in general relativity as the following considerations will show. Let us suppose that, given the ten components of the metric and their first time derivatives initially, the metric in the future is uniquely determined from the field equations. We can picture the situation schematically in Figure 14-1. Here we plot the metric as a function of time. The abscissa schematically represents the functional space of the metric.

However, we may perform a coordinate transformation that leaves

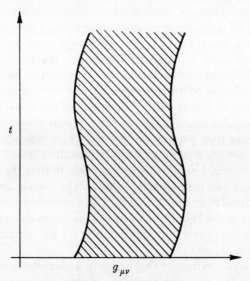

Figure 14-1 Schematic representation of the time development of metric components.

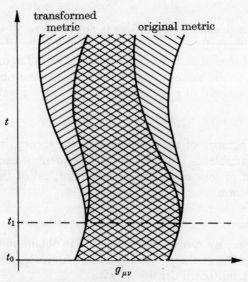

Figure 14-2 Schematic of time development of metric components, under time-dependent coordinate transformation.

everything unchanged up to some time $t_1 > t_0$ and thereafter deviates from the identity transformation. Such a transformation is a permissible transformation since all derivatives exist up to any order we desire. In this way we obtain what appears to be a different solution to the field equations starting from the same initial data. Of course, the two solutions do not represent different physical situations but merely the same situation expressed in two different coordinate systems. The effect of such a transformation is represented in Figure 14–2. The graph of the transformed metric is superimposed on the original metric. The region where the two graphs overlap represents that part of the metric which describes the physical situation and is not affected by a change of coordinates.

From these considerations one can conclude that the field equations do not determine the time development of the metric uniquely. In the Hamiltonian formulation of the theory, this nonuniqueness is reflected in a nonuniqueness in the Hamiltonian. If it were uniquely determined, then, of course, one could obtain a unique solution for the metric in the manner indicated by Eqs. (3) and (4).

There is another difficulty that arises in a Hamiltonian formulation of general relativity as a consequence of the general covariance of the theory. One can construct a momentum density $p^{\mu\nu}$ conjugate to $g_{\mu\nu}$ by differentiating the Lagrangian density of the theory with respect to $\dot{g}_{\mu\nu}$:

$$p^{\mu\nu} = \frac{\partial \mathscr{L}}{\partial \dot{g}_{\mu\nu}} \tag{5}$$

The Lagrangian density $\mathscr{L}$ used here is not equal to $\sqrt{-g}\, R$ but differs from it by an ordinary divergence $(\phi^\mu,_\mu)$ so chosen that the altered Lagrangian density is free of second derivatives of the metric. Both Lagrangian densities, of course, lead to the same field equations for the metric. Thus $p^{\mu\nu}$ is a well-defined functional of $g_{\mu\nu}$, $\dot{g}_{\mu\nu}$ and their spatial derivatives

$$p^{\mu\nu} = p^{\mu\nu}(g_{\alpha\beta}, \dot{g}_{\alpha\beta}) \tag{6}$$

However, because of the covariance of the theory, it turns out that the canonical variables $g_{\mu\nu}$, $p^{\mu\nu}$ are not independent of each other but are related by a set of four equations of constraint, called the primary constraints, of the form

$$p^{0\mu} + \Gamma^\mu(g_{\alpha\beta}) = 0 \tag{7}$$

As a consequence, we cannot invert Eqs. (6) to obtain unique expressions for the $\dot{g}_{\mu\nu}$ in terms of the $p^{\mu\nu}$ and $g_{\mu\nu}$. Consequently, when one tries to construct the Hamiltonian density $\mathscr{H}$ with

$$\mathscr{H} = p^{\mu\nu}\dot{g}_{\mu\nu} - \mathscr{L}(g_{\alpha\beta}, \dot{g}_{\alpha\beta}) \tag{8}$$

one cannot eliminate the $\dot{g}_{\alpha\beta}$'s from the right-hand side of Eq. (8) to obtain $\mathscr{H}$ as a function of the canonical variables alone. This was one of the main problems that confronted people in formulating a Hamiltonian theory for general relativity. It was solved in different ways by Pirani and Schild[10] and Dirac.[11]

A similar situation occurs in electrodynamics. There, things are simple enough so that one can see in detail just what is happening. The electromagnetic field is described by a vector potential **A** and a scalar potential ϕ together with any matter variables, such as Dirac fields, that might occur. The theory is invariant under the group of gauge transformations

$$\bar{\mathbf{A}} = \mathbf{A} - \nabla\lambda \tag{9}$$

and

$$\bar{\phi} = \phi + \dot{\lambda} \tag{10}$$

where λ is an arbitrary space-time function.

In general relativity, the transformation group depends upon four arbitrary space-time functions. They are the four new coordinates expressed as functions of the old coordinates. In electrodynamics there is just one arbitrary function. However, many of the consequences are the same. Thus, by means of arguments similar to those used in the general relativity case, one can show that a knowledge of the field quantities **A** and ϕ together with their first time derivatives does not lead to a unique solution for these quantities into the future. Thus all our comments concerning the Hamiltonian formulation of general relativity apply in this case with equal force.

The Lagrangian density of electrodynamics is given by

$$\mathscr{L} = \tfrac{1}{2}(\dot{\mathbf{A}} + \nabla\phi)^2 - \tfrac{1}{2}(\nabla\times\mathbf{A})^2 - \rho\phi + \mathbf{j}\cdot\mathbf{A} \tag{11}$$

We can define the momentum density **p** conjugate to **A** as the derivative of $\mathscr{L}$ with respect to $\dot{\mathbf{A}}$ and so obtain

$$\mathbf{p} = \dot{\mathbf{A}} + \nabla\phi \tag{12}$$

We note, however, that $\mathscr{L}$ does not contain any $\dot{\phi}$ terms so that π, the momentum conjugate to ϕ, satisfies the equation

$$\pi = 0 \tag{13}$$

This is the primary constraint associated with the gauge invariance of the theory and is analogous to the primary-constraint equations (7). Here we see directly that we cannot determine $\dot{\phi}$ in terms of the momentum densities. However, we can obtain the $\dot{\mathbf{A}}$'s in terms of the canonical variables and so obtain a Hamiltonian H given by

$$H = \int \mathscr{H} \, d^3x \tag{14}$$

where the Hamiltonian density $\mathscr{H}$ is

$$\mathscr{H} = \tfrac{1}{2}\mathbf{p}^2 + \tfrac{1}{2}(\nabla\mathbf{\times A})^2 - \mathbf{j}\cdot\mathbf{A} + \phi(\nabla\cdot\mathbf{p} + \rho) + \dot{\phi}\pi \qquad (15)$$

In this expression, ϕ is taken to be an arbitrary space-time function. Its appearance reflects the nonuniqueness in the Hamiltonian that is necessary if the canonical equations of motion are not to determine the canonical variables uniquely in terms of their initial values.

Unfortunately, this is not the whole story. There is another constraint equation that arises as a consequence of the requirement $\dot{\pi}$ be zero so that Eq. (13) is maintained throughout the evolution of the system. The time derivative of π is obtained in the usual way by taking its Poisson bracket with H. When we do this, we find that

$$\dot{\pi} = (\pi, H) = \nabla\cdot\mathbf{p} + \rho \qquad (16)$$

so that we must require that

$$\nabla\cdot\mathbf{p} + \rho = 0 \qquad (17)$$

This is just one of Maxwell's equations, since $\mathbf{p}$ is equal to $-\mathbf{E}$, the electric field. Equation (17) is referred to as the secondary constraint of the theory. Fortunately, all higher time derivatives of π and all time derivatives of $\nabla\cdot\mathbf{p} + \rho$ vanish so that there are no additional constraints associated with the theory.

Obtaining a Hamiltonian formulation of general relativity was carried out along similar lines. However, because of the complexity of the primary constraints (7), the resulting expressions for the Hamiltonian and the secondary constraints were virtually impossible to work with. Recently Dirac, DeWitt, and myself, all independently, were able to introduce a new set of canonical variables into the theory in such a way that the new primary constraints took on the simple form

$$\mathrm{p}^{o\mu} = 0 \qquad (18)$$

In terms of these new variables, the Hamiltonian density took on the relatively simple form

$$\mathscr{H} = (g^{oo})^{-1/2}\mathscr{H}_L + g_{or}\mathscr{H}^r \qquad (19)$$

where $\mathscr{H}_L$ and $\mathscr{H}^r$ are certain functionals of the g_{rs} and p^{rs} and their spatial derivatives. (Here Latin indices take on the values 1, 2, 3).

Since we require $p^{o\mu} = 0$ for all times, $\dot{p}^{o\mu}$ must also be zero for all times. $\dot{p}^{o\mu}$ is calculated by computing the Poisson bracket between $p^{o\mu}$ and the Hamiltonian H. Since $\mathscr{H}_L$ and $\mathscr{H}^r$ do not depend on $g_{o\mu}$ or $p^{o\mu}$, by taking the commutator of $\mathscr{H}$ with respect to $p^{o\mu}$, one can further show that the secondary constraints become

$$\mathscr{H}_L = \mathscr{H}^r = 0 \qquad (20)$$

The constraint on $\mathscr{H}^r$ is known as the longitudinal constraint; that on $\mathscr{H}_L$ is known as the Hamiltonian constraint. These constraint equations are the main cause of all difficulties in formulating a quantized version of the theory. The existence of these constraints is a direct consequence of invariance of the theory under arbitrary coordinate transformations. For this reason, it is most likely that the difficulties associated with the Hamiltonian formulation of the theory will generally appear in one way or another in any formulation of the theory. In the present formulation, they tell us that the canonical variables g_{rs} and p^{rs} are not independent of each other. But when we formulate a Hamiltonian quantization by imposing commutation relations on canonical variables, it is essential that these variables be independent. This means that, in effect, we have too many variables and some should be eliminated from the theory. Unfortunately, the standard methods of eliminating the redundant parts of $g_{0\mu}$ and $p^{0\mu}$ are not directly applicable because of the complexity of the constraint equations (20).

A simplified form of these constraints was first given by Dirac. The equation for $\mathscr{H}^r$ reduces to

$$\mathscr{H}^r = p^{sr}_{|s} \tag{21}$$

Subscript $|s$ denotes covariant differentiation using the metric g_{rs} and its inverse e^{rs}. It is not the full four-dimensional covariant derivative, but only the three-dimensional covariant derivative.

Equation (21) is very similar to the equation that appears in electrodynamics in the case of zero-charge density.

$$\nabla \cdot p = 0 \tag{22}$$

Equation (21) is a generalization of the divergence applied to a symmetric tensor in curved spaces. In electrodynamics we have simply the ordinary divergence of a vector. But this difference is the cause of many difficulties. The constraint on $\mathscr{H}_L$ is

$$\mathscr{H}_L = \frac{1}{K}(g_{ra}g_{sb} - \tfrac{1}{2}g_{rs}g_{ab})p^{rs}p^{ab} + {}^3R(g_{ab}) \tag{23}$$

where

$$K^2 = |g_{rs}| \tag{24}$$

and ${}^3R(g_{ab})$ is the curvature scalar constructed from the metric g_{rs} and its inverse. The first term resembles a kinetic energy, whereas the second term resembles potential energy. In the linearized version of the theory, these terms are in fact interpreted as kinetic and potential energy.

In order to understand better the type of difficulties introduced into the theory by the constraint equations (20), let us return to our example of electrodynamics. There we have the variables **A** and **p**. They are not independent variables, because they satisfy Eq. (18). This means that not all the variables of the theory are independent dynamic variables. If we can perform some kind of transformation and make $\nabla \cdot p + \rho$ a new momentum density for the theory, then, together with the canonical coordinates conjugate to the new momentum, they will play the same role as π and ϕ and can be eliminated from the theory.

One very simple way of doing this is to introduce the longitudinal and transverse components of **A** and **p**. Let

$$\mathbf{A} = \mathbf{A}^L + \mathbf{A}^T \tag{25}$$

where $\mathbf{A}^L$ and $\mathbf{A}^T$ satisfy the following conditions:

$$\nabla \cdot \mathbf{A}^T \equiv 0 \tag{26}$$

$$\nabla \cdot \mathbf{A}^L \equiv 0 \tag{27}$$

Similarly, **p** may be written as

$$\mathbf{p} = \mathbf{p}^L + \mathbf{p}^T$$

Then Eq. (18) reduces to

$$\nabla \cdot \mathbf{p}^L + \rho = 0 \tag{28}$$

$\mathbf{p}^T$ does not appear in the constraint equation, and we are free to consider

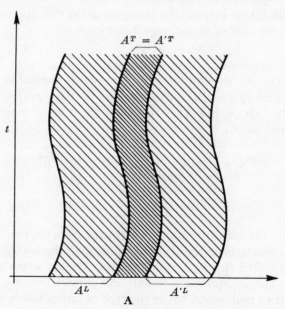

Figure 14-3 Representation of A field under gauge transformation.

$\mathbf{p}^T$ and $\mathbf{A}^T$ as the basic dynamic variables. $\mathbf{p}^L$ is expressed in terms of ρ. If ρ is zero, $\mathbf{p}^L$ is also zero. $\mathbf{A}^L$ may be made to be zero by introducing a proper gauge condition. Hence one can construct the Hamiltonian in terms of $\mathbf{A}^T$ and $\mathbf{p}^T$, which are then the canonical variables.

The commutation relations between $\mathbf{A}^T$ and $\mathbf{p}^T$ contain some terms other than the usual delta-function commutation relations. However, these terms are independent of $\mathbf{A}^T$ and $\mathbf{p}^T$ and no new complications arise. $\mathbf{A}^T$ and $\mathbf{p}^T$ are also invariant under a gauge transformation. Under a gauge transformation, only $\mathbf{A}^L$ changes. In Figure 14-3 we have schematically represented two different A fields describing the same physical situation, i.e., the same E and B fields. The central portion of the figure represents the transverse parts of the two A fields and is the same for both. The two outer portions represent the different longitudinal parts of the two fields.

With almost no modification, the above result applies to the case of gravitation. That is, in the p^{rs}, g_{rs} representation, there is some invariance under coordinate transformations. This represents the intrinsic geometry. In Figure 14-4, the noninvariant part of the representation is indicated by the fluff about an invariant core. This fluff depends upon the particular coordinate system one chooses. Under any coordinate transformation, the central core remains unchanged.

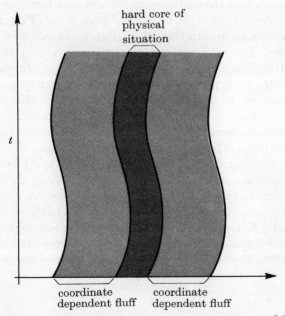

Figure 14-4 Schematic representation of invariant core of intrinsic geometry and coordinate-dependent fluff.

As in the electromagnetic case, one would like to separate from g_{rs} and p^{rs} a physical part that remains unchanged under coordinate transformations. How easily this separation can be made depends upon the form of the constraint equations. In the electromagnetic case, the separation is achieved by breaking up $\mathbf{A}$ and $\mathbf{p}$ into longitudinal and transverse parts. As we saw, the longitudinal part of p is uniquely determined by the constraint equation (28). On the other hand, $\mathbf{A}^L$ can be transformed away by choosing a proper gauge condition.

It is possible to break up the g_{rs} and p^{rs} in a manner analogous to the electromagnetic example. However, the redundant variables cannot be eliminated from the theory very easily.

At best, one can accomplish this solution by an approximation procedure based on a weak-field approximation. To date, no one, to my knowledge, has suggested a decomposition scheme of g_{rs} and p^{rs}, such that the physical part does not appear in the constraint equations, or a scheme allowing one to solve the constraint equations directly and to write down the redundant variables in terms of the other variables.

Quantum Version of the Theory

With the above discussion of the classic Hamiltonian formulation of general relativity and electrodynamics, we can now turn our attention to the quantum versions of these theories. Again, many of my remarks will be devoted to the electromagnetic case, since we know fairly well what is going on there. There are two different ways to quantize these theories within the Hamiltonian framework. The most straightforward of these, and the one used by Bergmann and Komar[2] and DeWitt,[4] is to treat only the physical part of the field variables as operators defined in some Hilbert space. The remaining field variables are to be eliminated from the theory by the use of the constraint equations and the imposition of gauge or coordinate conditions. Thus, in the electromagnetic case, one would treat only $\mathbf{A}^T$ and $\mathbf{p}^T$ as operators and replace $\mathbf{p}^L$ by $-\nabla(1/\nabla^2)\rho$. Once one has fixed the gauge (for example, by $\mathbf{A}^L = 0$), one can obtain the Hamiltonian directly in terms of these transverse parts. Then one can write down the Schrödinger equation. Finally, the commutation relations between the transverse parts follow from their Poisson-bracket relations in the usual way. A possible representation analogous to the x representation in ordinary quantum mechanics would be to define the operators $\mathbf{A}^T$ and $\mathbf{p}^T$ as follows:

$$\mathbf{A}^T\phi = \mathbf{A}^T\phi$$

$$\mathbf{p}^T\phi = i\hbar\frac{\delta}{\delta\mathbf{A}^T}\phi$$

(29)

In this way, state vectors would then be functionals of $\mathbf{A}^T$.

The same procedure has been applied to the gravitational case for which g_{rs}^{TT} and p^{rsTT} correspond to the transverse parts of the canonical coordinates and momenta.[12] Using a representation similar to Eq. (29), we take

$$g_{rs}^{TT}\phi \equiv g_{rs}^{TT}\phi$$

$$p^{rsTT}\phi \equiv i\hbar\frac{\delta\phi}{\delta g_{rs}^{TT}} \tag{30}$$

State vectors would then be functionals of g_{rs}^{TT}. However, because we could not solve the constraint equations for any four of the redundant variables in closed form, we do not have a closed form for the Hamiltonian in terms of the g_{rs}^{TT} and p^{rsTT}. We are forced to make a weak-field expansion. This is a return to the linearized theory that Feynman has treated.

There is another difficulty that arises when one takes this approach to quantization. The above scheme for separating the physical part is by no means unique in either the electromagnetic or the gravitational case. One can set up a scheme that allows one to calculate the physical part in many different ways. For example, in electrodynamics one can fix the gauge by imposing conditions on some of the $\mathbf{A}$'s. The remaining $\mathbf{A}$'s will then be gauge invariant. As an example, one can fix the gauge by requiring that

$$\mathbf{A}_1 = 0 \tag{31}$$

$$\mathbf{A}_2(x = 0) = 0 \tag{32}$$

$$\mathbf{A}_3(x = y = 0) = 0 \tag{33}$$

In this gauge, the values of $\mathbf{A}_2(x \neq 0)$ and $\mathbf{A}_3(x \neq 0, y \neq 0)$ are gauge-invariant quantities and, together with their canonical conjugate momenta, can be used to describe the physical state of the electromagnetic field. This description is, of course, quite different from the previously discussed condition $\mathbf{A}^L = 0$. Thus there are many different ways of fixing the gauge in electrodynamics. Each different way in turn leads to a different set of expressions that can serve as the physical variables.

The situation in general relativity is quite analogous. Once the coordinates are fixed by imposing suitable conditions on the g_{rs}'s and p^{rs}'s, the remainder variables automatically become invariant under coordinate transformations and can serve as physical variables. These are commonly referred to as observables. An interesting question is whether a quantized version using one set of observables is equivalent to a quantized version using another set. I shall discuss some of the difficulties involved in answering that question.

Imagine that two different decompositions of the g_{rs} and p^{rs} have been found. Symbolically, we write

$$\{g_{rs}, p^{rs}\} = \{y_{\text{physical}}, y_{\text{coordinate}}\} \tag{34}$$

and

$$\{g_{rs}, p^{rs}\} = \{y'_{\text{physical}}, y'_{\text{coordinate}}\} \tag{35}$$

The y's represent physical or coordinate conditions. Since y_{physical} and y'_{physical} both represent the same physical conditions, they must be functions of each other. However, in general, $y'_{\text{coordinate}}$ will depend both on $y_{\text{coordinate}}$ and y_{physical} and vice versa. As, for example, in the formulation of Eq. (21), we wish to treat only the physical parts of the field as operators and to consider the coordinate part as a c number (classical, or commuting number, that is, not an operator). This separate treatment of the physical and coordinate parts leads to the following difficulty: What is treated as a c number in one formulation will appear as an operator in the other formulation, and vice versa. It is not inconceivable that one can eliminate the above-mentioned difficulties and construct a general proof of the physical equivalence of different decomposition schemes, which are within the framework of the quantization procedure discussed above. However, I strongly doubt this possibility for reasons that I shall now discuss.

We have mentioned before that there are actually two ways of effecting a quantization within the Hamiltonian framework. In the one, discussed above, only the physical parts of the field are to be treated as operators defined in a Hilbert space. The physical parts are invariant under a gauge or coordinate transformation. Hence the gauge or coordinate group disappears from this "Hilbert space quantization," making it difficult to carry out the proof of equivalence discussed above.

In the other approach to quantization, one treats all the field variables as operators. These operators, either the **A** and **p** or the g_{rs} and p^{rs}, are assumed to have the standard commutation relations between canonical variables. Thus we have, for example

$$[g_{rs}, g'_{ab}] = [p^{rs}, p'^{ab}] = 0 \tag{36}$$

$$[g_{rs}, p'^{ab}] = i\hbar \delta^{ab}_{rs}\delta(x - x') \tag{37}$$

The prime over a variable means that it is evaluated at the space point x'. These operators operate in a linear vector space whose elements are functionals of the g_{rs}. In this representation, the operators are given by

$$g_{rs}\phi(x) = g_{rs}\phi(x)$$

$$p^{rs} = i\hbar \frac{\delta}{\delta g_{rs}} \phi(x) \tag{38}$$

In this case, all the coordinates and momenta, and not just the transverse (physical) parts are treated as operators. Because of the constraint equations (20), this vector space is not normalizable and hence is not a Hilbert space.

We now ask, how do these constraints modify the quantization of the theory. With the Hilbert space method of quantization, the constraints were no problem because they were eliminated from the theory prior to quantization. Now they must be taken into account. However, the constraint equations cannot be treated simply as operator equations directly. If we do this, they will be inconsistent with the commutation relations (38). That is, if we evaluate the covariant derivative of both sides of Eq. (37) at x'^b and, if we assume that $\mathscr{H}'^a = p'^{ab}_{|b} = 0$ everywhere, the left-hand side will be zero everywhere, whereas the right-hand side will not be zero at many points of space. There is one way to avoid this difficulty. To describe the physical states of the gravitational field, we shall use only those elements of the linear vector space ψ that satisfy

$$\mathscr{H}^a\psi = 0 \tag{39}$$

and

$$\mathscr{H}_L\psi = 0 \tag{40}$$

It is possible to show that, with these restrictions on the state vectors, the quantum version of the theory passes over to the classical version in the correspondence limit. This will not be so if this assumption is not imposed.

In order to complete this formulation, we must impose additional gauge or coordinate conditions. However, as is the case of the constraint equations, they cannot be treated as operator equations but must be assumed to hold only for a subclass of the state vectors that satisfy conditions (39) and (40). Thus the subspace of the original linear-vector space spanned by the vectors that satisfy these conditions is further broken up into subspaces by the imposition of various kinds of gauge or coordinate conditions. We schematically picture the space of all vectors defined by Eqs. (36) and (37) in Figure 14-5. The shaded area represents the subspace of vector space of vectors satisfying conditions (39) and (40). The two smaller cross-hatched areas represent subspaces, in which two different sets of coordinate conditions hold.

We can draw a similar picture in the classical theory as well, only now the over-all space is the phase space with coordinates **A** and **p** or g_{rs} and p^{rs}. The shaded area will now represent the subspace of points satisfying the constraint equations; the two smaller, cross-hatched areas will represent points satisfying two different sets of gauge or coordinate conditions. As we have seen, the points in the large shaded area are, in a certain sense, redundant; many represent the same physical situation. They differ only because different coordinates are used to describe the same state of the

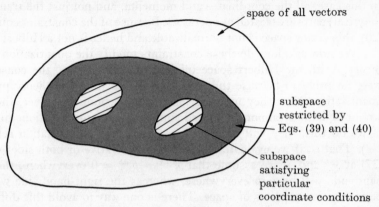

Figure 14-5　Representation of a vector space.

field. Thus we should expect that the totality of points within any one cross-hatched area should stand in a one-to-one relation with the possible states of the system. This also means that there should be a one-to-one correspondence between the points of one cross-hatched area and those of any other cross-hatched area.

Indeed, it has been proved in the classic version of the theory that there always exists a canonical transformation that maps the points of one cross-hatched area in a one-to-one manner onto the points of any other cross hatched area.[13]

These transformations are generated by linear combinations of the constraints. Since the transformation, which maps one cross-hatched area onto another, is obviously a finite gauge or coordinate transformation, we see that linear combinations of the constraints form the generators of the invariance group of the theory. In the course of the proof it was necessary to show that these generators did indeed form a group. The necessary and sufficient condition for this to be true is that the Poisson bracket between any two constraints is a linear combination of contraints. The constraints do possess this property. It is thus concluded that the subspace spanned by those points in phase space, for which the constraint equations are valid (the shaded area in Figure 14-5), is simply connected. Therefore, there can be no physical experiment within the theory by which a preferred coordinate system could be singled out. Thus the principle of general covariance is not violated.

From the above discussion, we can see the intimate relation between the invariance group of the theory and the constraint equations. This relationship is a general one and holds whenever a theory is derivable from a variational principle and possesses an invariance group whose elements are defined by one or more space-time functions.

These concepts can be best illustrated in terms of electromagnetic theory. If we include ϕ and π, as well as $\mathbf{A}$ and $\mathbf{p}$ as our canonical variables, we can form the following generator of an infinitesimal gauge transformation:

$$c = \int d^3x\{\dot{\gamma}\pi + \gamma(\nabla \cdot \mathbf{p} + \rho)\} \tag{41}$$

The variation of the field quantities ϕ and $\mathbf{A}$ may be easily computed in the subspace of interest in which the constraint equations are also satisfied:

$$\bar{\delta}\phi = \{\phi, c\} = \dot{\gamma} \tag{42}$$

and

$$\bar{\delta}\mathbf{A} = \{\mathbf{A}, c\} = -\nabla\gamma \tag{43}$$

Equations (42) and (43) represent an infinitesimal gauge transformation. Also, it is easy to prove that the generators π and $\nabla \cdot \mathbf{p} + \rho$ have vanishing Poisson brackets among themselves so that the generators of the form given in Eq. (41) do indeed form an infinitesimal group. The elements of this infinitesimal group can be added to give a finite gauge transformation. Exactly the same situation pertains in general relativity where a linear combination of the constraints generate an infinitesimal coordinate transformation.

Let us now return to the quantum version of electromagnetic theory. What we have said about the classical theory is also valid in the quantum theory if we replace canonical transformations by unitary transformations and Poisson brackets by commutors. In the electromagnetic theory, this is easily done; when the canonical variables are treated as operators, c is the generator of an infinitesimal unitary transformation. The commutator of two such transformations is a unitary transformation of the same kind.

It is not difficult to show that the two methods of quantization outlined above are equivalent. We may start from the classic theory, impose gauge conditions, and then quantize, treating only the physical parts of the field as operators in a Hilbert space; or we may treat all the field variables as operators in a linear vector space and impose gauge conditions afterward to restrict the vectors that are used to describe the physical state of the system. The essential point of the latter formulation is that we can carry out a unitary transformation that transforms from one coordinate frame to another. From this we can prove the equivalence of all gauge frames. Since the two methods are equivalent, we have thereby proved the equivalence of starting out in two different classical gauge frames.

There is another difficulty to be overcome that appears in Eqs. (42) and (43). In order to generate a transformation from one set of potentials to another that satisfies a particular set of gauge conditions, the gauge function γ will, in general, depend upon the potentials. Thus, if we wish to transform an arbitrary set of potentials to the Coulomb gauge where $\nabla \cdot \mathbf{A} = 0$, we must use a gauge function given by

$$\Gamma = (\nabla^2)^{-1}\nabla \cdot \bar{\mathbf{A}} \tag{44}$$

where $\bar{\mathbf{A}}$ is the original potential. This has the consequence, that if $\bar{\mathbf{A}}$ and $\bar{\mathbf{p}}$ are assumed to satisfy the standard commutation relations

$$[\bar{\mathbf{A}}_r, \bar{\mathbf{p}}'^s] = i\hbar\delta_r^s\delta \tag{45}$$

then it follows that

$$\mathbf{A} = \bar{\mathbf{A}} - \nabla(\nabla^2)^{-1}\nabla \cdot \bar{\mathbf{A}} \tag{46}$$

and

$$\mathbf{p} = \bar{\mathbf{p}} \tag{47}$$

will not satisfy Eq. (45). To by-pass this difficulty, one makes use of Eqs. (42) and (43) for generating gauge transformations. Since c is the generator of an infinitesimal unitary transformation, the transformed variables will satisfy the commutation relations (45). Equations (42) and (43) are valid only in the subspace of the linear-vector space where the constraint equations hold. In the full linear-vector space there are additional terms in the expressions for $\bar{\delta}\phi$, $\bar{\delta}\mathbf{A}$, $\bar{\delta}\pi$ and $\bar{\delta}\mathbf{p}$ that are linear combinations of the constraints. These terms arise from the nonvanishing commutators between ϕ, π, $\mathbf{A}$ and $\mathbf{p}$ and the quantities $\dot{\gamma}$ and γ. They maintain the validity of the commutation relations between the transformed field variables. It is then a straightforward procedure to prove the invariance of the theory under arbitrary q-number (noncommuting quantum operator) gauge transformations even in the presence of interaction with a Dirac field.

We can illustrate these remarks with a simple example (Figure 14-6). Two observers, A and B, observe the electric properties of a resistor. They both realize that the potential difference between two points is the only meaningful concept, but that it is much easier to assign an arbitrary value of potential to one fixed point and then measure all other potentials with respect to that fixed point. A decides to assign the value zero to the potential at the left end of the resistor, and B decides to assign the value zero for the potential to the right side of the resistor. For an idealized resistor they will have no trouble comparing their results. For instance, B will merely add to all his potential readings the value of the total potential difference between the two ends of the resistor. In order to transform his

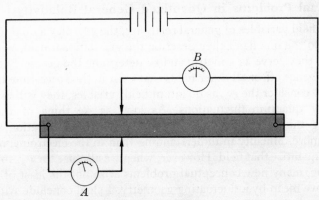

Figure 14-6 Illustration of effect of fluctuating gauge transformation by measurement of potential difference along a resistor.

result to that of A's, B performs a gauge transformation. Their results are then directly comparable.

Now let the resistor cease to be ideal. They will be looking at a resistor in which the potential is fluctuating as a result of thermal noise. A will conclude that the potential at the right end fluctuates, whereas B will conclude that the potential at the left end fluctuates. This will puzzle both of them for a moment since each had assigned the value zero to the potential at one of these two ends, respectively and, by definition, the value zero does not fluctuate. In order for B to check his results with those of A, he will now have to perform a gauge transformation that fluctuates with time. Such a transformation is the analogue of a q-number gauge transformation in the quantum theory.

In general relativity the situation is much the same as in electrodynamics, with one crucial difference. Although one can still construct the generator of an infinitesimal q-number coordinate transformation, one cannot integrate to obtain a finite transformation. The infinitesimal generators do not appear to form a group. In fact, one can prove that there exists no ordering of factors in the classical expressions for the constraints such that the commutator of $\mathcal{H}_L$ and $\mathcal{H}'_L$ is again a linear combination of the constraints. Thus it appears that the shaded area in Figure 14-5 is not simply connected; the use of different coordinate conditions appears to lead to essentially nonequivalent quantum theories. This conclusion stands in direct contradiction to the principle of general covariance. If true, it it would mean that, in principle at least, it should be possible to decide which, of the infinity of possible coordinate systems, is the one appropriate for a description of our universe.

Conceptual Problems in Quantized General Relativity

The field variables of general relativity, the $g_{\mu\nu}$, play a dual role in the theory. On the one hand they describe the gravitational field, whereas on the other they serve as a metric and so determine the geometry of space-time and hence affect all other fields that exist in the space-time manifold. If we now consider the $g_{\mu\nu}$ as quantum field variables, they will exhibit the customary quantum fluctuations. As long as we think of the $g_{\mu\nu}$ as describing the gravitational field, this additional complication seems to offer no more difficulty in understanding than in the electromagnetic case when we quantize that field. However, when we also use the $g_{\mu\nu}$ to describe the metric, many new conceptual problems arise not the least of which is what do we mean by a fluctuating geometry. I shall conclude with a brief discussion of some of these problems.

Many of the conceptual problems associated with quantizing general relativity are related to measurement processes. Since general relativity is first a geometric theory, the most natural types of measurements will involve the determination of space-time intervals, measurement of the gravitational field $g_{\mu\nu}$ and the Christoffel symbols $\{^{\rho}_{\mu\nu}\}$ in a given coordinate system. Wigner[14] has investigated the question of measuring time intervals in general relativity. He concluded that there seems to be a contradiction.

Wigner's argument is as follows: When one measures an interval of time in some region of space, what one actually measures is how long it takes for something to happen. For this purpose one needs an accurate clock. The accuracy in time measurement is limited by the quantum uncertainty relation

$$\Delta E \Delta t \geq \hbar \tag{48}$$

Therefore, if one wants an accurate clock (small Δt), there will be an uncertainty in its energy, and this uncertainty in its energy is related to an uncertainty in its mass through the relation

$$(\Delta m)c^2 = \Delta E \tag{49}$$

Thus the smaller Δt is, the bigger Δm must be. This means the fluctuations in the clock mass must be very large. In the limit of infinite accuracy the fluctuations in the clock mass must be infinite. These fluctuations in mass will, in turn, produce similar fluctuations in the gravitational field. In special relativity, where the metric is forever fixed, such fluctuations are not a problem since one need not include the gravitational field in the theory. In general relativity we can no longer neglect such fluctuations since the gravitational field is also the metric field and, hence, affects all other fields. As a consequence the very notion of a space-time interval and with it the notion of a point in space-time becomes questionable, and the whole nature of the space-time manifold becomes uncertain. It has even been conjectured, on the basis of such arguments, that one must eliminate the concept of points from the theory since they are unobservable elements. At the very least it does bring into question the process of setting up a coordinate system and the measurement of distances.

A possible way out of this apparent dilemma is to abandon the demand for accurate time measurement at a particular space point and adopt the approach of *S*-matrix theory wherein one talks only of asymptotic behavior of interacting systems. Such a procedure has been suggested by Misner. However, I believe we can learn about the structure of space and time only by examining the character of the coordinate system. This does not mean that we have actually to observe these coordinates. Rather our structure of space-time will determine to a large extent the type of coordinates we can introduce. For example, if space-time were in some way discrete, we would employ different coordinates from those we would employ if it were continuous. This in turn would affect the types of theories we could construct in space-time. Thus, even if we were never able to make local space-time measurement of the kind envisaged by Wigner, we could still have a space-time manifold whose properties would be known to us through the properties of the coordinate systems that exist in it.

Another difficulty arises when we try to work out a Bohr-Rosenfeld argument for the measurement of a gravitational field.[15] Bohr and Rosenfeld noted that in electromagnetic theory, when one wants to measure the electric field with great accuracy, one has to employ very large charges. Furthermore, since the measurement of the field involves a measurement of the momentum imparted to the particle we must, in some way, minimize the uncertainty in this measurement. The uncertainty ΔE_x in the x component of the electric field is related to the uncertainty Δp_x, of the x component of the momentum of the test particle by

$$\Delta E_x = \frac{\Delta p_x}{\epsilon \Delta t} \tag{50}$$

where ϵ is the charge on the test body and Δt is the time taken for the measurement of E_x. The uncertainty in the momentum measurement is itself limited by the uncertainty relation $\Delta p_x \Delta x \geq \hbar$ so that we have

$$\Delta E_x \geq \frac{\hbar}{\epsilon \Delta x \Delta t} \tag{51}$$

where Δx is the uncertainty in the position of the test particle. Since we want all three quantities ΔE_x, Δx, and Δt to be small, we must use a test body with a very large charge. However, a large ϵ entails a further difficulty since we measure the total field present. This includes the field produced by the test body. Thus, for large ϵ, this self-field $\mathscr{E}$ is also large.

Furthermore, we obtain no knowledge of this field since we do not know the position and motion of the test body exactly because of the uncertainty relations. However, Bohr and Rosenfeld showed that, by the use of purely mechanical devices such as springs, it is possible to compensate automatically for the effect of this self-field. They concluded that it is meaningful to talk about the value of an electric field at a point in space-time.

In the gravitational case, one can write an expression analogous to Eq. (35). Here the objects of measurement are components of the Christoffel symbols $\{^{\rho}_{\mu\nu}\}$. The component analogous to E_x is $\{^1_{44}\}$. If we assume that the test body moves along a geodesic, we can show, in a manner analogous to the derivation leading to Eq. (35), that the uncertainty in $\{^1_{44}\}$ is

$$\Delta\{^1_{44}\} \geq \frac{\hbar}{m\Delta x\Delta t} \tag{52}$$

where m is the gravitational mass of the test body. Again, in order to specify the gravitational field at a space-time point, we must make all three quantities, $\Delta\{^1_{44}\}$, Δx, and Δt vanishingly small. The requirement that $\Delta\{^1_{44}\}$ is small means that m must be very large. This large mass will produce a large field. But now the effects of this field cannot be compensated for as in the electromagnetic case. First, there are no devices such as springs that will not produce a gravitational field. Second, we have no way of determining the amount of compensation needed. Third, once the mass of the test body becomes large, it will no longer follow along a geodesic of the field we are trying to measure but will follow a geodesic of the combined fields. Fourth, since the theory is nonlinear, the two fields, external and self-, will not add, so that we can no longer make use of the geodesic equation to measure the $\{^{\rho}_{\mu\nu}\}$.

In both the above examples, we are confronted with a new situation that does not occur in ordinary Lorentz invariant theories. Whenever we try to make a measurement of gravitational fields at a point, we must use quite heavy bodies to overcome the effects of the uncertainty principle. The introduction of heavy bodies as measuring instruments distorts the result in an unpredictable way.

Another difficulty is associated with setting up the initial-value problem. The initial conditions are imposed upon space-like surfaces. However, one must know the geometry of the space-time in order to pick out a space-like surface. Classically, one can overcome this difficulty by choosing some surface determined by a condition on the coordinates such as $t = 0$, such that this surface is indeed space-like. For example, one can fix g_{rs} in a coordinate system where $g_{o\mu} = -\delta_{o\mu}$, such that, on the surface $t = 0$, $ds^2 = g_{rs}\,dx^r\,dx^s - dt^2 > 0$. Lichnerowicz and Mme.

Fourès-Bruhat showed that, as the system develops, the adjoining surface $t = dt$ is also space-like.

When we come to the quantum version of the theory, we are faced with the same problem. The initial state is represented by functions of g_{rs}. We can employ a coordinate system in which $g_{o\mu} = -\delta_{o\mu}$, and choose the initial surface to be that defined by $t = 0$. Then we must choose the ensemble of gravitational fields that makes up the eigen states of the field so that $ds^2 > 0$. This is easy, although it imposes rather complicated restrictions on our initial-state functionals. Now, the problem is, can we be sure that our initial space-like surfaces remain space-like into the future for all members of the ensemble? In the classical case, for a given set of g_{rs}, one can find a corresponding set of momenta p^{rs} that satisfy the constraint equations that lead to the surface $t = dt$ being space-like. In the quantum version it is possible that a surface that was initially space-like might become time-like or light-like. Such a possibility exists because of the difficulty mentioned earlier that one cannot find quantum expressions for the constraints (20) such that the commutator of any two of them is a linear combination of the constraints, with all coefficients standing to the left of the constraints. Since the Hamiltonian is itself a linear combination of the constraints, we find that they are not necessarily zero for the physical states ψ that satisfy Eqs. (39) and (40). As a consequence, the p^{rs} may have fluctuations that do not satisfy the constraint equations at later times and so lead to nonspace-like surfaces.

Thus, both from the formal and the conceptual points of view, there are serious problems associated with quantizing gravity. In all our examples there appear to be incompatibilities between the requirements of quantum mechanics as we know them and the requirements of general relativity. It is of course possible that, in a complete theory of quantum gravidynamics, such difficulties might, in some way, be ameliorated. One can argue that it is meaningful to discuss the measurement process only on the basis of the complete theory. However, one does not yet have such a complete theory. Hopefully, such discussions as we have given here, even with the crude methods used, might indicate this theory and the direction it should go, or whether it is reasonable to try to construct.

References

1. P. G. Bergman, *Phys. Rev.*, **75**, 680 (1949).
2. For a detailed bibliography, the reader is referred to P. G. Bergman, *Helv. Phys. Acta.* **Suppl. IV**, 79 (1956), and *Recent Developments in General Relativity*, Pergamon, New York, 1962, p. 31.
3. P. G. Bergmann and A. Komar, *Les Theories Relativistes de la Gravitation*, Centre National de la Recherche Scientifique, Paris, 1962, p. 309.

4. B. S. DeWitt, *Recent Developments in General Relativity*, Pergamon, 1962, p. 175.

5. R. E. Peierls, *Proc. Roy. Soc. (London)*, **A214**, 143 (1952).

6. J. A. Wheeler, *Ann. Phys.*, **2**, 604 (1957), C. W. Misner, *Rev. Mod. Phys.*, **29**, 377 (1957).

7. R. Arnowitt and S. Deser, *Phys. Rev.*, **113**, 745 (1959).

8. R. P. Feynman, "Quantum Theory of Gravitation," Lecture delivered on Sept. 24, 1963, Yeshiva University (unpublished).

9. R. W. Fuller and J. A. Wheeler, *Phys. Rev.* **128**, 919 (1962).

10. F. A. E. Pirani and A. Schild, *Phys. Rev.*, **79**, 986 (1950).

11. P. A. M. Dirac, *Proc. Roy. Soc. (London)*, **A246**, 333 (1958); *Phys. Rev.*, **114**, 924 (1959).

12. R. Arnowitt, S. Deser, and C. W. Misner, *Recent Developments in General Relativity*, Pergamon, New York, 1962, p. 127; further references to their work are contained here.

13. J. L. Anderson and P. G. Bergmann, *Phys. Rev.*, **83**, 1018 (1951).

14. E. P. Wigner, *Rev. Mod. Phys.* **29**, 255 (1957), *J. Math. Phys.*, **2**, 207 (1961).

15. J. L. Anderson, *Rev. Mex. Fis.*, **3**, 176 (1954).

15
Mach's principle as boundary condition for Einstein's equations

John A. Wheeler

The Search for an Acceptable Formulation of Mach's Principle

Inertia as the Radiative Component of the Gravitational Force

Mach's principle has already been discussed in Chapter 7. In its simplest form this principle states that acceleration can have no meaning unless there is something with respect to which the acceleration takes place. In other words, it says that the acceleration with respect to absolute space that Newton speaks about has to be understood as an acceleration with respect to the stars and matter in the universe. Thus it leads to the following *Formulation 1* of Mach's principle: *The inertial properties of an object are determined by the distribution of mass-energy throughout all space.* In Chapter 7 this idea was considered as calling for a modification of Einstein's relativity. In contrast, here Mach's principle is considered from a different point of view, in which it serves, not to *modify* Einstein's field equations, but to provide a *boundary condition* for those equations.

Mach's principle, together with Riemann's idea that the geometry of space responds to physics and participates in physics, were the two great currents of thought which Einstein, by means of his powerful equivalence principle, brought together into the present day geometrical description of gravitation and motion. The interplay between geometry and physics is the subject of Chapters 3 and 9. In the course of this work Einstein identified gravitation itself as the source of the interaction by which—according to Mach—one object affects the inertial properties of another. What is important in this connection is not the familiar $1/r^2$ static component of the gravitational force, but the acceleration-proportional radiative component of the interaction (Table 15-1). Einstein

Table 15–1

Static and Radiative Components of Electromagnetic and Gravitational Forces
Compared and Contrasted

(The meaning of f is explained in the text)

	Electromagnetism	Gravitation
Static or near part of interaction	$\dfrac{e_1 e_2}{r^2}$	$\dfrac{Gm_1 m_2}{r^2}$
Radiative or distant component	$\dfrac{e_1 e_2 a_2 f}{c^2 r}$	$\dfrac{Gm_1 m_2 a_2 f}{c^2 r}$

discussed this point in his book[1] in connection with the idealized experiment of Thirring. This description of the inertia of a given particle as arising from the radiative component of its interaction with all other masses in the universe has been examined further by Sciama[2] and Davidson.[3] The inertial term, ma, is dropped from Newton's equation of motion. In its place appears the sum of the radiative interactions

$$ma \sum_k \frac{Gm_k f}{c^2 r_k} \tag{1}$$

where the sum is taken over all masses in the universe, m_k, at distances r_k from m. The quantity f is an abbreviation for a dimensionless function of the angles between the lines of acceleration of source and receptor and the line connecting these two objects. This term gives a reasonable order of magnitude account of inertia if the dimensions of the universe are of the order of 10^{10} light-years and if the effective average density of matter is of the order of 10^{-29} g/cm³.[4]

Inertia, Geometry, and the Distribution of Mass-Energy and Energy Flow

The analysis of Thirring and Einstein brings this "sum for inertia" [Eq. (1)] into closer connection with the ideas of general relativity. On the one hand, the inertial properties of a test particle are expressed in terms of the metric tensor $g_{\mu\nu}$. On the other hand, the agencies responsible for changes in this measure of inertia are characterized not merely by density of matter, but by the entire stress-energy tensor $T_{\mu\nu}$. Thus Thirring and Einstein expressed the change of the metric in a local Lorentz system, owing to a change $\delta T_{\mu\nu}$, in the form

$$h_{\mu\nu} = g_{\mu\nu} - \hat{g}_{\mu\nu} \tag{2}$$

$$h = \hat{g}^{\mu\nu} h_{\mu\nu} \tag{3}$$

where $g_{\mu\nu}$ and $\hat{g}_{\mu\nu}$ are the components of the new and old metric, respectively. $h_{\mu\nu}$ is obtained from the equation

$$h_{\mu\nu} - \tfrac{1}{2}\hat{g}_{\mu\nu}h = (8\pi G/c^4)\int \frac{[\delta T_{\mu\nu}]_{\text{ret}}\,d^3x}{r} \tag{4}$$

This expression remains a good approximate solution of Einstein's field equation so long as the geometry of the regions where the mass-energy is located does not differ substantially from the local Lorentz geometry at the position of the test particle. From Eq. (4), and the fact that in relativity theory the inertial properties of a test particle are determined by the metric, one is led to the following formulation of Mach's principle (Formulation 2). *The geometry of space-time and therefore the inertial properties of every infinitesimal test particle are determined by the distribution of energy and energy flow throughout all space.*

Objections to Mach's Principle

The consistency of Mach's principle as expressed in Formulation 2 and Eqs. (3) and (4) has been questioned for the following reasons:

1. Einstein's field equations

$$R_{\mu\nu} - \tfrac{1}{2}g_{\mu\nu}R = (8\pi G/c^4)T_{\mu\nu} \tag{5}$$

are nonlinear. It is wrong in principle to try to express the solution $g_{\mu\nu}$ as a linear superposition of effects from the $g_{\mu\nu}$ in various regions of space.

2. The quantity $1/r$ in the integrand is not a well-defined quantity in an irregularly curved space.

3. If in the Friedmann universe the contributions to the inertia at a definite point in space-time due to matter at more and more remote points are considered, one is forced to go back to earlier and earlier moments of time for the value of the retarded stress-energy tensor, $(T\mu\nu)_{\text{ret}}$. Ultimately one comes to a time when the system was in a singular state. What does one do then about the contribution of $(T_{\mu\nu})_{\text{ret}}$ to the inertia?

4. The elementary sum in Eq. (1) for the coefficient of inertia envisages a radiative interaction between particle and particle which propagates instantaneously. But how can stars at distances of 10^9 and 10^{10} light-years respond to the acceleration of a test particle here and now in such a way as to react back upon this test particle at this very moment? This difficulty alone should be sufficient cause for dropping the elementary formulation of Eq. (1).

But when one turns from this picture to the Thirring-Einstein formulation [Eqs. (2), (3), and (4)] one encounters an ambiguity in the sense that one could use advanced interactions just as well as retarded interactions—or any combination of the two—in obtaining a solution of the linearized field equations [Eq. (4)]. If the advanced and retarded expressions for the metric in terms of the distribution of mass-energy differ from each other—as expected—will not one be forced to conclude that one expression is wrong? And if one is wrong will it not be likely that both are wrong?

5. Will not the $1/r$-dependence of the supposed inertial interaction make the inertial properties of a test particle depend upon the expansion and recontraction of the universe, and the proximity of nearby masses, in a physically unreasonable way?

6. How can it make sense to speak of the distribution of mass-energy (and energy flow) as determining the geometry? One cannot specify where one mass is, let alone the entire distribution of mass, until one has been given the geometry! But then what is there to be determined?

7. Why spoil the beautiful logical structure of relativity theory by mixing up with it anything so vague and so lacking in mathematical sharpness as Mach's principle? Why try to word it in careful 20th-century language when it is an outworn 19th-century idea that ought to be dropped at once and for all time?

Solutions of Einstein's Equations Not Produced but Selected by Mach's Principle

The answer is that Einstein's equations are not enough. Differential equations themselves do not define a solution. They must be supplemented by suitable boundary conditions. This need for boundary conditions leads to Formulation 3 of Mach's principle. *Mach's principle provides a boundary condition to separate allowable solutions of Einstein's equation from physically inadmissible solutions.* This concept of Mach's principle as the principle for the *selection* of solutions of Einstein's equations has been discussed earlier by J. A. Wheeler[5] and recently by H. Hönl.[6] Hönl proposes two theses: (1) As a cosmological principle, Mach's principle is a selection principle; that is, from the large number of possible solutions of the cosmological problem it enables one to select a small number of solutions which give physically reasonable world models. (2) Mach's principle can be applied unambiguously only to spatially closed world models; thus it is likely that the requirement of Mach's principle is identical with the requirement of a finite universe. The use of boundary conditions as a selection principle (Formulation 3) is so familiar in electrostatics (Table 15-2) that it generally goes without even a name. Only when Poisson's equation is supplemented by such a boundary condition does it lead to the $1/r$ law of action of a charge. This $1/r$ law of action furnishes the usual basis for saying that the distribution of electric charge uniquely determines the distribution of electric potential.

Table 15–2

Boundary Conditions in Electrostatic and in Gravitation Theory According to Formulation 3 of Mach's Principle

	Electrostatics	Gravitation theory
Differential equations	$\nabla^2 V = -4\pi\rho$	The four of Einstein's equations which have to do with geometry on a space-like hypersurface
Source terms	Electric charge density	Density of energy and energy flow
General solution	$V = \int \dfrac{\rho \, d^3x}{r}$ $+ \Sigma c_{n\,m} r^n Y_n^m(\theta,\phi)$	Geometry which (a) extends to spatial infinity or (b) is somewhere singular or (c) is closed up and free of singularity
Principle of selection of physical solution	Potential must fall off at great distances	Geometry must be of class (c) (to admit singularities is to admit points where the equations are not really satisfied)
Consequence of this principle and also another way of formulating this principle	Potential is uniquely determined by the distribution of charge	Geometry of *space-time* must be uniquely determined by the distribution of energy and energy flow over the original *spacelike* hypersurface

Cases Where a Given Boundary Condition Cannot Be Applied Are Regarded as Idealizations of Cases Where It Does Apply and Where It Does Make Sense

The boundary condition that the electrostatic potential shall fall off at large distances is noteworthy for what it does not do as well as for what it does do. It does not provide a way to *calculate* the $(1/r)$-law of action. Only the differential equation does that—giving in addition many other solutions. Moreover, one often considers in electrostatics problems where the requirement that the potential must fall off at great distances cannot be satisfied. As an illustration, consider the problem: "Given ρ

$(x, y, z) = \rho_0 \cos kz$, find $V(x, y, z)$." Thus one can choose between accepting the problem and giving up the generality of the boundary condition; or upholding the boundary condition at all times and modifying the problem.

One can say that the infinite cosine wave distribution of charge is only a mathematical idealization of a physical distribution of charge which is nearly of cosine character over a great region, as illustrated, for example, by an expression of the form

$$\rho(x,y,z) = (\rho_0 \cos kz)[\exp - (x^2 + y^2 + z^2)/a^2] \qquad (6)$$

where the Gaussian breadth a is very large. On this choice of interpretation the boundary condition can be applied, and the potential is determined uniquely by the distribution of charge.

Asymptotically Flat Geometry Expressed as Limit of Closed Space

Similarly, in general relativity one can find situations which are not compatible with the boundary condition of Table 15–2—and therefore not compatible with Formulation 3 of Mach's principle—and which nevertheless can be translated over into situations which *are* compatible with the boundary condition. Consider, for example, a single spherically symmetric concentration of mass in otherwise empty space. Associated with this mass is the familiar Schwarzschild four-geometry. This geometry is asymptotically flat at infinity. In this space-time the inertial properties of an infinitesimal test particle approach indefinitely closely to the Newtonian expectations at indefinitely great distances from the mass. Consequently it is unreasonable to think of the central mass as responsible for these inertial properties. If one accepts this situation, he cannot uphold Mach's principle either as Mach originally stated it, or as it is reformulated here as a boundary condition to *select* solutions of Einstein's field equations. The reason for this is that (1) for the Schwarzschild solution, the inertial properties of test particles are not attributable to the central and hence entire mass present, and (2) this solution does not describe a closed universe. Therefore we rule out the solution for a mass point which becomes flat at infinity. In other words, the Schwarzschild geometry is excluded by the geometric boundary condition of Table 15–2. This is analogous to electrostatics. There, for example, an infinite cosine distribution of charge was ruled out (Table 15–2) because it was incompatible with the boundary condition for the electrostatic potential at infinity.

The idealized situation that is pushed out of the back door as physically unacceptable comes in again at the front door in new clothes both in electrostatics and in general relativity (Table 15–3). Consider a geometry which *is* compatible with the boundary condition—which *is* closed and free of singularity at some initial time, or more precisely on some initial spacelike hypersurface. To construct such a geometry, take not a single spherically symmetrical distribution of mass, but many such mass centers. Let the number of centers and their spacing be so chosen as to curve up the space into closure[7] (Appendix A). The dynamics of such a lattice universe before and after the moment of time symmetry agrees within a few per cent or less with the dynamics of the Friedmann universe. The lattice universe is also consistent with the assumptions of the Friedmann universe: uniform dust distribution with zero pressure and uniform curvature. The corresponding expansion and recontraction of the lattice universe occurs as a change in the place of joining between one zone and the next rather than as a change in the geometry interior to the typical Schwarzschild zone. The interface moves outward from the centers of attraction on each side of it following the law of motion of a stone thrown out radially. It reaches a maximum distance. Then it falls back again toward both mass concentrations simultaneously. In this way the motion of these centers toward each other becomes appparent. The time for the expansion and contraction of the lattice universe—and of the boundaries of each Schwarzschild zone—is

$$
\begin{pmatrix} \text{time for expansion and re-} \\ \text{contraction in} \\ \text{length units} \end{pmatrix} = \pi \begin{pmatrix} \text{radius of lattice universe} \\ \text{at} \\ \text{maximum expansion} \end{pmatrix}
$$

$$
\simeq \begin{pmatrix} \text{radius of one Schwarzschild} \\ \text{zone at} \\ \text{maximum expansion} \end{pmatrix}^{3/2} \begin{pmatrix} \text{twice mass at center of zone} \\ \text{expressed in} \\ \text{length units} \end{pmatrix}^{-1/2}
$$

The time for expansion can be made arbitrarily large relative to the time required for light to cross one Schwarzschild zone by making the radius b of the typical zone sufficiently large.

In Table 15–3 the Schwarzschild geometry is envisaged as the limit of the geometry of a closed lattice universe when the size of the typical lattice zone is allowed to go to infinity. This limiting process is compared in the table with the analogous limiting procedure in electrostatics. We use the following notation. m^* is mass measured in centimeters at the center of each lattice cell, $m^* = Gm/c^2$. $4\pi b^3/3$ is the volume of a lattice cell at the "instant" (defined by a spacelike hypersurface) of maximum expansion. a is the radius of curvature of a comparison universe of uniform density and uniform curvature, also at the instant of mirror symmetry between past and future. This radius is determined as follows in terms of m^* and b: The "Schwarzschild cells" are joined together on boundaries which are not sufficiently far out for the geometry to be flat.

Table 15–3

Treatment of the Schwarzschild Geometry as the Limit of the Geometry of a Closed Lattice Universe Whose Lattice Size Goes to Infinity; and Comparison of This Treatment with Electrostatics

	Electrostatic example	Example from general relativity
Source (before modification)	Infinite periodic charge distribution $\rho = \rho_0 \cos kz$	Single spherically symmetric concentration of mass in otherwise empty space
Effect of interest	Electric potential—and thence the electric field	Metric of space-time—and thence the inertial properties of every infinitesimal test particle
Is "effect" so uniquely associated with "source" in this idealized case that one can say effect is "produced" by source?	No. We can add to V any number of harmonics of the form $r^n Y_n^m(\theta,\phi)$	No. The Einstein equations for the source "distribution" are satisfied by the asymptotically flat Schwarzschild geometry and many other empty space geometries
Does "effect" satisfy the boundary condition listed in Table 15–2?	No. None of these expressions for V falls off as fast as $(1/r)$ at great distances	Schwarzschild geometry as normally conceived does not describe a closed universe
Modified situation which *is* compatible with the boundary condition	$\rho = \rho_0(\cos kz)\,\exp(-r^2/a^2)$	Many such masses spaced with reasonable uniformity through a closed universe
Scale factor associated with this new source	*Range* of a charge distribution	Effective radius b of typical Schwarzschild zone
Is source now well defined?	Yes	No. We must specify what gravitational waves if any are present. In other words, we must specify the otherwise undetermined features intrinsic to three-geometry in which the masses are imbedded at the moment of time symmetry[a]

Table 15-3 (continued)

	Electrostatic example	Example from general relativity
When the specification of the "source" has been completed, is it reasonable to think of an "effect" as well determined by this specification plus boundary condition?	Yes. In this event one can prove the potential is uniquely determined by distribution of electric charge	Yes. We expect other features intrinsic to this three-geometry to be now uniquely determined by the (00) component of Einstein's equation plus the boundary condition of closure.[b] Mach's principle is now satisfied
Limiting procedure now envisaged?	Range a of charge distribution goes to ∞	Effective radius b of Schwarzschild zone goes to ∞
For each finite value of the parameter a or b is the relevant boundary condition satisfied?	Yes. V falls off as $1/r$ or faster at large r	Yes. Schwarzschild zone is a piece of a closed universe in which Mach's principle can be considered to apply
Is the boundary condition satisfied for infinite value of this parameter?	No. V does not fall off	No. Schwarzschild geometry is asymptotically flat

[a] See, for example, the "modified Taub universe" discussed in the text and in Appendix B as an alternative to the lattice universe as a solution of Einstein's field equations which also satisfies the condition of closure.

[b] This uniqueness can be established in the case where the lattice universe contains no gravitational waves along the lines outlined in Appendix A. No investigation has been made of uniqueness when gravitational waves are present in this universe. However, there is a related problem where the uniqueness of the three-geometry—for specified distribution of gravitational radiation—has been established as a consequence of the closure condition.[8]

The curvature of the Schwarzschild geometry in a local Lorentz frame in a plane perpendicular to the zonal radius is given by

$$R_{2323} = 2m^*/b^3 \tag{7}$$

The radius of curvature in a typical plane in the uniform comparison universe is given by

$$R'_{2323} = 1/a^2 \tag{8}$$

If we identify R'_{2323} with R_{2323}, we find

$$a^2 \simeq b^3/2m^* \tag{9}$$

Alternatively we can write down the 00 component of Einstein's field equations (the principal initial value equation of Yvonne Fourès–Bruhat) in the form

$$^{(3)}R + (\text{Tr } \mathbf{K})^2 - \text{Tr } \mathbf{K}^2 = 2(8\pi G/c^4)(\text{energy density}) \tag{10}$$

Note that the extrinsic curvature tensor, or "second fundamental form" K_{ij} vanishes on a time-symmetric spacelike hypersurface. Note also that the scalar curvature invariant of a three-sphere of radius a, expressed in terms of the physical components (indicated by a carat) of the curvature is

$$^{(3)}R = {}^{(3)}\hat{R}_{11} + {}^{(3)}\hat{R}_{22} + {}^{(3)}\hat{R}_{33} = (\hat{R}_{1212} + \hat{R}_{1313}) + (\hat{R}_{2121} + \hat{R}_{2323})$$
$$+ (\hat{R}_{3131} + \hat{R}_{3232}) = 6/a^2 \tag{11}$$

We may identify the density of mass in Eq. (10) with $m/(4\pi b^3/3)$. Then from Eqs. (10) and (11) we obtain

$$(6/a^2) \simeq (16\pi G/c^4)(3mc^2/4\pi b^3) \tag{12}$$

This gives the result

$$a^2 \simeq b^3/2m^* \tag{13}$$

The number of lattice cells N is approximately given by

$$N \simeq (\text{volume of comparison universe})/(\text{volume of cell})$$
$$\simeq 2\pi^2 a^3/(4\pi b^3/3) = (3\pi/2^{5/2})(b/m^*)^{3/2} \tag{14}$$

Thus the number of cells goes to infinity as the size of a typical cell goes to infinity.

Nonuniform Convergence of Lattice Universe to Flat Space Limit

The order of taking the limits as the cell size becomes large is important. Let observer **A** select (1) any arbitrary but finite distance from one center of mass and (2) any arbitrary but finite length of time and (3) any arbitrarily small but nonzero departure from the ideal Schwarzschild geometry which he is willing to tolerate. Then another observer, **B**, can pick an effective radius for the typical Schwarzschild zone at the moment of maximum expansion which is so great that the geometry inside that zone agrees with the ideal Schwarzschild geometry (1) to within the specified limits of accuracy (2) out to the stated distance and (3) for the stated time. However, if **B** acts first, and specifies the zone radius at the moment of maximum expansion, than **A** can always point to places so far away that the geometry there totally disagrees with the continuation of the Schwarzschild geometry of the original zone. **A** can even point out that the space is closed and compatible with Mach's principle. Thus **A** concludes that the geometry is asymptotically flat or closed according to whether he is forced to make the first move or is asked to wait until **B** has fixed the dimensions. That **A**'s conclusions depend upon the order of his move can be stated mathematically: The convergence to the limit of an infinitely great lattice universe is nonuniform.

Other Examples

The ideal lattice universe is one of many conceivable examples which illustrate how one can consider as closed—and compatible in general terms with Mach's principle—geometries that ostensibly are asymptotically flat. Three more examples may give a slight impression of how wide the range of allowable geometries is.

Lattice Universe with Gravitational Radiation

In the lattice universe there may be present, in addition to the "real" masses, the effective mass indirectly contributed by gravitational radiation. Then the inertial properties of test particles are affected by both sources of mass energy.[7]

Modified Taub Universe

It is not necessary to supply any "real" masses in addition to the one original mass in order to secure a closed universe. Gravitational waves of sufficient strength will supply the required curvature. This one sees from the example of the Taub universe.[9] There gravitational radiation alone suffices to curve up the space into closure. In this four-geometry consider the hypersurface or three-geometry defined by the instant of time symmetry or maximum expansion. Perturb this geometry to the extent necessary to introduce a spherical ball of matter, at first arbitrarily small, eventually large or denser, or both. Close to this mass, the geometry is nearly Schwarzschild. However, deviations from that limiting geometry become very great at distances comparable to the effective radius of the Taub universe.[10] In this universe it is not reasonable to speak of a geometry primarily determined by "real mass" and perturbed in only a minor way by gravitational radiation. On the contrary, the gravitational radiation is the primary determiner of the four-geometry and of the inertial properties of test particles. The one "real mass" produces only minor perturbations in the geometry except in its own immediate neighborhood.

Unmodified Taub Universe

The fourth example is the Taub universe itself, free of any "real matter" at all. This solution of Einstein's equations for a closed empty space is interpreted in Appendix B as a special case of a Tolman radiation-filled universe in which (1) Tolman's electromagnetic radiation is replaced by gravitational radiation; (2) this gravitational radiation, instead of being effectively isotropic, is described by a single hyperspherical harmonic; and (3) this harmonic has the lowest possible order, or greatest possible wavelength, compatible with the dimensions of the model universe.

Does a Relation between Inertia at One Place and Gravitational Radiation at Other Places Signify Circular Reasoning?

Regardless of the details of the Taub universe, it is a closed space in which the inertial properties of every infinitesimal test particle are well determined. Yet there are no ordinary masses present to which one can attribute the inertia of a test particle. Therefore, if Mach's principle is still to make sense, it is necessary to conclude that the distribution, not only of mass energy, but also of gravitational radiation, has to be specified in order to determine inertia completely—or, in the words of general relativity, to determine the geometry of space-time completely. But gravitational radiation itself is described as an aspect of geometry and nothing more. Consequently one seems to be caught in a logical circle in trying to formulate Mach's principle. Apparently one has to give the *geometry* in advance, in order not only

(1) to say in any well-defined way what one means by the term "distribution of mass-energy", but also

(2) to specify what gravitational radiation is present, so that one shall thereby be enabled

(3) to determine the geometry of space-time.

Evidently one can never feel happy about a formulation of Mach's principle that seems to contain this kind of circular reasoning. Therefore it is essential to demand a mathematically well defined statement of Mach's principle if his ideas are to be considered as having any relevance at all for present day relativity physics.

Not Circular: Specify Three-Geometry, Determine Four-Geometry

Now for this mathematical formulation. We shall resolve the question of circular reasoning by the following procedure. We *specify* the three-dimensional geometry. From this the four-dimensional geometry is *determined*. Furthermore, we shall clarify which features of gravitational radiation are freely disposable (field "coordinate" and its rate of change), and which features of the geometry are thereby determined (field "momentum").

3-Geometry and Its Rate of Change as Keys to the Plan of General Relativity

What Is the "Plan" of General Relativity?

It often helps in answering one question to ask another. Therefore it is fortunate for the search for a mathematical formulation of Mach's principle—a search now physically motivated—that another issue is currently under discussion. This issue is the one which Professor J. L. Synge raised at the Warsaw conference[11]: What is the *plan* of general relativity? What quantities can one freely specify, and what quantities are thereby determined? What is the inner structure of the dynamic theory of a geometry governed by Einstein's field equations?

Plan 1: Initial Data on a Lightlike Hypersurface

One plan of dynamics starts with a lightlike hypersurface. In this approach as applied to the mechanics of a system of particles, one specifies the appropriate number of coordinates and momenta at the times when the respective world lines cross this null hypersurface. This formulation of mechanics has been investigated by P. A. M. Dirac and V. Fock.[12] The corresponding formulation of geometrodynamics, particularly as relevant to the study of gravitational radiation, has been explored by R. Penrose, H. Bondi, R. Sachs, and others, and has been described in a comprehensive report by Sachs at the Warsaw conference.[11] However, this approach is not closely connected with the formulations of dynamics which are most widely used in other branches of physics. The relationship of this approach to Mach's principle has not been investigated.

Plan 2: Coordinates and Momenta—or Intrinsic Geometry and Extrinsic Curvature—on a Spacelike Hypersurface

Another plan of dynamics is more familiar. In particle dynamics we give as initial conditions the coordinates and momenta for the various particles at points on the respective world lines which are separated by spacelike intervals. In electrodynamics we give the field "coordinates" and "momentum"—the magnetic field $\mathbf{B}(x^1, x^2, x^3)$ and the electric field $\mathbf{E}(x^1, x^2, x^3)$—everywhere on a spacelike hypersurface. In geometrodynamics we also give the field coordinates and momenta on a spacelike hypersurface. These are: (1) the three-dimensional geometry intrinsic to this hypersurface,

$$ds^2 = {}^{(3)}g_{ik}(x^1,x^2,x^3)dx^i dx^k \tag{15}$$

and (2) the "extrinsic curvature" or so-called "second fundamental form"[13] telling how this hypersurface is to be curved with respect to the enveloping (yet to be constructed) four-dimensional geometry. When the four-geometry is written in the form

$$d\sigma^2 = -d\tau^2 = {}^{(4)}g_{\alpha\beta}\,dx^\alpha\,dx^\beta = {}^{(3)}g_{ik}(x^0,x^1,x^2,x^3)dx^i\,dx^k$$
$$+ 2N_i\,dx^i\,dx^0 + ({}^{(3)}g^{ik}N_iN_k - N_0^2)(dx^0)^2 \qquad (16)$$

with the condition

$$x^0 = x^{0*} \qquad (17)$$

specifying the spacelike hypersurface in question, then the extrinsic curvature tensor is given by the expression[14]

$$K_{ik} = -(1/2N_0)(\partial^{(3)}g_{ik}/\partial x^0 - N_{i|k} - N_{k|i}) \qquad (18)$$

x^0 is understood as being fixed at the particular value x^{0*}. The vertical stroke is used to denote covariant differentiation with respect to the three-geometry of the hypersurface, in contradistinction to the semicolon that marks covariant differentiation with respect to the four-geometry. The N_i are ADaM potentials to be discussed below. In term of the extrinsic curvature tensor and its trace, the geometrodynamical momentum is[14]

$$\pi^{ik} = -({}^{(3)}g)^{\frac{1}{2}}(K^{ik} - {}^{(3)}g^{ik}\,\mathrm{Tr}\,\mathbf{K}) \qquad (19)$$

Interpretation of the Four Potentials or Metric Coefficients N_0 and N_k as "Lapse Function" and "Shift Function"

Some interpretation of the ADaM potentials N_α is appropriate. Imagine two thin ribbons of steel, distinguished from each other by the labels $x^{0\prime} = 17.23$ and $x^{0\prime\prime} = 17.27$ (Figure 15–1). It is desired to construct out of these ribbons a rigid curtain. A workman paints cross-lines on one ribbon at intervals which need not be constant but which must not change irregularly or erratically. These are labeled $x^1 = \ldots 12$,

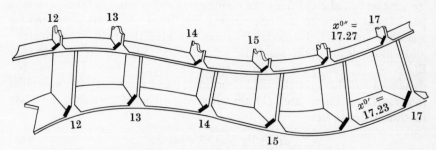

Figure 15–1 Use of ADaM potentials to construct a curved spacelike surface with specified time separation. The numerical information used to construct this surface is given in workman's table.

Workman's Table

x^1	$N_0(x^1)$	$N^1(x^1)$	$N_0(x^{0''}-x^{0'})$	$N^1(x_0''-x^{0'})$
12	30	10	1.2	0.4
13	25	17	1.0	0.68
14	20	12	0.8	0.48
15	22	9	0.88	0.36
16				
17				

13, 14 .... The same is done on the second ribbon, taking care that the new pattern of crosslines is not widely different from the old pattern. The workman then welds perpendicular uprights or "lapses" to the first strip at $x^1 = 12, 13, 14 \ldots$. Completion of the rigid structure requires a specification of the lengths of the uprights and the points where they are joined perpendicularly to the upper strip. We must provide the workman with two functions $N_0(x^1)$ and $N^1(x^1)$, the "lapse function" and the "shift function."[15] The worker tabulates both at $x^1 = 12, 13, 14 \ldots$. In two further columns he tabulates for the same values of x^1 the product of N_0 and N^1 by the number $(x^{0''} - x^{0'}) \doteq 0.04$. The one column tells him to what heights to cut off the uprights which he has welded to the strip that is lying down. The other tells him how far one way or the other to *shift* upper ends before he welds them to the upper strip. At $x^1 = 18$ let the value of what might loosely be called $N^1\, dx^0$ be 0.5. This implies that the corresponding upright is welded at its bottom to the cross line marked $x^1 = 18$. The upper strip is shifted 0.5 *coordinate* units to the right. Thus the "lapse" is welded to it at a cross line marked $x^1 = 17.5$. How the "shift" changes from place to place—and how much the spacing between one coordinate mark and the next differs between the upper and lower steel sheets—together determine how much curvature is built into the curtain. Along this line of reasoning, generalized to three dimensions, one sees at once the reason for the mathematical structure of Eq. (18).

Interpretation in Terms of the Length of the Normal and the Difference in Space Coordinates at Its Two Ends

To state the same interpretations of N_0 and N_k in other words, we return to equation (16) for the distance between a point (x^0, x^1, x^2, x^3) that lies on one hypersurface, $x^0 = $ constant, and another point $(x^0 + dx^0, \ldots, x^3 + dx^3)$ on another hypersurface, $x^0 + dx^0 = $ constant. Here the dx's are thought of as small but finite quantities. Let dx^0 be kept fixed (at the value $dx^0 = x^{0\,\prime\prime} - x^{0\,\prime} = 0.04$, for example) but on the hypersurface so selected let one point, then another, be tried until the invariant separation between it and the fixed point on the lower surface is extremized. Vary $d\sigma^2$ with respect to dx^k and set the coefficient of δdx^k equal to zero:

$$2^{(3)}g_{ik}\,dx^i + 2N_i\,dx^0 = 0 \tag{20}$$

The solution for Eq. (20) is

$$dx^i = -\,{}^{(3)}g^{ik}N_k\,dx^0 = -\,N^i\,dx^0 \tag{21}$$

The extremal value of the separation is, reasonably enough, timelike:

$$d\tau = N_0\,dx^0 \tag{22}$$

Thus the "lapse function" N_0 represents the *proper* time separation measured normally between two hypersurfaces per unit of difference in their time *coordinates*. The vectorial "shift function" N^i represents the *coordinates* at the base of the normal diminished by the coordinates at the summit of the normal, this difference again being referred to a unit difference between the time *coordinates* of the two hypersurfaces.

Lapse and Shift Functions Required in Addition to Three-Geometry to Define Four-Geometry

Evidently it is not enough to specify the geometries $^{(3)}g_{ik}$ *intrinsic* to a one-parameter family of hypersurfaces in order to have a well-defined four-geometry. One must in addition tell how these hypersurfaces are *related* to each other. One must tell how far apart the surfaces are ("lapse function") and how they are displaced space-wise one with respect to another ("shift function").

Arbitrary Lapse and Shift Functions Plus Arbitrary Three-Geometry Determine Field "Momentum"; but Arbitrary Field "Momentum" and Arbitrary Three-Geometry Are Ordinarily Incompatible

From the field "coordinate" $^{(3)}g_{ik}$ and its rate of change with respect to the parameter x^0, *plus* information about the "lapse" and "shift" functions of position, one can determine the "extrinsic curvature" K_{ik} and the associated field "momentum" [Eq. (18)]. However, the converse is not generally true. If the field "coordinate" $^{(3)}g_{ik}$ and the field "momentum" or the extrinsic curvature K_{ik} are both specified arbitrarily, they will ordinarily be incompatible. *The independent specification of the field coordinate and the field momentum is the wrong way to define initial-value conditions in general relativity.*

The Initial-Value Equations

The incompatibility of arbitrary intrinsic geometry of field "coordinate" $^{(3)}g_{ik}$ with arbitrary extrinsic curvature or field "momentum" π^{ij} follows from four of Einstein's ten equations, which we shall call *initial-value equations*.[16]

$$^{(3)}R + (\mathrm{Tr}\,\mathbf{K})^2 - \mathrm{Tr}\,\mathbf{K}^2 = 2(8\pi G/c^4)(\text{energy density}) \qquad (23)$$

$$(K_i^k - \delta_i^k\,\mathrm{Tr}\,\mathbf{K})|_k = (8\pi G/c^4)\,(\text{density of flow of energy in} \qquad (24)$$
$$i\ \text{direction})$$

These initial-value equations which relate the intrinsic geometry and extrinsic curvature on a spacelike hypersurface suggest the following questions: what quantities

(1) can be freely and independently specified, and yet

(2) suffice completely to specify the past and future of the four-geometry?

Plan 3: Specify Completely Independently the Field Coordinates on Two Hypersurfaces

These questions lead in turn directly to the two-surface formulation of dynamics, where one specifies no momenta, only coordinates (or conversely)—but coordinates on two hypersurfaces rather than one.[17] Moreover, *the field coordinates on the one surface are specified quite independently of those on the other surface.* The complete freedom that one has in this way of specifying the initial-value data would seem to be what one wants when he asks for a workable statement of the *plan* of general relativity (Table 15–4).

Meaning of the Phrase "Independently Specifiable Coordinates"

It is necessary to state in what sense one is to understand the phrase, "are specified quite independently of those on the other surface." What one says on this point depends upon whether he is thinking in the context of classical physics or quantum physics.

"Two-Surface" Formulation of Harmonic Oscillator Problem

By way of illustration we consider the simple harmonic oscillator. A specified set of coordinates x' at the time t' and x'' at the time t'' fixes the end points of a trial history,

$$x(t) = x_H(t) \qquad (25)$$

Table 15-4

The *Plans* of Electromagnetism and General Relativity as Expressed in Terms of the Two-Surface Formulation of Dynamics

(The field "coordinates" are specified on two spacelike hypersurfaces—most simply on two hypersurfaces which have an infinitesimal separation)

	Electromagnetism	Gravitation
The physically significant field quantities	Components of the electromagnetic field	Components of the Riemann curvature tensor
The coordinate-independent object which they define	A two-form: a honeycomb-like structure of tubes of force[18]	The intrinsic structure of the four-geometry in the neighborhood (corrections to the Euclidean pattern of distances between one point and another in a great table of *local* (geodesic) distances
The dynamic equations which tell how this object changes from place to place	Maxwell's eight equations	Equations that refer directly to the curvature components
The potentials normally introduced to simplify the analysis of these equations	The four-components of the electromagnetic potential A_α	The 10 components of the metric tensor $g_{\mu\nu}$
Notation used for these potentials when spacetime is sliced into spacelike hypersurfaces	The magnetic potential A with components A_k and the electrostatic or scalar potential $\phi = -A_0$	Six components of three-metric $^{(3)}g_{ik}$ intrinsic to a slice; the normal *proper* time separation N_0 between two hypersurfaces per unit of difference in their *time coordinates*; and the differences N^i (or, more conveniently, $N_k = {}^{(3)}g_{ki}N^i$) between space *coordinates* at the two ends of such a normal, again per unit of difference in the time coordinates of the two hypersurfaces

Table 15–4 (continued)

	Electromagnetism	Gravitation
The dynamical problem as formulated in variational language for a region of space-time bounded by two spacelike hypersurfaces σ' and σ''	Give $\mathbf{A}'$ on σ' and $\mathbf{A}''$ on σ''; inbetween take any trial functions $\mathbf{A}(x^0,x^1, x^2, x^3)$ and $\phi(x^0, x^1, x^2, x^3)$; calculate action integral; then vary the four potentials until the action is extremized	Give $^{(3)}g'_{ik}$ (x^1, x^2, x^3) (this *defines* σ') and arbitrarily call the value of x^0 on this surface some number $x^{0'}$; similarly, give $^{(3)}g''_{ik}$ and $x^{0''}$. Inbetween choose any trial values for the 10 potentials, compute action, and extremize with respect to choice of the potentials
The simpler version of this variational problem relevant for the formulation of initial-value problem and Mach's principle: the two hypersurfaces have an infinitesimal separation.	Give $A(x^1, x^2, x^3)$ and $\partial A/\partial t$; have a simpler action principle in which $\phi(x^1, x^2, x^3)$ is the only function to be adjusted	Give $^{(3)}g_{ik}$ (x^1, x^2, x^3) and $\partial^{(3)}g_{ik}/\partial t$; have a simpler action principle in which only the "lapse function" N_0 (x^1, x^2, x^3) and the "shift function" N_k (x^1, x^2, x^3) are to be varied
Variational problem well defined in an *open* space?	No	No
Payoff from this extremization in a *closed* space	Value of ϕ on the spacelike surface from which one can then calculate the electric field $\mathbf{E}$—the "momentum" conjugate to the already specified field "coordinate" $\mathbf{B}$	Values of N_0 and N_k from which one can calculate the "extrinsic curvature" K_{ik} of the thin sandwich or the "momentum" conjugate to the geometrodynamical "coordinate" or intrinsic geometry $^{(3)}g_{ik}$
What equation has automatically been solved by this extremization?	The initial-value equation div $\mathbf{E} = 4\pi\rho$, in which there appeared superficially to be three unknown functions of position	The initial-value equations $(K_i^k - \delta_i^k \operatorname{Tr} \mathbf{K})_{|k} = (16\pi G/c^4)\hat{T}_{\perp i}$ $^{(3)}R + (\operatorname{Tr} \mathbf{K})^2 - \operatorname{Tr} \mathbf{K}^2 = (16\pi G/c^4)T_{\perp\perp}$ in which there appeared ostensibly to be six unknown functions of position
Situation now in brief	We have *compatible* values for field coordinate and field momentum on initial spacelike hypersurface	We have compatible values for field coordinate and field momentum on initial space like hypersurface

Table 15–4 (continued)

	Electromagnetism	Gravitation
Further payoff	Now we have just the right amount of consistent initial-value data to predict the electromagnetic field everywhere in space and at all times	Now we have just the right amount of consistent initial-value data to determine the geometry of *space-time* in past, present, and future—and hence the inertial properties of every infinitesimal test particle
Recapitulation of what information was required for this prediction	(1) Maxwell's equations (2) Law of motion of charges (3) Specification of divergence-free magnetic field and its time derivative on a closed spacelike hypersurface (4) Specification of positions and velocities of charges at points where their world lines cross this hypersurface	(1) Einstein's equations (2) Dynamical law for the fields or objects responsible for the stress-energy tensor on the right side of Einstein's equations (3) Specification of closed spacelike three-geometry and its rate of change with respect to a parameter x^0—a parameter which otherwise has no direct physical meaning (4) Specification of initial-value data for fields or objects responsible for $T_{\mu\nu}$
Is the relation between "effect" and "source" well defined? (Mach's principle)	"Effect" - electromagnetic field. Relation well defined only if "source" is understood to imply specification on spacelike hypersurface of both (1) positions of charges *and* (2) magnetic field and its time rate of change	"Effect"-inertial properties of test particle = geometry of space-time. Relation well defined only if "source" is understood to imply specification on space-like hypersurface of both (1) density and flow of mass-energy *and* (2) intrinsic three-geometry and its rate of change with respect to some parameter x^0—this latter reasonably enough because how otherwise would one have a geometry with respect to *specify* the distribution and flow of mass

The *classical* history in the intervening time interval is to be selected in such a way as to extremize the action integral

$$I_H = \int_{x',t'}^{x'',t''} L(x_H(t), dx_H(t)/dt, t)dt$$

$$= (m/2) \int (\dot{x}_H^2 - \omega^2 x_H^2)dt \qquad (26)$$

The solution is well known. It is simple harmonic motion of circular frequency ω:

$$x_H(t) = x_{H_{\text{classical}}}(t) = \frac{x' \sin \omega(t'' - t) + x'' \sin \omega(t - t')}{\sin \omega(t'' - t')} \qquad (27)$$

Associated with this "classical history" is the action, the so-called "Hamilton's principal function," given by the expression

$$I_{H_{\text{classical}}} = [m\omega/2 \sin \omega(t'' - t')][(x'^2 + x''^2) \cos \omega(t'' - t') - 2x'x''] \qquad (28)$$

The Quantum Propagator and Its Relation to the Classical Action

In quantum mechanics one gives arbitrarily, not the coordinates at two times, but the state function or probability amplitude $\psi(x', t')$ at one time, t', and asks for its value $\psi(x'', t'')$ at some later time t''. The function at the new time can be found by solving the Schrödinger equation numerically or otherwise. The focus of attention shifts from this equation to its solution in Feynman's formulation of quantum mechanics.[19] A *propagator* gives the desired function in terms of the arbitrarily specified initial function:

$$\psi(x'',t'') = \int_{-\infty}^{+\infty} <x'',t''|x',t'> \; \psi(x',t')dx' \qquad (29)$$

Feynman writes this propagator as the sum of elementary propagation amplitudes,

$$<x'',t''|x',t'> \; = \mathcal{N} \sum_H \exp (iI_H/\hbar) \qquad (30)$$

Every conceivable history contributes with the same weight; only the phase differs from one history to another. Destructive interference automatically cuts down the *effective* contribution of the nonclassical histories. The sum reduces in the case of the harmonic oscillator to an expression of the form

$$<x'',t''|x',t'> \; = \mathcal{N}_1 \exp \left(\frac{i}{\hbar}[I_H]_{\text{classical}}\right) \qquad (31)$$

where in the exponent the Hamilton's principal function $[I_H]_{\text{classical}}$ has the value given by Eq. (28).

Specification of "Two-Surface" Data in the Classical Problem— Normally Compatible, Sometimes Incompatible

In the classical problem a difficulty arises when the time interval $(t'' - t')$ is an integral multiple of a half-period. After an even number of half-periods the coordinate must return to its initial value; after an odd number, it must come to the negative of its initial value. (1) If x'' does not agree with x' in the one case, or with $-x'$ in the other case, the end-point data have been inconsistently specified. (2) Even if they have been consistently given, the momentum with which the motion starts off at the one end point, and with which it returns to the other end point, is completely indeterminate. In both cases the variational problem is indeterminate.

No Problem of Incompatibility in Quantum Propagator

No such problem of incompatibility of the "end-point data" or "two-surface data" arises in the quantum formulation. When the interval $(t'' - t')$ is a half-period, the propagator reduces to one type of Dirac delta function,

$$<x'',t''|x',t'> \; = \; - \, i \, \delta(x'' + x') \tag{32}$$

and to another type when the interval is a full period,

$$<x'',t''|x',t'> \; = \; -\delta(x'' - x') \tag{33}$$

In other words, *the quantum propagator remains well defined for all specifications of the two-surface data*, regardless of any specialities in the classical problem in one case or another.

The Quantum Problem Always at the Background of Classical Analysis

No one has found any way to escape the conclusion that geometrodynamics, like particle dynamics, has a quantum character. Therefore the quantum propagator, not the classical history, is the quantity that must be well defined. Consequently it will not be considered a source of concern that one can specify the three-geometries $^{(3)}\mathscr{G}'$ and $^{(3)}\mathscr{G}''$ intrinsic to two hypersurfaces in such a way that the action functional for general relativity admits no extremum. Such cases are the geometrodynamical generalization of the special cases just encountered for the harmonic oscillator. Only on this understanding will it be justified to say that the three-geometry on one hypersurface is specified quite independently of the three-geometry on the other hypersurface.

Concentration on the Case of Two Nearby Hypersurfaces

Of greatest simplicity is the case where the two hypersurfaces are "close together." This is the only case we shall consider in any detail. Then the determination of the momenta from the values of the coordinates on the two surfaces is the most immediate. This step carries one halfway through the dynamic problem. Having consistent and singularity free initial-value data for momenta and coordinates at the initial time, one is in a position to complete the solution and to determine without any ambiguity the history of the system for at least a finite proper time into the past and future.[20] For this purpose one uses the standard dynamical equations:

1. Hamilton's equations for a system of particles.
2. Maxwell's equations in the electromagnetic case.
3. Einstein's equations in the case of geometrodynamics.

Alternative Ways to Apply the Two-Surface Formulation of Dynamics

Alternative ways of applying the two-surface formulation to particle mechanics, electrodynamics, and general relativity differ from one another by the apportionment of the analytic load between a variational principle and differential equations.

Option 1 for Electrodynamics: Well-Separated Hypersurfaces and Exclusive Reliance upon the Variational Method

One can avoid any use at all of differential equations in calculating the history of the system, whether a particle, the electromagnetic field, or geometry. Instead one can rely entirely on the idea of extremizing an action integral extended over the entire interval of time for which one wants to know the history. For the particle, one specifies x' at t' and x'' at t''. One regards as the function to be varied, either $x(t)$ alone, as in the familiar Lagrangian variation principle of Eq. (26), or *both* $x(t)$ and $p(t)$ *independently*, as in the Hamiltonian formulation

$$\delta \int_{x',t'}^{x'',t''} [p(t)\dot{x}(t) - \mathscr{H}(p(t),x(t),t)]dt = 0 \tag{34}$$

To express electrodynamics in variational form one uses the familiar vector and scalar potentials $\mathbf{A}$ and ϕ,

$$\mathbf{B} = \operatorname{curl} \mathbf{A} \tag{35}$$

$$\mathbf{E} = -\partial \mathbf{A}/\partial t - \operatorname{grad} \phi \tag{36}$$

so that half of Maxwell's equations are automatically satisfied. The other two Maxwell equations can be obtained from the variational principle:

$$\delta I = \delta \int [(1/8\pi)(\mathbf{E}^2 - \mathbf{B}^2) + (j \cdot \mathbf{A} - \rho \phi)](1/c)d^4x = 0 \qquad (37)$$

To solve these equations we must specify in advance:

1. The charge and current densities ρ and j (both in charge units/ (length unit)^3) throughout the four-dimensional region bounded by the two hypersurfaces.

2. $\mathbf{B}$ on each of the two surfaces in such a way that div $\mathbf{B}$ vanishes. This condition can be met by giving $\mathbf{A}$ on each of the two surfaces for an arbitrary gauge. (The physics is unchanged under a gauge transformation of the form $\mathbf{A} \to \mathbf{A} + \text{grad } \lambda$, where λ is an arbitrary function.)

ϕ and $\mathbf{A}$ are varied independently everywhere between the two surfaces to extremize I (subject only to the prior specification of $\mathbf{A}$ on the two hypersurfaces.)

Option 1 for General Relativity: Exclusive Use of the Variational Principle (An Impractical Approach)

The appropriate action principle in general relativity[17] supplemented by source terms is

$$\delta I_4 = \delta \int_{x^{0'}, {}^{(3)}g_{ij'}}^{x^{0''}, {}^{(3)}g_{ij''}} \left\{ \pi^{ij} \partial^{(3)} g_{ij} / \partial x^0 + N_0 ({}^{(3)}g)^{\frac{1}{2}} [{}^{(3)}R \right.$$

$$- {}^{(3)}g^{-1}(\text{Tr } \pi^2 - \tfrac{1}{2}(\text{Tr } \pi)^2)] + 2N_i \pi^{ij}|_j \qquad (38)$$

$$\left. - N_0 ({}^{(3)}g)^{\frac{1}{2}} L^{**}(g^{..}, A \ldots) \right\} d^4x$$

This variational principle results from adding complete derivatives to the familiar Lagrange integrand of general relativity $[{}^{(4)}R + L](-g)^{\frac{1}{2}}$, and using the notation of the ADaM potentials. Here L^{**} is $8\pi G/c^4$ times the invariant or scalar Lagrangian for whatever fields have energy and produce gravitational effects. This can be expressed in terms of (1) the *covariant* components of those fields (the field components $F_{\alpha\beta}$ in electromagnetism for example) and (2) the elements $g^{\mu\nu}$ of the matrix reciprocal to $g_{\alpha\beta}$:

$$g^{\mu\nu} = \left\| \begin{matrix} ({}^{(3)}g^{jk} - N^j N^k/N_0^2) & (N^k/N_0^2) \\ (N_j/N_0^2) & -(1/N_0^2) \end{matrix} \right\| \qquad (39)$$

Here $^{(3)}g^{jk}$ is the matrix reciprocal to $^{(3)}g_{jk}$ and

$$N^j \equiv {}^{(3)}g^{jk}N_k \tag{40}$$

In Eq. (38) there are 16 functions of space and time to be varied in the region between the two surfaces in such a way as to extremize the integral. Ten of these quantities are metric coefficients: the six $^{(3)}g_{ik}$, which can be freely varied except at the two hypersurfaces where their values are prescribed; and the four lapse and shift functions N_0 and N_i (not N^i!), which can be varied freely everywhere. The remaining six quantities, the momentum components π^{ij}, are also adjustable without restrictions. This adjustment of the momenta is analogous to that of the particle momentum $p(t)$ in Eq. (34). Initially the function is free even to the extent that its terminal values are free. However in the particle case one of the equations obtained from the variational principle,

$$\dot{x}(t) = \partial H(p,x,t)/\partial p \tag{41}$$

completely determines the momentum in terms of the velocity. In an analogous way[14] ("Palatini philosophy"), we carry out the extremization of Eq. (38) with respect to π^{ij}. From this we obtain six equations *determining* the six π^{ij} in terms of the N_α and $^{(3)}g_{ik}$ and their derivatives. These equations are equivalent to Eq. (19) for the momentum in terms of the extrinsic curvature *together with* the definition of this curvature given by Eq. (18).

If one wishes to use the variational principle (38) in order to obtain differential equations, he will (1) vary the lapse and shift functions, (2) set the coefficients of the four δN_α equal to zero, (3) find in this way the four initial-value equations [Eqs. (23) and (24)] that have to do primarily with geometry within the successive hypersurfaces, and (4) obtain the other six more "dynamic" components of Einstein's ten field equations by varying the six $^{(3)}g_{ik}$ and setting the coefficients of the six $\delta^{(3)}g_{ik}$ equal to zero.

We would like to make exclusive use of the variational principle to *replace* all differential equations (in the spirit of Rayleigh and Ritz). To do this we must (1) substitute into Eq. (38) the expressions for the six π^{ij} in terms of the six $^{(3)}g_{ij}$ and the four N_α and their derivatives, and (2) use numerical methods or ten analytic trial functions [$^{(3)}g_{ij}$, N] containing adjustable parameters to extremize the action integral I. Unhappily the extremum, rather than being a minimum or a maximum, is often a saddle of higher order, as one can convince himself even in the simpler problem of a single particle bound in a harmonic oscillator potential. This kind of variational principle does not normally lend itself either (1) at the theoretical level to establishing existence proofs or (2) at the practical level to doing calculations.

Option 2 (Most Favored): Use of Variational Principle to Solve Two-Surface Initial-Value Problem between Two Infinitesimally Separated Hypersurfaces (Thin Sandwich); and the Field Equations to Extend Solution to Past and Future; Electrodynamics as an Example

Proofs of the existence of solutions to field equations are much more widely known for manifolds with positive definite metric[21] than for manifolds with indefinite metric. Hence it is an advantage to formulate a variational problem such as to ensure a positive definite metric. This can be achieved by restricting the variational problem to the region between two infinitesimally separated spacelike hypersurfaces on which the initial-value data are specified and then extending this solution to the rest of space with the use of the differential field equations. It has been shown by Lichnerowicz[20] that in the case of general relativity the solution can be continued in this manner by Einstein's 10 field equations.

Therefore we shall concentrate on the thin-sandwich initial-value problem. The essential ideas are most easily seen in the case of electromagnetism. The magnetic potential has been specified on both surfaces ($\mathbf{A}'$ at $x^{0\prime}$ and $\mathbf{A}''$ at $x^{0\prime\prime}$) but the separation between them is allowed to go to zero. In this limit $\mathbf{B}^2$ and $\mathbf{j}\cdot\mathbf{A}$ *are not adjustable* in the region between the two surfaces because their values can depart only infinitesimally from the values specified on the surfaces. Then the variational principle reduces to the form

$$\delta I = \delta \int [(\mathbf{E}^2/8\pi) - \rho\phi]d^3x = 0 \tag{42}$$

to be extremized with respect to the single unknown potential ϕ. The theory of this variational problem is well known. From this extremization, conducted analytically or by the Rayleigh-Ritz method, we obtain a potential ϕ that satisfies the differential equations

$$\nabla^2\phi = -4\pi\rho - (\partial/\partial t)\text{div}\,\mathbf{A} \tag{43}$$

This potential generates an electric field

$$\mathbf{E} = -\partial\mathbf{A}/\partial t - \text{grad}\,\phi \tag{44}$$

that automatically satisfies the initial-value equation

$$\text{div}\,\mathbf{E} = 4\pi\rho \tag{45}$$

One now has $\mathbf{E}$ and $\mathbf{B}$, which can serve as the consistent starting points for the dynamic analysis. Starting with these values we can apply the other six equations of Maxwell and predict the entire past and future of the electromagnetic field.

Concept of the Thin Sandwich in Geometrodynamics

Similarly, in relativity one seeks to adjust four potentials, the lapse function N_0 and the three shift functions N_i, so as to generate an extrinsic curvature tensor K_{ij}, according to Eq. (18), which will satisfy the initial-value equations [Eq. (23) and (24)]. This done, the initial-value problem is solved. To formulate the appropriate "thin-sandwich" variational principle, we proceed here as in electrodynamics to the limit of infinitesimally thin separation of the initial-value surfaces. One can state this idea in two alternative ways.[17]

1. Give nearly identical $^{(3)}g'_{ik}$ and $^{(3)}g''_{ik}$. Take any arbitrary numbers $x^{0'}$ and $x^{0''}$ for the labels to be applied to these two hypersurfaces. In the definition of the extrinsic curvature K_{ik} [Eq. (18)] the term $\partial^{(3)}g_{ik}/\partial x^0$ appears. Replace this derivative by the difference $(^{(3)}g_{ik}'' - {}^{(3)}g_{ik}')/(x^{0''} - x^{0'})$. Apparently the value of K_{ik} will depend on $(x^{0''} - x^{0'})$. Actually it will not. All that ever matters in K_{ik} or anywhere else is the *product* of $(x^{0''} - x^{0'})$ by the lapse function N_0. If a big value is used for $(x^{0''} - x^{0'})$, a small one will come out of the variational principle for N_0, and conversely.

One sees this invariance property of the product also in another way: The normally measured interval of *proper* time between the two hypersurfaces [Eq. (22)] is $N_0(x^{0''} - x^{0'})$.

Therefore in this formulation one takes as the quantities to be varied only the *products*

$$\eta_0 = N_0(x^{0''} - x^{0'}) \tag{46}$$

$$\eta_k = N_k(x^{0''} - x^{0'}) \tag{47}$$

and not the individually arbitrary quantities N_0, N_k, $x^{0'}$, $x^{0''}$. To this conceptually simpler formulation there is an alternative and mathematically sharper statement of what is kept fixed during the variation [$^{(3)}g_{ik}'$ and $^{(3)}g_{ik}''$].

2. Consider a continuous one-parameter (x^0) family of three-geometries $^{(3)}g_{ik}(x^0, x^1, x^2, x^3)$. Then the initial-value problem under consideration is defined by a knowledge of $^{(3)}g_{ik}$ and $\partial^{(3)}g_{ik}/\partial x^0$ for some fixed value of x^0. The associated variational problem is found by dropping the factor dx^0 in the integrand d^4x in Eq. (38).

The "Intrahypersurface Variational Principle" for the Initial-Value Problem of General Relativity

Now that only a threefold space integration is called for, the next to the last term in Eq. (38) can be integrated by parts to give

$$2N_i \pi^{ij}|_j \rightarrow -\pi^{ij}(N_{i|j} + N_{j|i}) \tag{48}$$

In a non-Euclidean topology more than one coordinate system is generally required to cover a manifold without singularity. Each is defined in its own coordinate patch.[22] It might appear that a problem of transition arises in passing from one patch to another in the integration by parts. The absence of any such difficulty is guaranteed by the covariant character of the differentiations in Eq. (48). Moreover, the surface integral disappears in the simplest example of a closed space, a manifold with the topology of the three-sphere $S^{(3)}$. Thus, let the integration start in the neighborhood of one point P in $S^{(3)}$. Let it extend out to a boundary with the topology of the two-sphere $S^{(2)}$. As the range of integration is widened, $S^{(2)}$ at first swells more and more. Later it begins to decrease in size. Eventually, as the integration extends over the whole three-space, the boundary collapses to nothingness at some point other than P. No surface integral is left.[23] Also no derivatives of the π^{ij} are left in Eq. (38). Therefore everywhere that these momenta appear, they are easily expressed in terms of the curvature tensor K_{ij} by Eq. (19); and the K_{ij} are then expressed [via Eq. (18)] in terms of the quantities that one really thinks of varying: the lapse and the shift functions. The first substitution leads by simple algebra to the formula

$$I_3 = \int \{^{(3)}R - (\mathrm{Tr}\,\mathbf{K})^2 + \mathrm{Tr}\,\mathbf{K}^2 - L^{**}(g^{..},A...)\}(^{(3)}g)^{\frac{1}{2}}N_0\,d^3x \qquad (49)$$

for the quantity to be extremized. In this "intrahypersurface" (IHS) variational principle, as in other applications of the Lagrangian method to dynamics, the "kinetic" term $(\mathrm{Tr}\,\mathbf{K})^2 - \mathrm{Tr}\,\mathbf{K}^2$, appears with a sign opposite to that of the "potential" term $^{(3)}R$, whereas in the initial-value equation (23) for the *energy density* these terms appear, reasonably enough, with the same sign. The second substitution is made by writing the K_{ij} and the $g^{\alpha\beta}$ in terms of the four functions to be varied, N_α, according to Eqs. (18) and (39). This substitution is better left understood than carried out explicitly!

The Also Useful Option 3: Exclusive Reliance on Differential Equations to Analyze the Dynamics of General Relativity

Option 3 for analyzing the "plan" of general relativity, like option 2, starts with a specification of $^{(3)}g_{ik}$ and $\partial^{(3)}g_{ik}/\partial x^0$ over a closed spacelike hypersurface; in more picturesque language, it presumes a specification of two "nearby" three-geometries $^{(3)}\mathscr{G}'$ and $^{(3)}\mathscr{G}''$. Here "nearby" is to be tested after the event by calculating N_0 and from it [Eq. (22)] finding if the proper time separation between the two hypersurfaces is or is not small compared to the scale of the spacelike variations in $^{(3)}\mathscr{G}'$ and $^{(3)}\mathscr{G}''$. In addition, the energy density and energy flow have to be given, just as in option 2. The difference is only that the four potentials N_α are to be found by solving the four equations, Eqs. (23) and (24), not by directly trying to extremize the action integral I_3 of Eq. (49). Once the lapse and shift have been found, however, there is no difference in what one does between option 3 and option 2. (1) Calculate the extrinsic curvature K_{ik}. (2) Calculate the field momentum π^{ik}. (3) Use all ten of Einstein's equations to predict the four-geometry in past and future.

Verification That the Intrasurface Variational Principle and the Initial Value Equations Are Equivalent

On the right-hand side of the initial-value equations stand the energy density and energy flow, a total of four quantities. In contrast, the variational principle, Eq. (49), makes reference to *all* of the covariant components of the field contributing to this energy. One could therefore be concerned whether the two approaches will give the same result. To check this point, we must vary the N_α in the variational principle of Eq. (49) and set the coefficients of the δN_α equal to zero. Then we may compare the resulting equations with the initial-value equations. The variation of the field Lagrangian is the most complicated part of this program. It has the form.

$$\delta[N_0 L^{**}(g^{..}, A...)] = L^{**}\,\delta N_0 + N_0(\partial L^{**}/\partial^{(4)}g^{\alpha\beta})(\partial^{(4)}g^{\alpha\beta}/\partial N_\gamma)\delta N_\gamma \quad (50)$$

The derivatives of the components of the reciprocal metric tensor may be evaluated by using Eq. (39) for that tensor. First we express the derivatives of the Lagrange function in terms of the stress-energy tensor of the field in question, employing for this purpose the standard formula,[24]

$$\begin{aligned} T^{**}_{\alpha\beta} &= (-g)^{-\frac{1}{2}}(\partial/\partial g^{\alpha\beta})(-g)^{\frac{1}{2}}L^{**} \\ &= (\partial L^{**}/\partial g^{\alpha\beta}) - (1/2)g_{\alpha\beta}L^{**} \end{aligned} \quad (51)$$

Here $T^{**}_{\alpha\beta}(m^{-2})$ is an abbreviation for $(8\pi G/c^4)$ times the usual stress-energy tensor $T_{\alpha\beta}$ (kg-m²/sec²-m³). Next we find that all those terms in Eq. (50) which contain an undifferentiated L factor drop out. Those that remain become

$$2[T^{**}_{\perp\perp}\delta N_0 + T^{**k}_{\perp}\delta N_k] \quad (52)$$

$T^{**}_{\perp\perp}$ is given by

$$\begin{aligned} T^{**}_{\perp\perp} &\equiv (T^{**}_{00} - 2N^k T^{**}_{ok} + N^i N^k T^{**}_{ik})/N_0^2 \\ &= T^{**\perp\perp} = (8\pi G/c^4)(\text{energy density}) \end{aligned} \quad (53)$$

The energy density is corrected for the oblique coordinate system being used here. It is a scalar with respect to coordinate changes in the hypersurface. $T^{**k}_{\perp}$ and $T^{**k\perp}$ are given by

$$\begin{aligned} T^{**k}_{\perp} &\equiv {}^{(3)}g^{km}(T^{**}_{om} - N^s T^{**}_{sm})/N_0 \\ T^{**k\perp} &= -T^{**k}_{\perp} = (8\pi G/c^4)(\text{density of energy flow}) \end{aligned} \quad (54)$$

The density of energy flow is also corrected for the oblique coordinate system of the surface. It is a contravarient vector with respect to coordinate changes in the hypersurface.

The rest of the variational analysis is straightforward. One can verify the agreement with the initial-value equations in all detail.

Precisely What Features of the Energy Are Specified on the Hypersurface?

The specification of energy on the hypersurface in the *initial-value equations* is most naturally made in terms of the $T^{**}_{\perp\perp}$ and $T^{**k}_{\perp}$, not the much-more coordinate-dependent $T^{**}_{\alpha\beta}$. As regards the variational principle, it is clear that it can be changed, if only the change reproduces the initial-value equations. Therefore the Lagrange function, which may be complicated or unknown or both, can be replaced by an expression that will have the same variation [Eq. (52)]. Thus one obtains for the quantity to be extremized:

$$I^*_3 = \int\{[^{(3)}R - (\operatorname{Tr}\mathbf{K})^2 + \operatorname{Tr}\mathbf{K}^2 - 2T^{**}_{\perp\perp}]N_0 - 2T^{**k}_{\perp}N_k(^{(3)}g)^{\frac{1}{2}}\}d^3x \quad (55)$$

Elimination of the Lapse Function

The lapse function N_0 enters only algebraically in the time component [Eq. (23)] of the initial-value equations and in the variational principle [Eq. (55)]. To make this fact more evident, we introduce the abbreviation

$$\gamma_{ij} = \tfrac{1}{2}[N_{i|j} + N_{j|i} - \partial^{(3)}g_{ij}/\partial x^0] \quad (56)$$

and write

$$\gamma_2 = (\operatorname{Tr}\gamma)^2 - \operatorname{Tr}\gamma^2 \quad (57)$$

γ_2 is referred to as the "shift anomaly." Then

$$K_{ij} = \gamma_i /N_0 \quad (58)$$

where K_{ij} measures the true extrinsic curvature, having to do with changes in spacelike distances per unit *proper* time between two hypersurfaces. In contrast, γ_{ij} performs a similar function when one does not yet know the lapse function, or scale of proper time, so that one has to use a purely nominal time *coordinate* x^0. The "kinetic" term in the variational principle becomes

$$(\operatorname{Tr}\mathbf{K})^2 - \operatorname{Tr}\mathbf{K}^2 = \gamma_2/N_0^2 \quad (59)$$

The modified function to be extremized becomes

$$I^*_3 = \int\{(^{(3)}R - 2T^{**}_{\perp\perp}N_0 - \gamma_2/N_0) - 2T^{**k}_{\perp}N_k\}(^{(3)}g)^{\frac{1}{2}}\, d^3x \quad (60)$$

If there exists an extremum with respect to N_0, this occurs at the value

$$N_0 = \pm\,[\gamma_2/(2T^{**} - {}^{(3)}R)]^{\frac{1}{2}} \quad (61)$$

The two signs for the root give the same physical results. A change in the sign of N_0 results in a corresponding reversal in the sign of N_k. All that has been changed is the convention as to the direction in which time is increasing! Baierlein *et al.*[17] comment about the result [Eq. (61)]: "Thus not only is the thickness of the thin sandwich from $^{(3)}\mathscr{G}'$ to $^{(3)}\mathscr{G}''$ determined by $^{(3)}\mathscr{G}'$ and $^{(3)}\mathscr{G}''$, but also its location in the enveloping $^{(4)}\mathscr{G}$ is determinate. This is the sense in which we discover a 3-geometry to be the carrier of information about time in general relativity."

The Condensed Intrasurface Variational Principle as a Mathematical Formulation of Mach's Principle

Inserting Eq. (61) for the lapse function into Eq. (60) we obtain the "condensed intrasurface variational principle"[25] (CIVP),

$$I_{\text{CIVP}} = -I_3^*/2 = \int \{[\gamma_2(2T_{\perp\perp}^{**} - {}^{(3)}R)]^{\frac{1}{2}} + T_{\perp}^{**k}N_k\}({}^{(3)}g)^{\frac{1}{2}} d^3x \qquad (62)$$

$$= \text{extremum}$$

The analog of this intrasurface variational principle in electrodynamics is

$$\int [(\mathbf{E}^2/8\pi) - \rho\phi]d^3x = \text{extremum} \qquad (63)$$

Equation (63) when combined with

$$\mathbf{E} = -\partial\mathbf{A}/\partial t - \text{grad } \phi \qquad (64)$$

is equivalent to the single differential equation

$$\nabla^2\phi = -4\pi\rho - (\partial/\partial t)\text{div } \mathbf{A} \qquad (65)$$

for the single potential ϕ. In Eq. (62) the given quantities are still the metric $^{(3)}g_{ik}$ of the hypersurface, the rate of change of this metric with a parameter x^0, the scalar curvature invariant $^{(3)}R$ of the geometry, and the density of energy and energy flow. To be varied to obtain an extremum are now not four potentials but only three, the components N_k of the vectorial shift function. They enter Eq. (62), (1) as coefficients of the energy flow and (2) as the functions whose covariant derivatives determine the "shift anomaly" γ_2.

The variational principle CIVP of Eq. (62) expresses in precise mathematical form our fourth formulation of Mach's principle: *the specification of a sufficiently regular closed three-dimensional geometry at two immediately succeeding instants, and of the density and flow of mass-energy, is to determine the geometry of space-time, past, present, and future, and thereby the inertial properties of every infinitesimal test particle.* Thus from Eq. (62), when it possesses a solution, one obtains the shift N_k. Then from Eq. (61) one has immediately the lapse function. From these potentials, via Eq. (56) and Eq. (58), one obtains the extrinsic curvature. Then one has in hand an adequate and consistent set of initial-value data for integrating Einstein's field equations and for obtaining a uniquely specified four-geometry (the arbitrariness in the coordinate system in this spacetime having no relevance to its *geometry!*)

Condensed Initial-Value Equations

We may obtain condensed initial-value equations in the following way. We make small variations δN_k in the shift components in Eq. (62). Then we set the coefficients of these variations equal to zero. In this way we arrive at three coupled second-order differential equations for the determination of the vector field $\mathbf{N} = (N_1, N_2, N_3)$. The same equations may be obtained by solving Eq. (23) for N_0 [in agreement with Eq. (61)] and substituting this result into Eq. (24). The condensed initial-value equations read

$$\left\{\frac{(2T^{**\perp\perp} - {}^{(3)}R)^{\frac{1}{2}}[(N_{i|j} + N_{j|i} - {}^{(3)}\dot{g}_{ij}) - {}^{(3)}g_{ij}{}^{(3)}g^{mn}(N_{m|n} + N_{n|m} - {}^{(3)}\dot{g}_{mn})]}{[({}^{(3)}g^{ab}\,{}^{(3)}g^{cd} - {}^{(3)}g^{ac}\,{}^{(3)}g^{bd})(N_{a|b} + N_{b|a} - {}^{(3)}\dot{g}_{ab})(N_{c|d} + N_{d|c} - {}^{(3)}\dot{g}_{cd})]^{\frac{1}{2}}}\right\}$$

$= -T^{**}_{\perp i} = + (8\pi G/c^4)$ (*i*th covariant component of density of flow of energy)   (66)

Variational Principle Equivalent to Differential Equations Plus Boundary Conditions

These equations *plus boundary conditions* are equivalent to the condensed intrasurface variational principle, Eq. (62). The *boundary conditions are essential* in geometrodynamics as in electrostatics *if* one is to obtain a unique relation between the "source" [density and flow of energy and gravitational radiation as described by ${}^{(3)}g_{ij}$ and ${}^{(3)}\dot{g}_{ij} = (\partial {}^{(3)}g_{ij}/\partial x^0)$] and the "effect" (the vector shift $\mathbf{N}$ and the four-geometry and inertial properties of test particles). The boundary conditions in a closed space are obvious: the vector field $\mathbf{N}$ found by integration around the space one way has to join up properly with the vector field found by integration around the space another way; or more simply, the vector field (due account being taken of changes from one coordinate patch to another [22] (1) must be everywhere *regular* and (2) must lead to a regular and *single-valued* extrinsic curvature K_{ij}. If the space is *open*, the differential equations are still well defined; but they are not accompanied by any boundary condition. Moreover, one can no longer expect the variational integral ordinarily to have a finite and well-defined value in the case of an open space. Therefore there arises the built-in consequence of Mach's principle as formulated here, that the space should *be closed* and that the geometry [${}^{(3)}\mathcal{G}'$ and ${}^{(3)}\mathcal{G}''$, or ${}^{(3)}g_{ik}$ and $\partial {}^{(3)}g_{ik}/\partial x^0$] should be everywhere regular. (One could *supply* an artificial boundary condition at two-dimensional spatial infinity but this would not be a *physically natural* procedure.)

Comments on Mach's Principle and the Intrasurface Variational Principle

Issues Not Discussed Here: Uniqueness

It would be an enormous labor to take up one by one all the questions that are left unanswered here and treat them systematically. Moreover, there is wanting one key element in the discussion—a proof that the solution of the variational problem in Eq. (62) (when there is a solution) is unique.[25]

Effect of Additional Mass on Inertia Not Discussed

On the other hand, there are many questions about the physical content of Mach's principle that can and ought to be discussed. An example is the question how the inertial properties of a sun and planet are affected by matter distributed around them in a large spherical shell. The analysis of this situation requires great care. For example the inertial properties will not be said to have changed or will be said to have changed according as the time measurements are made by clocks within the shell or far outside it.

Instantaneous or Retarded Effect of Source on Test Particle?

Another question has to do with the *speed* with which the supposed inertial effects of sources are propagated to the test particles which they affect. This question arises even in electrodynamics where, according to Eq. (65), the effects of the charge distribution on the potential appear *formally* to be propagated instantaneously *within* the spacelike hypersurface. However, we know that in standard Maxwell electrodynamics, effects are all propagated, not instantaneously, but with the speed of light. It is also well known that there is no inconsistency between the instantaneous potential of Eq. (65) and the retarded potentials of the usual radiation theory.[26] Analogously one finds also in geometrodynamics a basically *elliptical* equation, describing what appears formally to be an instantaneous propagation of effects from one place to another in a spacelike hypersurface. Yet one knows that a disturbance in a source at one point in spacetime will propagate to another point only with the speed of light.[27] In geometrodynamics, as in electrodynamics, the formalism itself guarantees that there can be no discrepancy between effects calculated in the two different ways from the same sources. Therefore in principle there can be no trouble from the question mentioned in point 4 on page 305: How can Mach's principle make sense when it implies that the accelerated test mass acts on all the other masses in the universe, and that they in turn have to act back on this particle?[28] One would like here, as in Fermi's analysis of electrodynamics, to see more of the inner workings of the machinery by which (1) the propagation in time and (2) a formally instantaneous propagation necessarily yield the same solution of Einstein's field equations.

Do Sources Have to Be Followed Back into the Past When the Model Universe Was in a Singular State?

The all effects appear *formally* as propagated instantaneously within the spacelike hypersurface disposes of another question about Mach's principle. Let one evaluate the inertial effects on a given test particle (that is to say, the effects on the geometry in a given neighborhood) caused in the sense of Mach by more and more remote sources of mass-energy. One appears to be forced farther and farther back into the past. On this basis one ultimately comes to regions where according to the expanding universe model the geometry is singular and where it is not possible to follow back any further the dynamical evolution of the geometry by employing Einstein's field equations only at the classical level.[29] However, this is not the case. We can specify the dynamic problem by giving the "sandwich" type of data on an initial spacelike hypersurface. This is, give $^{(3)}\mathscr{G}$, $\partial^{(3)}\mathscr{G}/\partial x^0$, and the density and flow of energy. Then the integral that one has to extremize, or the triplet of differential equations that one has to solve, make no reference to anything going on back in the past at a time or place where the geometry—calculated classically—may be singular.

Model Universe Devoid of Constants of Motion?

Still another question is this: What are the true physical constants of the motion in general relativity? It is well known that total energy cannot be defined and has no meaning in a closed universe.[24] The question has recently been raised[29] whether such a system is not in principle devoid of all constants of motion whatsoever. One can compare a model universe in some respects with a billiard ball set into motion on a triangular billiard table which has sides e, π, and 1. The motion is quasi-ergodic. That is, if started in one way, it will not repeat itself, although it will come indefinitely close to repeating the motion it would have had if it were started in another way. To an observer with only a finite resolving power the only difference in the two motions might be in the speed or energy of the ball. Not even this difference can manifest itself in the case of a model universe.[29] In either case the dynamics can be determined by specifying initial-value data (x' and y' at t'; x'', y'' at t'' for the billiard ball or $^{(3)}\mathscr{G}'$ and $^{(3)}\mathscr{G}''$ for the geometry) without constants of the motion. In other words, if there are no constants of the motion they will hardly be missed!

Different Masses on the Two Hypersurfaces

Now for questions on which something more definite can be said. First, how can it possibly make sense to specify $^{(3)}\mathscr{G}'$ and $^{(3)}\mathscr{G}''$ arbitrarily? Are there not all sorts of conditions of compatibility that have to be satisfied? Consider, for example, the case of a space that is asymptotically flat. From the rate of approach to flatness at great distances as given by

$$ds^2 \sim (1 + 2m^*/r)dr^2 + r^2(d\theta^2 + \sin^2\theta \, d\phi^2) \tag{67}$$

one can evaluate the mass and energy of the system. If, independent of what hypersurface one chooses, *this* constant has to agree between $^{(3)}\mathscr{G}'$ and $^{(3)}\mathscr{G}''$, how many other quantities are there which must also agree on the two hypersurfaces? To discuss this question more fully, consider a specific example, the Schwarzschild solution of Einstein's field equations, for which the line element is given by

$$do^2 = - d\tau^2 = - (1 - 2m^*/r)dt^2 + (1 - 2m^*/r)^{-1}dr^2 \\ + r^2(d\theta^2 + \sin^2\theta \, d\phi^2) \tag{68}$$

Let $^{(3)}\mathscr{G}'$ be the hypersurface $t = t' =$ constant. On this the asymptotic geometry follows Eq. (67). Let the second hypersurface $^{(3)}\mathscr{G}''$ be described at small distances by giving t as some reasonable and regular function t'' of r, θ, and ϕ, which at large distances becomes

$$t'' \to (8m_1^*r)^{\frac{1}{2}} \tag{69}$$

with $m_1^* =$ a constant. Taking the differential of this expression and substituting into Eq. (65), one finds that the second hypersurface has the asymptotic geometry

$$ds^2 \sim [1 + 2(m^* - m_1^*)/r]dr^2 + r^2(d\theta^2 + \sin^2\theta \, d\phi^2) \tag{70}$$

The masses not only can be different but, in this example, must be different. One's first surprise at this result traces back to a semantic obscurity in the word "flat":

Meaning 1: The *intrinsic three-geometry* is asymptotically flat.

Meaning 2: The intrinsic three-geometry is asymptotically flat and also the *extrinsic curvature* is zero.

Only when "flat" is used in sense 2 do the apparent masses have to agree between two asymptotically flat geometries. However, the two-surface formulation of relativity focusses on *intrinsic* three-geometry, so that "flat" there is used in sense 1. There *is* no problem of compatibility between the two three-geometries in the example. René Thom[30] has even shown that one can fill in between two three-geometries of different *topology* with a nonsingular topology. Whether and when the geometry laid down on that topology can also be nonsingular is a deeper question.

Question of Effectively Elliptic Character of the Thin-Sandwich Problem

Does the variational principle CIVP [Eq. (62)] or the triplet of differential equations to which it corresponds have elliptic character? This issue brings to mind the question whether

$$d^2\psi/d\theta^2 + (\lambda - V_0 \cos \theta)\,\psi = 0 \tag{71}$$

is an eigenvalue equation. One might think not, to look at the regions of θ where the "oscillation factor" or "effective kinetic energy factor" $(\lambda - V_0 \cos \theta)$ is negative. There the solution is curved away from the θ axis. However, what counts in the end for the existence of nodes and eigenvalues is the region where this factor is positive and the solution is oscillatory. The equation is *effectively* oscillatory in character (for λ sufficiently in excess of $-V_0$). It is difficult in the case of Eqs. (62) and (66) to be precise at this stage; but one has the impression that it is in a comparable sense *effectively elliptic*. Space in the "thin-sandwich" problem is divided up ordinarily into regions where $(2T^{**\perp\perp} - {}^{(3)}R)$ is positive (also the shift anomaly γ_2 has to be positive) and regions where the second quantity has to follow the first in changing sign. At the interface between one such region and another the anomaly γ_2 has to change sign. This situation reminds one, to use another analogy, of the theory of buckling of shells, and of conditions at the boundary between one region of crumpling and another.

Since the shift anomaly γ_2 is central to this discussion, we shall discuss it in greater detail. Consider the equation for the eigenvalues of the extrinsic curvature tensor K_{ik}, or rather, of the closely related shift tensor $\gamma_{ik} = N_0 K_{ik}$. Consider the determinant

$$\begin{vmatrix} (\gamma_1^1 - \lambda) & \gamma_1^2 & \gamma_1^3 \\ \gamma_2^1 & (\gamma_2^3 - \lambda) & \gamma_2^3 \\ \gamma_3^1 & \gamma_3^2 & (\gamma_3^3 - \lambda) \end{vmatrix}$$
$$= \det(\gamma_i^k) - (\gamma_2/2)\lambda + (\mathrm{Tr}\,\boldsymbol{\gamma})\lambda^2 - \lambda^3 \tag{72}$$

A change in coordinates changes the $\gamma_i{}^k$ individually but not the eigenvalues λ, and consequently not the coefficients of the various powers of λ on the right-hand side of Eq. (72). Therefore consider a system of coordinates such that at the particular point of interest the shift tensor $\gamma_i{}^k$ is diagonal. Let the elements along the diagonal, (the eigenvalues λ) be denoted by A, B, C. Then the coefficient of $-\lambda$ in the expansion of the secular determinant $(A - \lambda)(B - \lambda)(C - \lambda)$ is

$$(BC + CA + AB) = \tfrac{1}{2}[(A + B + C)^2 - (A^2 + B^2 + C^2)]$$
$$= \tfrac{1}{2}[(\mathrm{Tr}\,\boldsymbol{\gamma})^2 - \mathrm{Tr}\,\boldsymbol{\gamma}^2] = (\tfrac{1}{2})(\text{shift anomaly}) = \gamma_2/2 \tag{73}$$

Associated with the point in question consider a three-dimensional space with coordinates A, B, C. Then the shift tensor is represented by a single point in this space. Moreover this point is independent of the choice of coordinate system in the hypersurface. In the space (A, B, C) we may construct through the origin a line with direction cosines $(3^{-\frac{1}{2}}, 3^{-\frac{1}{2}}, 3^{-\frac{1}{2}})$. We may also construct a double cone with this line as the axis with an angle of opening θ such that

$\cos \theta = 3^{-\frac{1}{2}} = $ scalar product of $3^{-\frac{1}{2}}(1, 1, 1)$ with

$$\left.\begin{pmatrix}(1,0,0) \text{ or}\\ (0,1,0) \text{ or}\\ (0,0,1)\end{pmatrix}\right\} \tag{74}$$

Then any point *on* a coordinate axis lies on one or the other half of the cone. Every point on a coordinate axis also annuls the shift anomaly, according to Eq. (73). It takes only a few more steps to show that the shift anomaly γ_2 is

(1) zero for *every* point *on* either cone,
(2) positive for every point *within* either cone, and
(3) negative in the neutral space *outside* the cones.

A particular character of the shift tensor $\gamma_i{}^k$ corresponds to each of these three cases. What is the detailed value of the shift tensor is only settled by extremization of the CIVP, or by integration of the initial-value equations with appropriate boundary condition, and is therefore governed by the initial-value data all over the hypersurface. However, only the *local* value of the quantity $(2T^{**\perp\perp} - {}^{(3)}R)$, determined by the initial-value data, is required to determine the *character* of the shift tensor. We now turn from comments on the general problem to a particular example.

Example Where Both Hypersurfaces That Bound the Thin Sandwich Have Ideal Three-Sphere Geometry

Let both hypersurfaces have the geometry of the ideal sphere

$$x^2 + y^2 + z^2 + w^2 = 1$$

thus for ${}^{(3)}\mathscr{G}'$ (which we shall denote by x^0)

$$ds^2 = a'^2[d\chi^2 + \sin^2\chi(d\theta^2 + \sin^2\theta\, d\phi^2)] \tag{75}$$

and for ${}^{(3)}\mathscr{G}''$ (denoted by $x^0 + \Delta x^0$)

$$ds^2 = a''^2[d\chi^2 + \sin^2\chi(d\theta^2 + \sin^2\theta\, d\phi^2)] \tag{76}$$

where a'' and a' are constants. Or to use another language, consider a one-parameter family of such hypersurfaces, characterized by a parameter x^0:

$$a = a(x^0) \tag{77}$$

and pick some fixed value of x^0, thus specifying

$$a \text{ and } da/dx^0 \ (\sim (a'' - a')/\Delta x^0) \tag{78}$$

(As remarked earlier, the value of Δx^0 will drop out of the results at the end.) The remaining initial-value data comprises the energy flow, which we set equal to zero, and the energy density, which we assume independent of position:

$$T^{**\perp\perp} = \text{constant (independent of } \chi, \theta, \phi) \tag{79}$$

The question now is: What four-geometry to fill in between the two hypersurfaces so as to satisfy the thin-sandwich equations? The timelike perpendicular erected to $^{(3)}\mathscr{G}'$ at the point χ, θ, ϕ will have to be assigned a certain length. Also it will be necessary to tell what point it touches on the hypersurface $^{(3)}\mathscr{G}''$, or to tell what the starred quantities are in the following formula for the coordinates of this point:

$$\chi - \chi^*, \quad \theta - \theta^*, \quad \phi - \phi^* \tag{80}$$

On account of the symmetry of the sphere it will be simplest to assume— as a trial—the same angles for both points, or to take all the starred quantities equal to zero. Thus the shift function is assumed zero:

$$N^\chi = \chi^*/\Delta x^0 = 0, \text{ etc.} \quad \text{(three equations)} \tag{81}$$

Now we may evaluate the shift tensor. It is determined by the fractional increase between one hypersurface and the other in the distance between points with corresponding coordinates, say, (χ, θ, ϕ) and $(\chi + d\chi, \theta + d\theta, \phi + d\phi)$. But this increase for the case we are considering is the same in all directions and at all places, and is in direct proportion to the fractional increase in the value of the radius. Thus the eigenvalues of $\gamma_i{}^k$ are identical:

$$A = B = C = \frac{\text{(fractional increase in radius)}}{\text{(change in the highly nominal parameter } x^0)}$$

$$= (1/a)\,(da/dx^0) \tag{82}$$

The point in the space (A, B, C) lies inside one half of the double cone, right on the axis. The shift anomaly is positive:

$$\gamma_2 = (\text{Tr } \gamma)^2 - \text{Tr } \gamma^2 = (6/a^2)(da/dx^0)^2 \tag{83}$$

but independent of position. Likewise the covariant derivative of $\gamma_i{}^k$ is zero and the N_i vanish. These circumstances guarantee that the condensed initial-value equations [Eq. (66)] are automatically satisfied. It only remains to find the lapse function N_0:

$$\gamma_2/N_0{}^2 = 2T^{**\perp\perp} - {}^{(3)}R \tag{84}$$

or

$$(6/a^2)(da/N_0\,dx^0)^2 = 2T^{**\perp\perp} - 6/a^2 \tag{85}$$

Instead of actually solving for N_0, it is better to recognize that $N_0\ dx^0$ is the *proper* time separation—call it dt—between hypersurfaces, the parameters attached to which are x^0 and $x^0 + dx^0$, and is therefore directly the physical quantity of interest. Thus write

$$(da/dt)^2 = (a^2/3)T^{**\perp\perp} - 1 \tag{86}$$

The dynamics of the model universe are completely determined by Eq. (86) as soon as one puts in the law of change of energy density with expansion:

$$T^{**\perp\perp} = (8\pi G/c^4)(Mc^2/2\pi^2 a^3) \tag{87}$$

for a universe filled with inchoate dust (Friedmann universe); and

$$T^{**\perp\perp} = \text{constant}/a^4 \tag{88}$$

for a system filled with isotropic radiation (Tolman universe).

Question of Uniqueness. The Linear Approximation

The purpose here was not to take up old problems anew, but to prepare the way in a simple example to investigate the *uniqueness* of the four-geometry determined by ${}^{(3)}g_{ik}$, $\partial{}^{(3)}g_{ik}/\partial x^0$, $T^{**\perp i}$, and $T^{**\perp\perp}$. Suppose the vector shift function $N^i = (\chi^*,\ \theta^*,\ \phi^*)\Delta x^0$ is *not* assumed to be zero but is investigated in terms of the equations themselves. Will one find oneself with no alternative *except* the familiar solution already sketched out? Unfortunately the three coupled second-order equations to be solved are only quasi-linear, not linear. The problem appears difficult without resorting to deeper mathematical considerations which are not immediately apparent. Therefore no decisive results can be offered here. What *has* been investigated is the case where the contribution of the shift vector N_i to the shift tensor

$$\gamma_{ik} = \tfrac{1}{2}(N_{i|k} + N_{k|i} - \partial{}^{(3)}g_{ik}/\partial x^0) \tag{89}$$

is so small compared to the "main term" [Eq. (82)] that one is justified in treating the condensed initial value equations [Eq. (66)] as *linear* in N^i. These equations then take the form

$$\begin{aligned}
(\sin \chi)^{-2}(\partial^2\chi^*/\partial\theta^2 &+ (\sin\theta)^{-2}\,\partial^2\chi^*/\partial\phi^2 + \cot\theta\,\partial\chi^*/\partial\theta \\
&+ 4\chi^*) - (\partial/\partial\chi)(\partial\phi^*/\partial\phi + (\sin\theta)^{-1}(\partial/\partial\theta)(\theta^*\sin\theta)) = 0
\end{aligned} \tag{90}$$

and

$$\sin \chi (\partial/\partial\chi)(\sin \chi \; \partial\theta^*/\partial\chi) + (\sin \theta)^{-2}(\partial^2\theta^*/\partial\phi^2)$$
$$+ 2\theta^* - (\sin \chi)^{-3}(\partial/\partial\chi)(\sin^3 \chi \; \partial\chi^*/\partial\theta)$$
$$- (\sin \theta)^{-2}(\partial/\partial\theta)(\sin^2 \theta \; \partial\phi^*/\partial\phi) = 0 \tag{91}$$

and

$$\sin^2 \theta \sin \chi (\partial/\partial\chi)(\sin \chi \; \partial\phi^*/\partial\chi) + \sin \theta(\partial/\partial\theta)(\sin \theta \; \partial\phi^*/\partial\theta)$$
$$- (\sin \chi)^{-3}(\partial/\partial\chi)(\sin^3 \chi \; \partial\chi^*/\partial\phi) - \sin \theta(\partial/\partial\theta)(\sin \theta \; \partial\theta^*/\partial\phi) = 0 \tag{92}$$

One can attempt to obtain a solution of this equation in the form of a spherical harmonic expansion.

$$\chi^*(\chi,\theta,\phi) = \sum f_{l,m}(\chi) Y_l^m(\theta, \phi) \tag{93}$$

No thoroughgoing analysis along this line has been completed. However, Professor C. W. Misner pointed out at the Warsaw conference that the equation ought in principle to admit *rotations*. This point has since been tested and verified. It obviously makes no difference to the geometry of the three-sphere $^{(3)} \mathscr{G}''$ whether one set of hyperspherical polar coordinates χ, θ, ϕ or a rotated set is used to describe the location of the points. However, it does make a difference to the coordinate-dependent shift vector N^k. To fill in between $^{(3)} \mathscr{G}'$ and $^{(3)} \mathscr{G}''$ with a thin-sandwich $^{(4)} \mathscr{G}$, compatible with the intrasurface variational principle or initial-value equations, does not in itself fix the values of these quantities. The timelike normals that reach between the one hypersurface and the other, which start at (χ, θ, ϕ) on one hypersurface, and also end at (χ, θ, ϕ) on the other hypersurface, will end at *different* values of (χ, θ, ϕ) when a rotated coordinate system is used:

$$(\chi - \chi^*, \theta - \theta^*, \phi - \phi^*).$$

Shifts Produced by the Six Independent Rotations

The calculation of the starred changes in the angles under a typical small rotation is most easily made by going to Cartesian coordinates:

$$\begin{aligned}
x &= a \sin \chi \sin \theta \cos \phi \\
y &= a \sin \chi \sin \theta \sin \phi \\
z &= a \sin \chi \cos \theta \\
w &= a \cos \chi
\end{aligned} \tag{94}$$

There are six independent small rotations out of which the most general small rotation is constructed by linear combination. Consider as an example a rotation through the small angle θ_{zw} in the (z, w) plane

$$dx = 0 \qquad dy = 0$$
$$dz = \theta_{zw}w \qquad (95)$$
$$dw = -\theta_{zw}z$$

The resulting change in the polar angle θ is

$$d\theta = \cos^2\theta \, d(\tan\theta) = \cos^2\theta \, d[(x^2 + y^2)^{\frac{1}{2}}/z]$$
$$= -\cos^2\theta(x^2 + y^2)^{\frac{1}{2}}z^{-2}\theta_{zw}w$$
$$= -\theta_{zw}\cot\chi\sin\theta \qquad (96)$$

Similarly one finds the changes in all three coordinate angles under all six independent rotations (Table 15–5).

It is easy to verify that each line of Table 15–5 represents a solution of the linearized initial value equations [Eqs. (90), (91), and (92)]. It is conjectured that there is no other independent solution of these equations which are free of truly geometrical singularity, as distinguished from coordinate singularity,[31] over the entire three-sphere.

Even if and when this conjecture can be established, there will remain the question of uniqueness of the equations for this two-sphere problem in their full nonlinear form [Eq. (66)]. After that will be the question of uniqueness in more general situations.

Assessment of Mach's Principle

Pending the investigation of these apparently difficult mathematical questions, it would not appear unreasonable to adopt as a working hypothesis the position (Formulation 4 of Mach's principle) that the specification

Table 15–5

Changes in Polar Angles on Three-Sphere Brought About by the Six Independent Types of Rotation

	χ^*	θ^*	ϕ^*
θ_{yz}	0	$\sin\phi$	$\cot\theta\cos\phi$
θ_{zx}	0	$-\cos\phi$	$\cot\theta\sin\phi$
θ_{xy}	0	0	-1
θ_{xw}	$\sin\theta\cos\phi$	$\cot\chi\cos\theta\cos\phi$	$-\cot\chi\sin\phi/\sin\theta$
θ_{yw}	$\sin\theta\sin\phi$	$\cot\chi\cos\theta\sin\phi$	$\cot\chi\cos\phi/\sin\theta$
θ_{zw}	$\cos\theta$	$-\cot\chi\sin\theta$	0

of a sufficiently regular closed three-dimensional geometry at two immediately succeeding instants, and of the density and flow of mass-energy, is to determine the geometry of spacetime, past, present, and future, and thereby the inertial properties of every infinitesimal test particle. In this sense it is proposed to view Mach's principle as the *boundary condition for Einstein's field equations*, and an essential part of the "plan" of general relativity. The condensed intrasurface variational principle [CIVP Eq. (62)] is the most compact mathematical statement available of this interpretation of Mach's principle. As conceived here, it carries with it the tacit requirement that the model universe be *closed*.

Appendix A

Dynamics of the Lattice Universe[7]

For a precise analysis of the dynamics of the lattice universe consider the initial-value problem at the moment of time symmetry or maximum expansion: $^{(3)}\mathbf{R} = (16\pi G/c^2)\rho$. Here ρ is the density of mass, equal, for example, to ρ_0 inside each center of attraction and vanishing elsewhere. We solve this equation by modifying the geometry of a three-sphere of uniform curvature and radius a for which the line element is

$$ds^2_{\text{ideal}} = a^2[d\chi^2 + \sin^2\chi(d\theta^2 + \sin^2\theta\, d\phi)] \tag{A-1}$$

by a conformal factor ψ:

$$ds^2 = \psi^4\, ds^2_{\text{ideal}} \tag{A-2}$$

The initial-value equation takes the form

$$\nabla^2\psi + (2\pi G/c^2)\rho\psi^5 - (3/4a^2)\psi = 0 \tag{A-3}$$

Here the operator ∇^2 is calculated from the metric of the ideal three-sphere. This equation is to be solved throughout one lattice zone subject to the conditions (1) that ψ have the appropriate symmetry within that zone and (2) that its normal derivative vanish at the zonal boundary. This is an eigenvalue problem which determines the radius a of the comparison sphere. When gravitational radiation is present the metric cannot be represented in such a simple form. However, there is still typically a factor like ψ to be found—governed now not only by the distribution of mass, but also by the distribution of gravitational radiation.

Appendix B

The Taub Universe Interpreted in Terms of Gravitational Radiation of Maximal Wavelength

The Taub universe[9] is free of any "real matter" at all. Taub derived this solution of Einstein's equations,

$$d\sigma^2 = -d\tau^2 = \gamma_1\,dx^2 + (\gamma_1\sin^2 x + \gamma_3\cos^2 x)dy^2$$
$$+ 2\gamma_3\cos x\,dy\,dz + \gamma_3\,dz^2 - \gamma_1^2\gamma_3\,dt^2 \tag{B-1}$$

with

$$\gamma_1 = \cosh(t/4)\cosh^2(t/2)$$
$$\gamma_3 = 1/\cosh t$$

from arguments of group theory having nothing directly to do with the kind of considerations which are the center of attention in this chapter. Therefore, it is of interest to see how one can obtain the same solutions by a physical line of reasoning.

Replace the dust in the Friedmann universe by electromagnetic radiation distributed uniformly in space and in direction. One arrives at the Tolman universe.[33] During its expansion and recontraction the wavelength of every standing wave varies as the radius a of the model universe. In consequence the density of mass-energy varies not as $1/a^3$, as in the Friedmann universe, but as $1/a^4$. Now we may replace the electromagnetic radiation of the Tolman universe by gravitational radiation of short wavelength. There is no longer any "real" density of mass-energy on the right-hand side of Einstein's equation. However, the fine-scale ripples in the geometry bring about the same type of larger-scale curvature as would be caused by a "real" distribution of mass-energy. Let δg denote the local root-mean-square amplitude of the fluctuations in the metric, and let $\lambdabar = \lambda/2\pi = $ (wavelength)$/2\pi$ denote their reduced wavelength. Then the *effective* density of mass-energy associated with the gravitational radiation is of the order

$$\hat{T}_{\perp\perp\,\text{effective}} \sim (c^4/8\pi G)(\delta g/\lambdabar)^2 \tag{B-2}$$

To curve a space into closure with a radius which at the moment of maximum expansion has the value a_0 requires an energy density given by

$$^{(3)}R = (16\pi G/c^4)\hat{T}_{\perp\perp} \tag{B-3}$$

or

$$6/a_0^2 \sim 2(\delta g/\lambdabar)^2 \tag{B-4}$$

Thus the amplitude of the ripples need not be great:

$$\delta g \ (\text{at maximum expansion}) \sim 3^{\frac{1}{2}}\lambdabar/a_0 \tag{B-5}$$

if the wavelength is short.

During the expansion and recontraction the energy density, proportional to $(\delta g/\lambdabar)^2$, necessarily varies as $1/a^4$. Consequently the amplitude of the ripples varies in accordance with the formula

$$\delta g(t) \sim \text{constant}_1 \lambda(t)/a^2(t)$$
$$\sim \text{constant}_2/a(t)$$
$$\sim 3^{\frac{1}{2}}\lambda_0/a(t)$$
$$\sim (3^{\frac{1}{2}}/n)(a_0/a(t)) \tag{B-6}$$

The last expression above refers to the case where the perturbation in the otherwise ideal spherical geometry is described by a hyperspherical harmonic[34] of order n. The factor $3^{\frac{1}{2}}$ is not to be taken seriously in this order-of-magnitude formula.

From considering a gravitational wave of very short wavelength it is natural to turn to the opposite limiting case, where the order n has the minimum possible value and the wavelength has the maximum possible value which will fit into the three-sphere. The corresponding hyperspherical harmonic has well-defined symmetry properties.[34] These symmetry properties, and the critical amplitude required for closure, are *the features of the special gravitational wave that gives the Taub universe.*

The Taub universe is homogeneous but not isotropic; the curvature differs from one direction to another, but the principal values of the curvature do not change from place to place.

The curvature provides a more reasonable way of talking about perturbations in the geometry than does the quantity δg. This is for a well-known reason. One cannot form coordinate-independent independent quantities with the metric coefficients nor their first derivatives. For the order of magnitude of typical components of the fluctuation part of the curvature in a local Lorentz frame one has the estimate

$$\hat{R}(t)_{\text{wave}} \sim \delta g/\lambda^2$$
$$\sim \delta g/(a/n)^2$$
$$\sim na_0/a^3(t)$$

as compared to the typical component of the curvature of the background geometry,

$$\hat{R}_{\text{background}} \sim 1/a^2(t)$$

Thus the mode of longest wavelength and lowest n is the one for which the perturbations in the geometry—as measured by the differences in the curvature in different directions—are not greatest (as one might have thought from the expression for δg) but least.

At early and late stages this perturbation becomes fractionally larger and larger and every *space-like* three-geometry ultimately develops infinite curvature, in accordance with what appears to be a general principle.[35]

Appendix C

The Uniqueness of the Solution of the Initial-Value Problem in Electrodynamics and Geometrodynamics

The uniqueness of the initial-value problem is well understood in the case of electrodynamics for a closed orientable three-manifold. Given everywhere $\mathbf{B}$ and $\dot{\mathbf{B}}$, one arrives at a unique $\mathbf{E}$ when one specifies the jump $\Delta_k\phi$ in the potential in traveling the circuit of the kth-independent handle or "wormhole" of the topology, where k runs over the values from $k = 1$ to $k = R_1 = R_2 =$ the second Betti number of the manifold. These numbers determine the charge or flux of lines of force trapped in the topology. That the numbers $\Delta_k\phi$ have to be fixed follows most evidently from the occurrence of a surface integral $\int\delta\phi(\mathbf{E}\cdot d\mathbf{S})$ in the passage from the variational principle Eq. (42) to the differential equation (43). Does topology make an equally forceful appearance in the initial-value equations of general relativity? *Is there a geometrodynamical analog of electric charge? No argument for the existence of such a charge follows from the variational principle as discussed in the text* ("*coordinate representation*"). The surface integral of the quantity $\pi^{ij}N_i$ shows up in the integration by parts of Eq. (48). In the discussion of the text following Eq. (48) it is remarked that this surface integral vanishes when the topology is that of an ordinary, simply connected three-sphere. However, it was shown by Misner that the surface integral *also* vanishes for *any* closed orientable three-manifold. The nature of the two-surfaces encountered in these integrals is the same in geometrodynamics as in electromagnetism. Most simply, one such surface is conceived as the point of contact between two balloonlike expanding fingers that are feeling their way down into a wormhole from opposite mouths. The first factor in each integrand—$\mathbf{E}$ in the one case, π^{ij} in the other case—is the same in this respect, that the quantity in question has *physical meaning* and is a *field momentum*. The difference comes in the character of the second factor—the potential jump $\delta\phi$ in electrodynamics, the metric potential N_i in geometrodynamics. Only the gradient of ϕ has significance in electromagnetism, so that ϕ itself can suffer a net change in going around the circuit of a handle. On the other hand, the quantity N_i directly governs the distance between points on the two nearby hypersurfaces that have specified coordinates. Unlike the electric potential ϕ, this quantity must return to its original value after the circuit of a handle. Therefore a geometrodynamic analog to electric charge—if one is to come in at all—will have to show up in the conjugate representation of the initial-value problem (not analyzed here).[36]

Acknowledgment. Thanks are expressed to R. F. Baierlein, H. Bondi, R. H. Dicke, E. Guth, J. E. Hogarth, A. Komar, L. Markus, C. W. Misner, E. Schücking, M. Schwarzschild, D. Sciama, D. H. Sharp, A. H. Taub, R. Utiyama, E. P. Wigner, R. P. Zia, and other colleagues for discussions of Mach's principle.

References and Notes

1. A. Einstein, *The Meaning of Relativity*, Princeton University Press, Princeton, N.J., 3rd ed., 1950, p. 107; *Sci. Am.*, p. 209, April 1950.
2. D. W. Sciama, *Monthly Notices Roy. Astron. Soc.*, **113**, 34 (1953); *Sci. Am.*, p. 99, February 1957.
3. W. Davidson, *Monthly Notices Roy. Astron. Soc.*, **117**, 212 (1957).
4. For a discussion of present information on the density and size of the universe see, for example, J. Oort and J. A. Wheeler in *Onzième conseil de physique Solvay: La Structure et l'évolution de l'univers*, Editions Stoops, Bruxelles, 1959 (referred to hereafter as SÉU).
5. J. A. Wheeler, *SÉU*, pp. 49–51.
6. H. Hönl, in E. Brüche (ed.), *Physikertagung Wien*, Physik Verlag, Mosbach/ Baden, 1962, p. 95.
7. For a detailed but approximate treatment of the dynamics of such a lattice universe, see R. W. Lindquist and J. A. Wheeler, *Rev. Mod. Phys.*, **29**, 432 (1957). For a more nearly precise treatment at the moment of time symmetry, see Appendix A.
8. D. Brill, *Ann. Phys.*, **7**, 466 (1959); H. Araki, *Ann. Phys.*, **7**, 456 (1959); J. A. Wheeler, *Geometrodynamics*, Academic, New York, 1962, p. 56. This book is cited hereafter as GMD.
9. A. H. Taub, *Ann. Math.*, **53**, 472 (1951).
10. A first-order analysis of deviations from Schwarzschild geometry has been given by T. Regge and J. A. Wheeler, *Phys. Rev.*, **108**, 1063 (1957), but no attempt is made there to fit on to the Taub solution at greater distances.
11. International Conference on Relativistic Theories of Gravitation, Warsaw, Poland, July 1962. Proceedings to be published.
12. P. A. M. Dirac, V. A. Fock, and Boris Podolsky, *Physik. Z. Sowjetunion*, **2**, 468 (1932).
13. See, for example, L. P. Eisenhart, *Riemannian Geometry*, Princeton University Press, Princeton, N.J., 1926, pp.150ff.
14. See R. Arnowitt, S. Deser, and C. W. Misner, *Phys. Rev.*, **122**, 997 (1961), and earlier papers cited by them. This group of papers is referred to hereafter as ADaM. See also their chapter in L. Witten (ed.), *Gravitation: an Introduction to Current Research*, Wiley, New York, 1962. This book is referred to hereafter as GICR. See also P. A. M. Dirac, *Proc. Roy. Soc. (London)*, **A246**, 333 (1958); *Phys. Rev.*, **114**, 924 (1959); *Phys. Rev. Letters*, **2**, 368 (1959).
15. The quantities N_0 and N_i were introduced in (16) to describe the time-time and time-space components of the metric (covariant tensor; subscript indices). However, the contravariant space components N^i (21) have a more readily apprehended significance as coordinate "shifts" (Fig. 15–1) than do the original N_i.
16. K. Stellmacher, *Math. Ann.*, **115**, 136 (1937); A. Lichnerowicz, *J. Math. Pure Appl.*, **23**, 37 (1944); *Helv. Phys. Acta Suppl.*, **4**, 176 (1956); *Théories*

relativistes de la gravitation et de l'électromagnétisme, Masson, Paris, 1955; Y. Fourès-Bruhat, *Acta Math.*, **88**, 141 (1952); *J. Rational Mech. Anal.*, **5**, 951 (1956); and the chapter by Y. Foures in GICR.

17. The following is based on a paper of R. F. Baierlein, D. H. Sharp, and J. A. Wheeler, *Phys. Rev.*, **126**, 1864 (1962), which in turn is based on (1) the A. B. senior thesis of David Sharp, Princeton University, May 1960 (unpublished) and (2) an analysis by R. F. Baierlein which led to the variational principle of Eq. (38).

18. For a discussion of this structure see G. de Rahm: *Variétés différentiables: formes, courants, formes harmoniques*, Hermann, Paris, 1955.

19. R. P. Feynman, the Principle of Least Action in Quantum Mechanics, Ph.D. thesis, Princeton University, 1942 (unpublished); *Rev. Mod. Phys.*, **20**, 367 (1948); Phys. Rev., **76**, 769 (1949); see also Philippe Choquard thesis, École Polytechnique Féderale, Zurich, 1955; and F. J. Dyson, Advanced Quantum Mechanics, photolithoprinted notes, Cornell University, Ithaca, New York, 1954.

20. The proof that this can be done in the case of general relativity is given in the book of A. Lichnerowicz, *Théories relativistes de la gravitation et de l'électromagnétisme*, Masson, Paris, 1955.

21. C. B. Morrey, *Pacific J. Math.*, **2**, 25 (1952); John Danskin, *Rivista Mat. Univ. Parma*, **3**, 43 (1952).

22. See, for example, GMD, p. 259.

23. See Appendix C.

24. See, for example, L. Landau and E. Lifshitz, translated by M. Hammermesh, *The Classical Theory of Fields*, Addison-Wesley, Reading, Mass., 1951.

25. The question of uniqueness of the solution of the initial-value problem is well understood in the case of electrodynamics in a closed or orientable 3-manifold. This, together with the possibility of a geometrodynamical analog of electric charge, is discussed further in Appendix C.

26. E. Fermi, *Rev. Mod. Phys.*, **4**, 87 (1932).

27. Marcel Riesz, *Acta Math.*, **81**, 1, 223 (1949).

28. For more on the equivalence between retarded and other ways of evaluating potentials in electrodynamics, see, for example, J. A. Wheeler and R. P. Feynman, *Rev. Mod. Phys.*, **17**, 157 (1945); **21**, 425 (1949).

29. J. A. Wheeler, *The Monist*, **47**, No. 1 (1963).

30. R. Thom, *Comment. Math. Helv.*, **28**, 17 (1954), Chap. IV. See also J. W. Smith, *U.S. Natl. Acad. Sci. Proc.*, **46**, 111 (1960).

31. In principle all question of what is a coordinate singularity and what is a truly geometrical singularity can and should be eliminated by the use of two or more coordinate patches (Ref. 22) to eliminate all singularities in the coordinate systems that cover the three-sphere.

32. See Ref. 7.

33. R. C. Tolman, *Relativity, Thermodynamics and Cosmology*, Clarendon Press, Oxford, 1934.

34. E. Lifshitz, *J. Phys. U.S.S.R.*, **10**, 116 (1946).

35. GMD, pp. 61–64.

36. For more on this topic see J. A. Wheeler, "Absence of a Gravitational Analog to Electrical Charge" in Charles P. Wells and Robert Wasserman, eds., *Fundamental Topics in Relativistic Fluid Mechanics and Magnetohydrodynamics*, Academic, New York, 1963.

INDEX

351

801046017